5-15-67

D0385122

WALTER CLARK HAMILTON, Ph.D. California Institute of
Technology, is Chemist at the Brookhaven National Laboratory engaged in research in theoretical and experimental
molecular structure and the applications of digital computers
to crystallographical problems. Dr. Hamilton held a National
Science Foundation Post-doctoral Fellowship at the Mathematical Institute at Oxford University and has lectured at
the Columbia University School of General Studies.

STATISTICS IN PHYSICAL SCIENCE

ESTIMATION, HYPOTHESIS TESTING, AND LEAST SQUARES

WALTER CLARK HAMILTON

BROOKHAVEN NATIONAL LABORATORY

THE RONALD PRESS COMPANY · NEW YORK

"In an infinite series, the impossible will certainly happen."
—G. SPENCER BROWN, *Probability and Scientific Inference*

Preface

In the chemistry and physics of today, particularly in the borderline field of chemical physics, more and more problems involve the estimation of a relatively small number of parameters from a large number of experimental observations, each of which is subject to error. In other problems, only a few observations may be available for the test of a complex physical theory. In either case, it is the purpose of statistical analysis to determine the best values for the parameters and to assess the probability of error when one makes statements or tests hypotheses concerning the parameter values.

Often the problems which arise in practice involve the concept of statistically correlated observations and parameters; the treatment of these problems demands an understanding of multivariate probability distributions and the method of least squares. Given a set of observations, each of which is related to a few or dozens of physical parameters by a complex but known mathematical expression, how are we to determine the best parameter values, their limits of error, and whether or not they agree with values for the same parameters obtained from other experiments?

The writing of this book was motivated by the need for a comprehensive treatment of the methods of least squares, linear hypothesis testing, and multivariate analysis in a form easily assimilated and put to use by the laboratory scientist. Although the emphasis is on least squares and associated techniques, it is hoped that the introductory sections are so complete that the mathematically mature scientist with little experience in statistical problems will become familiar enough with the concepts of elementary statistical estimation to be able to apply the methods with confidence and to read the more specialized statistical texts for treatment of the problems with which we do not deal here.

A critical Bibliography lists a number of recent texts or monographs in probability and statistics which the author has found useful or interesting and often both. In addition, a list of references to the statistical literature pertinent to the material of each chapter is appended to the individual chapter. Both the books and the papers will serve as entry points to the vast statistical literature, into which the reader may penetrate as deeply as his taste or time permits.

None of the material presented here is new. It is hoped, however, that the presentation is one which will give the average physicist or chemist new insight into the matters discussed. Many useful results are given without proof, and no attempt is made to present all of modern statistical theory in a rigorous manner. There are a number of books which almost adequately perform the latter important and interesting task, and it was felt that a great deal was to be gained here by making the presentations as brief and to the point as possible. On the other hand, some short proofs and derivations are given in the hope that the reader may gain some familiarity with the types of manipulation and reasoning involved and be tempted to work out new examples and proofs for himself.

As an aid to the study of the material presented, exercises are provided at the end of each chapter. These are often problems intended to extend further the material presented in the text proper and to lead the student or reader to a deeper insight into this material. Although some numerical exercises are provided, the scientific literature provides a wealth of material which can be used for illustration of all the points in the book. The reader may find it amusing to consider statements of statistical significance or estimates of probable error which he finds in the scientific literature and to decide whether he would make the same statements of significance or assign the same estimates of error.

Chapter 1 introduces the basic ideas of probability and statistics which are used in subsequent chapters. The concepts of probability distributions, expected values and moments, statistical estimation, and hypothesis testing are discussed at length. The chapter closes with a brief discussion of the theory of matrices and linear equations without which a discussion of multivariate least-squares techniques becomes unnecessarily cumbersome.

Chapter 2 discusses the estimation of parameters from univariate populations and introduces the basic distributions in common use: the normal, Student's t, chi-square, and the variance ratio F.

Chapter 3 treats briefly the classical methods of the analysis of variance: the estimation of population means and their differences from several samples.

Chapter 4 is the real heart of the book, presenting as it does the theory of linear least-squares adjustments, the error distribution of quadratic forms, and the theory of linear hypothesis tests.

Chapter 5 contains discussions of a number of miscellaneous statistical problems, most of which are related to the applications of the least-squares method. Some of these problems, e.g., non-linear least-squares and hypothesis tests and optimum experimental design, are the subjects of vigorous work by statisticians at the present time, and the discussions are necessarily incomplete and perhaps speculative. In this connection, it might be remarked that physical data and experimentation rarely conform in every respect to the idealized conditions implicit in every rigorous statistical test, and the scientist must therefore be prepared to use approximate methods and tests, realizing that his statements regarding probability of error are often more qualitative than they might appear.

Chapter 6 contains more extended numerical examples of the least-squares method than was possible in Chapter 4. In particular, applications to crystallography, radiochemistry, and infrared spectroscopy are illustrated.

Many of the topics commonly found in statistical texts have been omitted. The treatment of others is perhaps briefer than usual. The intent has been to present those methods which the author has found to be of most use in chemical physics. The Bibliography indicates other texts which he has found useful.

The author's interest in statistical methods originated during a collaboration with Dr. Verner Schomaker on the application of least-squares methods to electron diffraction data, and he owes a great debt to Dr. Schomaker for his stimulating conversations during that collaboration.

Appreciation is also due to Professors Robert D. Morrison, David Weeks, and Olan H. Hamilton, each of whom carefully read a semifinal version of the manuscript and made many suggestions to improve the correctness and clarity of the presentation. The author takes full responsibility for any remaining grotesque notation or obliquities in argument which may prove annoying to the professional statistician.

A number of the author's colleagues kindly supplied numerical examples and preprints of work pertinent to the textual material. Marjorie, Kim, Douglas, and Karl Hamilton provided an atmosphere of continual encouragement and interest.

WALTER CLARK HAMILTON

Upton, New York
May, 1964

Contents

STATISTICS IN
PHYSICAL SCIENCE

1

Basic Concepts and Mathematical Preliminaries

1–1. INTRODUCTION

Much of modern experimental physical science is concerned with the assignment of numerical values to quantities which occur in physical theories. This assignment is never absolutely accurate. No matter how well a measuring instrument is designed, there will always be limitations inherent in the materials and methods of construction which will make the reproducibility of the measurement impossible at some level.* The position of a pointer on a meter dial may with great care be determined to within perhaps one-hundredth of an inch, but we would be sorely pressed to distinguish the difference between two positions one-thousandth of an inch apart.

If there is some quantity which we want to know extremely well, we often measure it many times, by different methods, with different instruments, perhaps by different experimenters. We combine all the results in some way and then make the statement that the combination is more accurate than any single measurement, i.e., that it is likely to be closer to the

---

* This is aside from any uncertainties in the theoretical framework. We speak here of quantities theoretically measurable with arbitrary accuracy, the experimental determination being limited by the deficiencies in real materials and human observers.

true value. This statement may well not be true, especially if each of the measurements is subject to bias. We must ask ourselves what these statements mean; we must ask ourselves whether we have indeed determined the best value for the quantity of interest and what the relationship of this value is to the unknown true value. We must also decide whether there are significant differences between the different experimental results. We must be prepared with an answer in case a critic asks, "How well do you know this number? What assurances can you give me that I will get the same results when I repeat the experiment?"

The inability to make precise measurements is but one of the problems which arise when the results of experiments are to be tested against physical theories. Another problem which is becoming more and more important, as the sophistication of our experiments and our theories increases, arises in the fact that the quantities which we can most conveniently measure are not the quantities of basic interest in the theory. If we are to go from one to the other, we must invoke mathematical relationships between the two; these relationships may be simple or complex. In any case, if we have measured a quantity A with a given precision, we will want to know how well we know the value of a derived quantity B. A more general problem arises when we measure a multitude of quantities

$$A_1, A_2, \ldots, A_n \tag{1}$$

and wish to determine the values of a set of theoretical parameters

$$B_1, B_2, \ldots, B_m, \tag{2}$$

all of which are again interrelated, each being dependent on all the A_i. How are we to do this, given the fact that there are errors in the measurement of each A_i?

The solutions to these and related problems are the concern of statistical analysis, and the applications of statistical analysis to the treatment of experimental data in physical science are the concern of this book.

In this chapter, we will attempt to make more precise the relationship between measurement and statistics. We will introduce the concepts of *sample space* and *probability measure* over a sample space. This will be followed by a general discussion of probability density functions and expected values of random variables. The statistical part of the chapter concludes with a discussion of the estimation of parameters and the testing of hypotheses. We present in the closing section a brief introduction to matrix notation and the manipulation of large-scale linear systems; this material will be particularly useful in the discussion of the theory of least squares in Chapter 4.

The intent of this chapter is to provide an understanding of the basic concepts and terminology, rather than to give a thorough discussion of all the ramifications of each topic. The examples are thus brief and suggestive, while a more detailed application of the ideas introduced here is reserved to later chapters.

1–2. SAMPLE SPACES AND PROBABILITY

Let us first introduce a few of the concepts of abstract probability theory and show how they are related to quantitative experiments.

We assume that we are able to create a set of circumstances C that allow any number of repetitions; i.e., we perform an experiment, the initial conditions of which are reproducible. On establishing these circumstances, certain observations, the nature of which is unimportant to this discussion, may be made. Each such distinguishable set of observations resulting from a single establishment of the conditions C may be described as an *outcome* of the experiment. Denoting one such outcome by x_i, we may make a list of all possible outcomes:

$$x_1, x_2, x_3, \ldots, x_n. \tag{1}$$

This set of all possible outcomes is, in the language of probability theory, the *sample space;* each of the x_i is a point in this sample space, that is, a *sample point.* Any time the circumstances C are established (the experiment performed), the outcome must be one of the x_i.

This set of possible outcomes may also be called a *population.* In examining one of the x_i, i.e., in performing the experiment, we are drawing a sample of size one from the population of all possible outcomes. Hence the name *sample point* is a reasonable one. Depending on the nature of the experiment, the number of points in the sample space may be finite or infinite.

Although each sample point should be conceptually realizable, it is not necessary that it be physically possible in a given experiment; it is of course necessary that all possible physical outcomes be represented. A mathematical model for the sample space, chosen for its simplicity, may well include points other than those which we expect to find in the experiment.

Furthermore, the description of individual sample points may be more detailed than is necessary; it may be convenient to use the same sample space as a model for two experiments, where, for example, the points x_1, x_2, x_3 are distinguishable in one experiment but not in another.

It should also be carefully noted that each of the points in the sample space may represent a rather complicated array of numbers, not necessarily just one. The outcome x_i may be a complex set of experimental results.

Example 1–2–1

Suppose that a coin is tossed and that we can distinguish two possible outcomes: the coin lands heads up, or the coin lands tails up. An adequate sample space would consist of two points:

$$x_1 \equiv \text{heads}$$
$$x_2 \equiv \text{tails}.$$

Example 1–2–2

A coin is tossed twice, and each fall of the coin may be classified as heads or tails. An adequate sample space could consist of the following four points:

$$x_1 \equiv \text{heads followed by heads}$$
$$x_2 \equiv \text{heads followed by tails}$$
$$x_3 \equiv \text{tails followed by heads}$$
$$x_4 \equiv \text{tails followed by tails.}$$

Example 1–2–3

Suppose that we take a beaker containing 25 ml of a 0.1 N NaOH solution and a few drops of a suitable indicator. From a burette initially containing 50 ml of a 0.1 N HCl solution, we run out the solution into the beaker until the indicator changes color. At this point, we read the level of the liquid in the burette and record to the nearest 0.01 ml the volume of HCl used. Each sample point is a number with two decimal places, and a possible sample space is the set of 5001 numbers:

$$0.00, 0.01, 0.02, \ldots, 49.99, 50.00.$$

Most chemists would be surprised if certain of these numbers were the results of actual experiments. This illustrates the possibility that the sample space may contain sample points which are never realized in practice.

Example 1–2–4

The titration in the preceding example is carried out five times in succession. Each point in the sample space is now an ordered sequence of five numbers. The set of five titrations is regarded as a single experiment; one typical outcome might be the following:

$$x_i \equiv (24.83, 25.02, 25.61, 24.36, 24.99).$$

The entire sample space might consist of all possible ordered sequences of five numbers chosen from the set in Example 1–2–3. Since each titration can result in any one of 5001 numbers, the total number of points in such a sample space is 5001^5.

Example 1–2–5

The counting rate from a radioactive source is observed, to the nearest integral number of counts per minute, at one-minute intervals for 1000 minutes. Each point in the sample space is an ordered sequence of 1000 integers. The sample space may consist of all possible such sequences. We may wish to consider that every positive integer is a possible result for each rate. The number of points in the sample space is again infinite. Again, certain of these points will not be realized in practice.

Example 1–2–6

A crystal is exposed to x-rays in a camera of the type used by crystallographers. The intensities of the resulting 10,000 spots on the film are measured and recorded. Each point in the sample space is a list of 10,000 numbers, each identified as to position on the film and orientation of the crystal with respect to the x-ray beam.

The description of the sample space may depend upon the purpose of the experiment. That is, our definition of a distinguishable outcome may vary from case to case. For example, in most coin-tossing experiments, we choose to regard any one fall of heads as indistinguishable from another; we do not consider it relevant that in one case the top of the head is toward the north and in another case toward the south. The sample points could include such information, but it is usually desirable to make the description of the sample points, and hence the sample space, as simple as possible. On the other hand, if we are tossing the coin to determine whether to go to the beach, we might wish to consider a sample space containing a more detailed description of the coin, e.g.,

$$x_1 \equiv \text{heads, and the temperature of the coin is } 5° \text{ C.}$$

To be safe, the description of the sample points should include all information of likely use. Then in any particular experiment, if the description is too detailed, we can combine a few or many points for the purposes of the single experiment. For this purpose, it is convenient to define an *event* as a subset of points in the sample space. A notation frequently used for the description of an event A is

$$A \equiv \{x_1, x_2, \ldots, x_k\} \tag{2}$$

or

$$A \equiv \{x_i | i = 1, 2, \ldots, k\}.$$

This means that the event A consists of the sample points x_1 through x_k. An event A is said to have *occurred* if the sample point representing the outcome of the experiment is a member of the set A.

The event consisting of all the points in the sample space will be denoted here by S, i.e.,

$$S \equiv \{x_i | i = 1, 2, \ldots, n\}. \tag{3}$$

Example 1–2–7

A coin is tossed twice, with the purpose of guessing whether it has two heads. It is sufficient to consider the sample space as consisting of two events,

$$A \equiv \{x_1\}$$
$$B \equiv \{x_2, \, x_3, \, x_4\},$$

where the sample points are labeled as in Example 1–2–2. If the outcome of the experiment is x_2, x_3, or x_4, we say that event B has occurred and may conclude that the coin does not have two heads. (The conclusion is not relevant to the present discussion.)

We define the *intersection* of two events A and B as the event C which contains the points common to A and B. This is written as

$$C \equiv A \cap B. \tag{4}$$

Example 1–2–8

If

$$A \equiv \{x_i | i = 1, 2, \ldots, 10\}$$
$$B \equiv \{x_i | i = 5, 6, \ldots, 15\},$$

then the intersection of A and B is

$$A \cap B \equiv C = \{x_i | i = 5, 6, \ldots, 10\}.$$

If there are no points in common, we say that the event or set C is *empty,* and write

$$A \cap B \equiv 0. \tag{5}$$

In this case, we also say that the events are *distinct* or *disjoint.*

We define the *union* of the sets A and B as the event C which contains all points lying in either A or B (or in both), and write

$$C \equiv A \cup B. \tag{6}$$

Example 1–2–9

If the events A and B are defined as in Example 1–2–8, we have

$$A \cup B \equiv C \equiv \{x_i | i = 1, 2, \ldots, 15\}.$$

It is useful also to consider the event "not-A" which contains all the points of the sample space not in A. Recalling that S is the entire set of points in the sample space, this event may be written as

$$\overline{A} = S - A. \tag{7}$$

and is called the *complement* of A. The concepts discussed in the preceding few paragraphs may be made more clear by an examination of Figure 1–1.

$A \cap B$ and $A \cup B$ may also be read "A and B" and "A or B" respectively, where *or* includes the possibility *and.*

In order for the concept of sample space to be useful to us in our dis-

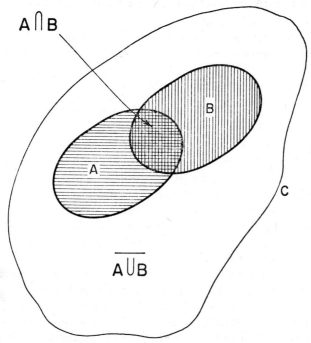

Fig. 1–1. Symbolic representation of some concepts associated with a sample space. The sample space S consists of all points on the interior of the curve C. The event A consists of all points in the horizontally shaded area; the event B consists of all points in the vertically shaded area. The intersection $A \cap B$ is represented by the area where the two shaded areas overlap. The union $A \cup B$ is represented by the entire shaded area. The non-shaded area lying inside the curve C is the complement of $A \cup B$ and may be denoted by $\overline{A \cup B}$ or $S - (A \cup B)$.

cussion of statistics, we must introduce one further notion, that of probability. Formally, we may proceed as follows: To every event A in the sample space S, we will assign a number $P(A)$, called the *probability of A*, having the following characteristics:

(a) $P(A)$ is a positive real number not greater than 1.

(b) $P(A \cup B) = P(A) + P(B)$ if and only if $A \cap B$ is empty.   (8)

(c) $P(S) = 1$ where S is the event consisting of all points in the sample space.*

These are the fundamental requirements for a probability measure in abstract probability theory. In order for the concept to be in agreement with our "common-sense" notions of probability, i.e., to be useful to us in

---

* It follows from conditions (b) and (c) that $P(\overline{A}) = 1 - P(A)$.

applications to experimental science, we would like $P(A)$ to have additional properties:

1. If the experiment C is performed n times, where n is a large number, and in these n trials the number of occurrences of the event A is m, we would like to be certain that the ratio m/n differs little from $P(A)$.
2. If $P(A)$ is very small, we would like to be almost certain that if we perform the experiment once, the event A does not occur at all.
3. If $P(A)$ is near 1, we would like to be almost certain that if we perform the experiment once, the event A will occur.

These conditions are not very precise and probably cannot be made so in a way which will satisfy everyone. In applying the rigorous theorems of probability theory and mathematical statistics to actual physical events, we can say little more than is expressed in the numbered statements above. In many cases, we do not repeat an experiment many times but base our arguments on hypothetical repetition with some arguments about our past experience in cases where the experiments have been repeated. Thus, when we say that the probability of our obtaining a result different from the one actually found is low, we mean that if we *did* repeat the experiment, we should be rather surprised if a different result were found.

If we do indeed perform an experiment many times, we may wish to take the ratio m/n which actually occurs as a definition for $P(A)$. That is, the probability is determined by what has actually occurred. We then may set up a theoretical model for the sample space and the associated probability measure which satisfies the experimental determination. This theoretical model may then be used as a probability model for future experiments of a similar type. Unfortunately, if future results turn out to be extremely improbable under the assumed model, we are tempted to throw out the model, and it is here that the paradox arises.*

To summarize these last few ideas, let us ask again what the situation is with regard to the application of probability ideas to experimental measurement. Before performing an experiment, we will assume that $P(A)$, or at least the functional form of $P(A)$, for the pertinent sample space is known. This knowledge will generally have been obtained from the application of the pragmatic definition to experiments of a similar type.

Example 1-2-10

In the coin-tossing experiment in Example 1-2-1, a probability assignment

$$P(x_1) = P(x_2) = \tfrac{1}{2}$$

would be agreed upon as a sensible model by most people.

---

* Many interesting philosophical questions arise in the application of probability theory to statistics. These can only be hinted at here. An eye-opening discussion may be found in the delightful little book by Brown (see Bibliography).

Example 1–2–11

A suitable model for Example 1–2–7 might be

$$P(A) = \tfrac{1}{4}$$
$$P(B) = \tfrac{3}{4}.$$

This assumes a fair coin, i.e., the coin *defined* by $P(x_i) = \tfrac{1}{2}$. If we have advance information that the coin does indeed have two heads, we might more reasonably choose a model with

$$P(A) = 1$$
$$P(B) = 0.$$

Example 1–2–12

In Example 1–2–3, most competent chemists would agree that a reasonable model would have a maximum value of $P(A)$ for $A \equiv \{25.00\}$ and that

$$P(\{x|x < 24.00\}) * = 0$$
$$P(\{x|x > 26.00\}) \quad = 0.$$

Example 1–2–13 (The Binomial Distribution)

We consider that an experiment has two possible outcomes only. These outcomes are labeled *success* and *failure;* the sample space for the experiment consists of two points only. The probabilities are assigned as follows:

$$P(\text{success}) = p$$
$$P(\text{failure}) = 1 - p = q.$$

Such an experiment is known as a *Bernoulli trial.* Consider now the more general experiment of n Bernoulli trials. The outcome will be a sequence of n terms, each being either success or failure. The number of sample points will be 2^n, and the probability associated with each point will be

$$p^k q^{n-k}$$

if this point represents an outcome which includes k successes and $n - k$ failures, regardless of order. If we are interested only in the total number of successes and not in their order, the probability for k successes in n trials is the probability for each point as given above, $p^k q^{n-k}$, multiplied by the number of points which include exactly k successes, i.e.,

---

* This is to be interpreted as the probability of the event G, where G consists of all sample points x satisfying the condition $x < 24.00$.

$$C(n, k) \equiv \binom{n}{k}.^*$$

Thus the probability for the event A, where A consists of all sample points having k successes for n trials, is given by

$$P(A) = b_n(k) = \binom{n}{k} p^k q^{n-k}.$$

The function $b_n(k)$, defined for $k = 0, 1, 2, \ldots, n$, is the binomial probability function for n trials. It is important to note that this is a theoretical model, but one which experience tells us is applicable to such experiments as coin-tossing, where, for example, the condition

$$p = q = \tfrac{1}{2}$$

defines a fair coin.

Example 1–2–14 (Poisson Distribution)

If we assume that the occurrence of a particular phenomenon is random in time but with a fixed probability of occurrence in unit time, then the probability of k events occurring in unit time is given by

$$p(k) = \frac{e^{-\lambda}\lambda^k}{k!},$$

where λ is a parameter which will be shown in Section 1–4 to be equal to the average number of occurrences in unit time. This is the Poisson distribution, which seems to provide a satisfactory probability model for many naturally occurring processes, the most familiar of which is probably radioactive decay. It is interesting to note that the Poisson distribution is the limit of the binomial distribution as n increases without limit and p decreases in such a way that $pn = \lambda$ is a constant. Thus, an observation for a small interval of time Δt may be considered as a Bernoulli trial, $p = \lambda \Delta t$ being the probability of success in this interval. As Δt approaches 0, so does p, and the number of observations $1/\Delta t = n$ increases without limit, so that

$$pn = \lambda \Delta t \cdot \frac{1}{\Delta t} = \lambda.$$

1–3. CONDITIONAL PROBABILITY

Suppose that the outcome x_1 of an experiment belongs to event B, i.e., event B has occurred; what can be said about the probability that event

---

* The *binomial coefficient* $C(n, k)$ is the number of ways of distributing k articles (successes) into n boxes (trials), where each box can hold but one article. This may be shown by elementary combinatorial theory (which we do not pretend to cover in this book) to be equal to $n!/k!(n - k)!$. See, for example, Feller (Bibliography).

A has occurred? This is known as the conditional probability of A, knowing B, and is usually written $P(A|B)$. An examination of Figure 1-1 will convince the reader that

$$P(A|B) = P(A \cap B)/P(B) *$$ (1)

provided only that $P(B) \neq 0$. If $P(B) = 0$, the conditional probability is undefined. When we say that B has occurred, we have restricted the sample space so that there is no longer any possibility that the sample point which has occurred lies in $S - B$. We effectively renormalize the probability measure, so that $P(B|B) = 1$. The event B has occurred; its probability, after the fact, is unity.

Clearly, if the intersection of A and B is empty, the conditional probability of A, knowing B, is zero. If, on the other hand, B is completely contained in A,

$$A \cap B = B$$ (2)

and

$$P(A|B) = 1.$$ (3)

Example 1-3-1

Two coins are tossed. Each has a probability of $\frac{1}{2}$ for heads and $\frac{1}{2}$ for tails. I am told that at least one of the coins has fallen heads. What is the probability that the other is tails? Let the event A denote at least one tail and the event B, at least one head. Then the event AB has probability $\frac{1}{2}$ corresponding to the two falls HT and TH. The probability of event B is $\frac{3}{4}$. Hence

$$P(A|B) = (\tfrac{1}{2})/(\tfrac{3}{4}) = \tfrac{2}{3}.$$

The probability that the other coin is tails is $\frac{2}{3}$, a result that one naïvely might not expect.

Suppose the entire sample space is divided into mutually exclusive and exhaustive events B_i, $i = 1, \ldots, n$:

$$B_i \cap B_j = 0 \quad \text{for} \quad i \neq j.$$ (4)

We know from the considerations in the preceding paragraph that

$$P(B_k|A) = P(B_k \cap A)/P(A)$$ (5)

and also that

$$P(B_k \cap A) = P(B_k)P(A|B_k).$$ (6)

Since the events B_i are mutually exclusive, it may be shown that

$$\sum_{j=1}^{n} P(A|B_j)P(B_j) = P(A).$$ (7)

* $P(A \cap B)$ is sometimes written $P(AB)$.

Substituting expression (7) for $P(A)$ into (5), we obtain

$$P(B_k|A) = \frac{P(B_k)P(A|B_k)}{\sum\limits_{j} P(B_j)P(A|B_j)}. \tag{8}$$

Expression (8) is known as *Bayes' rule* for conditional probabilities.

Example 1-3-2

Suppose we are given three boxes, one containing two red balls, one containing two black balls, and the third containing one red ball and one black ball. We choose a box at random, i.e., with equal *a priori* probability, and then draw one ball from it. We find that the ball is red. What is the probability that the second ball will also be red, i.e., that we have chosen box number one? The mutually exclusive events are

$B_1 \equiv$ chosen box has two red balls
$B_2 \equiv$ chosen box has two black balls
$B_3 \equiv$ chosen box has one red and one black ball.

When we say that we have chosen the box at random, we mean that

$$P(B_1) = P(B_2) = P(B_3) = \tfrac{1}{3}.$$

Let A denote the event: A red ball is drawn. Then

$$P(A|B_1) = 1$$
$$P(A|B_2) = 0$$
$$P(A|B_3) = \tfrac{1}{2}.$$

Then the probability that the first box was the chosen one is

$$P(B_1|A) = \frac{\tfrac{1}{3}\cdot 1}{\tfrac{1}{3}\cdot 1 + \tfrac{1}{3}\cdot 0 + \tfrac{1}{3}\cdot\tfrac{1}{2}}$$
$$= \tfrac{2}{3}.$$

1-4. CONTINUOUS PROBABILITY DISTRIBUTIONS

In Section 1-2, we have defined a probability function $P(A)$ over a sample space as a real-valued function satisfying certain conditions. To each event of the sample space we have assigned a real number having characteristics which allow it to be identified in a suitable way with the pragmatic probability of experimental measurement. In the examples given in the previous two sections, we have assumed that the sample space consisted of discrete points and hence that $P(A)$ was a function of a discrete variable. For most of our applications, however, it will be more convenient to consider probability functions which are continuous functions of some variable associated with the sample space.

Let us assume that the sample space is such that each point of the sample space can be characterized by the value of a continuous variable x which can take on all values between $-\infty$ and $+\infty$. If the event A is defined as the set of all sample points characterized by the inequality

$$x \leqslant x^0, \tag{1}$$

we define the *cumulative probability distribution function* $F(x^0)$ and the *probability density function* $\phi(x^0)$ by

$$P(A) \equiv F(x^0) = \int_{-\infty}^{x^0} \phi(x)\, dx. \tag{2}$$

The density function $\phi(x)$ has the additional significance that

$$P(x^0 \leqslant x \leqslant x^0 + dx) = \phi(x^0)\, dx.^* \tag{3}$$

In accordance with our requirements that the total probability for the sample space be equal to unity, we require that $\phi(x)$ include a normalization factor such that

$$F(\infty) = \int_{-\infty}^{+\infty} \phi(x)\, dx = 1.\dagger \tag{4}$$

The basic requirement for any probability density function is that this integral exist. We furthermore require that

$$\phi(x) \geqslant 0 \quad \text{for} \quad -\infty < x < +\infty. \tag{5}$$

One of the most widely used concepts in statistics is that of the *random variable*. A random variable is a function which takes on a definite value at every point of a sample space. Thus, if we have a sample space S with an associated probability measure P and a random variable X defined over the sample space, to each point x_i of S, we can assign a probability measure $P(x_i)$ and a definite numerical value $X(x_i)$ for the random variable.

Example 1-4-1

The *uniform density function* is defined by

$$\phi(x) = \frac{1}{2a} \quad \text{for} \quad -a \leqslant x \leqslant a$$

$$\phi(x) = 0 \quad \text{otherwise.}$$

The differential and integral forms are shown in Figure 1-2a. The number a is a parameter which specifies a particular density function from the infinitely many of the same form.

---

* It is not uncommon in the non-specialist literature to find the probability density function called a distribution function. However, it seems best to distinguish between the two.

† Other appropriate limits may be substituted. The integral is to be taken over the entire sample space, whatever it may be.

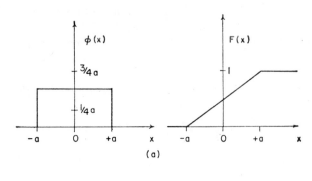

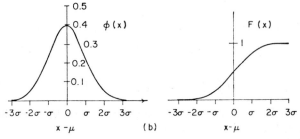

Fig. 1–2. Probability density functions $\phi(x)$ and cumulative probability density functions $F(x)$ for (a) the uniform density function and (b) the normal density function with mean μ and standard deviation σ.

Example 1–4–2

The *normal* or *Gaussian density function* is defined as follows:

$$\phi(x) = \frac{1}{\sigma(2\pi)^{1/2}} \exp\left[-\frac{(x-\mu)^2}{2\sigma^2}\right].$$

This probability function, illustrated in Figure 1–2*b* is perhaps the most common one used in experimental science; it is frequently assumed for the result of a measurement x if the true probability density function is unknown. This assumption, although open to question in many cases, has a certain validity, especially as a limiting case, as will be shown in Section 2–3. The quantities σ and μ are the parameters of the density function.

Further examples of continuous probability density functions will be given in Chapter 2.

Multivariate Density Functions. If there are several numerical variables

$$x_1, x_2, \ldots, x_n \tag{6}$$

associated with each point in the sample space, we may define a multi-variate probability density function as follows:

$$\phi(x_1^0, x_2^0, \ldots, x_n^0) \, dx_1 \, dx_2 \cdots dx_n$$
$$= P(x_i^0 \leqslant x_i \leqslant x_i^0 + dx_i, \quad i = 1, 2, \ldots, n). \quad (7)$$

The term on the right side of Eq. (7) is to be interpreted as the probability that the inequalities

$$
\begin{aligned}
x_1^0 &\leqslant x_1 \leqslant x_1^0 + dx_1 \\
x_2^0 &\leqslant x_2 \leqslant x_2^0 + dx_2 \\
&\cdots\cdots\cdots\cdots \\
x_n^0 &\leqslant x_n \leqslant x_n^0 + dx_n
\end{aligned}
\qquad (8)
$$

all hold simultaneously. The density function so defined is also known as the *joint density function* of the x_i, and the integrated form

$$F(x_1^0, x_2^0, \ldots, x_n^0) = \int_{-\infty}^{x_1^0} \cdots \int_{-\infty}^{x_n^0} \phi(x_1, x_2, \ldots, x_n) \, dx_1 \, dx_2 \cdots dx_n \quad (9)$$

is the *joint cumulative distribution function*. Again the density function is assumed to be normalized so that

$$\int_{-\infty}^{+\infty} \cdots \int_{-\infty}^{+\infty} \phi(x_1, x_2, \ldots, x_n) \, dx_1 \, dx_2 \cdots dx_n = 1. \quad (10)$$

The *marginal density function* for x_j is the density function for x_j obtained when the entire density function is integrated over the whole range of all variables with the exception of x_j. We will denote this function by $\phi^M(x_j)$; for example,

$$\phi^M(x_1) = \int_{-\infty}^{+\infty} \cdots \int_{-\infty}^{+\infty} \phi(x_1, x_2, \ldots, x_n) \, dx_2 \, dx_3 \cdots dx_n. \quad (11)$$

It is thus a univariate density function which gives the probability that x_j lies in a given range, irrespective of the values of the other variables. We may also define a marginal density function of any m of the n variables as the density function obtained by integrating over the whole range of the remaining $n - m$ variables. For example, the marginal density function for the first m variables is given by

$$\phi^M(x_1, x_2, \ldots, x_m) = \int_{-\infty}^{+\infty} \cdots \int_{-\infty}^{+\infty} \phi(x_1, x_2, \ldots, x_n) \, dx_{m+1} \cdots dx_n. \quad (12)$$

This is again a multivariate density function of dimension m. In a sense it is a projection of the n-dimensional probability space onto an m-dimensional space.

The *conditional probability density* function of any m of the variables is the probability density function of these m variables, given that the other $n - m$ variables have certain fixed values. In exactly the same manner as for the discrete sample spaces (see Section 1–3), the conditional density function is obtained by dividing the density function for all the variables by the marginal density function for those variables whose values are fixed:

$$\phi^C(x_1, x_2, \ldots, x_m | x^0_{m+1}, x^0_{m+2}, \ldots, x^0_n)$$

$$= \frac{\phi(x_1, \ldots, x_m, x^0_{m+1}, \ldots, x^0_n)}{\phi^M(x^0_{m+1}, \ldots, x^0_n)}$$

$$= \frac{\phi(x_1, \ldots, x_m, x^0_{m+1}, \ldots, x^0_n)}{\int_{-\infty}^{+\infty} \cdots \int_{-\infty}^{+\infty} \phi(x_1, \ldots, x_m, x^0_{m+1}, \ldots, x^0_n) \, dx_1 \cdots dx_m}. \quad (13)$$

If

$$\phi(x_1, \ldots, x_n) = \phi_1(x_1, \ldots, x_m)\phi_2(x_{m+1}, \ldots, x_n), \quad (14)$$

then the two sets of variables $(x_1, \ldots, x_m)$ and $(x_{m+1}, \ldots, x_n)$ are said to be statistically *independent*. If this is the case, the conditional probability is equal to the marginal probability as follows:

$$\phi^C(x_1, \ldots, x_m | x_{m+1}, \ldots, x_n) = \phi^M(x_1, \ldots, x_m), \quad (15)$$

whatever the values of $(x_{m+1}, \ldots, x_n)$.

Example 1–4–3

One of the most familiar multivariate probability functions is the multivariate normal density function, which will be treated in greater detail in Section 4–3. We give here an example of the bivariate normal density function with zero means:

$$\phi(x_1, x_2) = \frac{1}{2\pi D^{1/2}} \exp\left[-\frac{1}{2D}(m_{22}x_1^2 - 2m_{12}x_1x_2 + m_{11}x_2^2)\right],$$

where

$$D = m_{11}m_{22} - m^2_{12}.$$

By integrating over y or x, we obtain respectively the marginal density functions:

$$\phi^M(x_1) = \frac{1}{(2\pi m_{11})^{1/2}} \exp\left(-x_1^2/2m_{11}\right)$$

$$\phi^M(x_2) = \frac{1}{(2\pi m_{22})^{1/2}} \exp\left(-x_2^2/2m_{22}\right),$$

which are again normal density functions in one variable. The conditional density functions are obtained as follows:

$$\phi^C(x_1|x_2) = \frac{\phi(x_1, x_2)}{\phi^M(x_2)} = \left(\frac{m_{22}}{2\pi D}\right)^{1/2} \exp\left[-\frac{m_{22}}{2D}(x_1 - m_{12}x_2/m_{22})^2\right],$$

with an analogous expression for $\phi^C(x_2|x_1)$ obtained by interchanging the subscripts. When x_1 and x_2 are independent, $m_{12} = 0$, and

$$\phi(x_1, x_2) = \phi^M(x_1)\phi^M(x_2) = \phi^C(x_1|x_2)\phi^C(x_2|x_1).$$

1–5. FUNCTIONS OF A RANDOM VARIABLE

Frequently, we know the probability density function for a random variable but find that it is some function of this random variable that is interesting to us from an experimental point of view. How is the probability density function for this new variable to be obtained?

If x is a random variable with associated continuous probability density function $\phi_x(x)$, and if $y = y(x)$ is a monotonic strictly increasing or strictly decreasing function of x such that $x = x(y)$ has a unique solution for every y of interest, then y has a continuous probability density function given by

$$\phi_y(y) = \phi_x\{x(y)\}\left|\frac{dx}{dy}\right|. \tag{1}$$

That is, we solve the defining equation $y = y(x)$ for x in terms of y, substitute this value in the density function for x and multiply by the *absolute value* of the derivative of x with respect to y, again replacing x by its equivalent expression in terms of y.

Example 1–5–1

Suppose that x is a continuous random variable, defined over the range $-\infty < x < +\infty$, with density function

$$\phi_x(x) = \frac{1}{(2\pi)^{1/2}} \exp\left(-\tfrac{1}{2}x^2\right),$$

what is the density function for the linear function of x defined by

$$y = ax + b?$$

We first solve for x and dx/dy:

$$x = \frac{y - b}{a}$$

$$\frac{dx}{dy} = \frac{1}{a}$$

Using Eq. (1) above, we find

$$\phi_y(y) = \frac{1}{(2\pi)^{1/2}} \exp\left[-\frac{1}{2}\left(\frac{y - b}{a}\right)^2\right]\left|\frac{1}{a}\right|$$

$$= \frac{1}{|a|(2\pi)^{1/2}} \exp\left[-\frac{1}{2}\left(\frac{y - b}{a}\right)^2\right]$$

A common application of the latter expression is the standardization of a normally distributed random variable to a random variable of zero mean and unit variance (see Section 2–3).

Consider now the more general cases where y is not a monotonic function of x but has a continuous non-zero derivative at all but a finite number of points. Then the range of the variable x may be broken up into a finite number of sections, in each of which y is a monotonic strictly increasing or strictly decreasing function of x with a continuous derivative. Then at all points where dy/dx is non-zero and where the equation $y = y(x)$ has a real finite solution for $x = x(y)$, we have

$$\phi_y(y) = \sum \phi_x\{x(y)\} \left|\frac{dy}{dx}\right|^{-1}, \tag{2}$$

where the sum is over all values x which are solutions of $y = y(x)$. At points where $dy/dx = 0$ or where $y = y(x)$ has no real finite solution for $x = x(y)$, we set $\phi_y(y) = 0$.

Example 1–5–2

Again let the random variable x have the normal density function:

$$\phi_x(x) = \frac{1}{(2\pi)^{1/2}} \exp\left(-\tfrac{1}{2}x^2\right)$$

and consider the function

$$y = x^2.$$

Now $x = \pm y^{1/2}$, and $dy/dx = 2x = \pm 2y^{1/2}$, the sign being negative for $x < 0$ and positive for $x > 0$. Since x is not real for $y < 0$, we have

$$\phi_y(y) = 0 \quad \text{for} \quad y < 0.$$

Furthermore, $dy/dx = 0$ for $y = 0$, and hence

$$\phi_y(y) = 0 \quad \text{for} \quad y = 0.$$

Finally, for positive values of y, we have

$$\phi_y(y) = \frac{1}{2y^{1/2}} \{\phi_x(-y^{1/2}) + \phi_x(+y^{1/2})\}$$

$$= \frac{1}{2y^{1/2}} \left\{ \frac{1}{(2\pi)^{1/2}} e^{-y/2} + \frac{1}{(2\pi)^{1/2}} e^{-y/2} \right\}$$

$$= \frac{1}{(2\pi y)^{1/2}} e^{-y/2}.$$

Example 1–5–3

Let $y = 1/x$ and consequently $x = 1/y$. Then $dy/dx = -1/x^2 = -y^2$. For $y = 0$, x is not finite. Hence

$$\phi_y(0) = 0.$$

If x is again normally distributed as in the preceding example, we have

$$\phi_y(y) = \frac{1}{y^2(2\pi)^{1/2}} \exp\left(-\tfrac{1}{2}y^2\right) \quad \text{for} \quad y \neq 0.$$

Example 1–5–4

Let $y = |x|$. This has no solution for $y < 0$. Furthermore dy/dx is discontinuous at $x = 0$. Therefore

$$\phi_y(y) = 0 \quad \text{if} \quad y \leqslant 0.$$

Again if $\phi_x(x)$ is the unit normal density function, then

$$\phi_y(y) = \frac{2}{(2\pi)^{1/2}} \exp\left(-\tfrac{1}{2}y^2\right) \quad \text{for} \quad y > 0.$$

Example 1–5–5

If y is equal to the principal value of $(2/\pi) \tan^{-1} x$, then $x = \tan(\pi y/2)$ and $dy/dx = (2/\pi)[1/(1 + x^2)]$. If $\phi_x(x) = [1/(2\pi)^{1/2}] e^{-x^2/2}$, then

$$\phi_y(y) = \frac{\pi}{2}\left\{1 + \tan^2 \frac{\pi y}{2}\right\} e^{-(1/2)\tan^2(\pi y/2)}$$

for $-1 < y < +1$. For other values of y, $\phi_y(y) = 0$.

The probability density functions for the functions described in the preceding examples are illustrated in Figure 1–3.

Similar relationships hold between multivariate density functions. Consider the case where n random variables

$$y_1, y_2, \ldots, y_n \tag{3}$$

can be expressed as functions of n random variables

$$x_1, x_2, \ldots, x_n \tag{4}$$

by a set of equations

$$y_i = y_i(x_1, x_2, \ldots, x_n); \quad i = 1, 2, \ldots, n \tag{5}$$

such that the y_i have continuous partial derivatives $\partial y_i/\partial x_j$ for all values of the x_j. Furthermore, assume that the Jacobian

$$J = \det\left\{\frac{\partial y_i}{\partial x_j}\right\} = \begin{vmatrix} \dfrac{\partial y_1}{\partial x_1} & \dfrac{\partial y_1}{\partial x_2} & \cdots & \dfrac{\partial y_1}{\partial x_n} \\[2mm] \dfrac{\partial y_2}{\partial x_1} & \dfrac{\partial y_2}{\partial x_2} & \cdots & \dfrac{\partial y_2}{\partial x_n} \\[2mm] \cdot & \cdot & \cdots & \cdot \\ \cdot & \cdot & \cdots & \cdot \\ \cdot & \cdot & \cdots & \cdot \\[2mm] \dfrac{\partial y_n}{\partial x_1} & \dfrac{\partial y_n}{\partial x_2} & \cdots & \dfrac{\partial y_n}{\partial x_n} \end{vmatrix} \tag{6}$$

does not vanish in the region of interest. Then in the region where there is a unique solution for the x_j in terms of the y_i, we can write

$$\phi_y(y_1, \ldots, y_n) = |J|^{-1}\phi_x(x_1, \ldots, x_n), \tag{7}$$

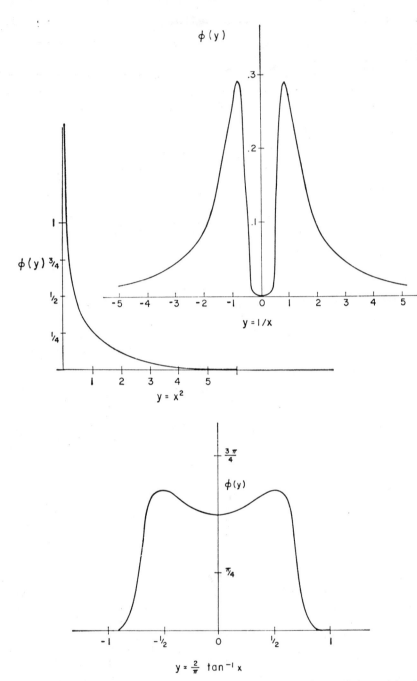

Fig. 1–3. Probability density functions $\phi_y(y)$ for various functions $y = y(x)$ when the probability density function for x is the normal density function with zero mean and unit variance.

where in the density function on the right-hand side we have substituted the solutions for the x_j in terms of the y_i.

As in the univariate case, extensions can be made to the case where more than one value of x_j may correspond to a single value of y_i, but, as we will make no direct use of these, we will not present the precise formulation.

Example 1–5–6

In the treatment of linear least-squares adjustments in Chapter 4, we will be interested in linear functions of the type

$$\mathbf{Y}_{n,1} = \mathbf{A}_{n,n}\mathbf{X}_{n,1} + \mathbf{B}_{n,1}.^{*}$$

Then

$$\mathbf{X} = \mathbf{A}^{-1}(\mathbf{Y} - \mathbf{B})$$

and

$$J = \det \mathbf{A}.$$

It follows that

$$\phi_y(\mathbf{Y}) = \phi_x\{\mathbf{A}^{-1}(\mathbf{Y} - \mathbf{B})\}|\det \mathbf{A}|^{-1}.$$

This does not exist if the matrix $\mathbf{A}$ is singular, i.e., has a vanishing determinant.

Example 1–5–7

Let x_1 and x_2 have the bivariate density function

$$\phi_x(x_1, x_2) = \frac{1}{2\pi} \exp\left[-\tfrac{1}{2}(x_1^2 + x_2^2)\right].$$

Thus x_1 and x_2 are independent, normally distributed random variables. Consider the functions

$$y_1 = \frac{x_1}{x_2} \quad \text{and} \quad y_2 = x_1.$$

The inverse solution is

$$x_1 = y_2 \quad \text{and} \quad x_2 = \frac{y_2}{y_1}.$$

The Jacobian is

$$J = \det \begin{pmatrix} \dfrac{1}{x_2} & -\dfrac{x_1}{x_2^2} \\ 1 & 0 \end{pmatrix} = \frac{x_1}{x_2^2} = \frac{y_1^2}{y_2}.$$

By substitution in Eq. (7), we find that

$$\phi_y(y_1, y_2) = \frac{y_2}{y_1^2} \frac{1}{2\pi} \exp\left[-\frac{1}{2}\left(y_2^2 + \frac{y_2^2}{y_1^2}\right)\right]$$

* This is a matrix equation, the dimensions of the matrices being given as subscripts. See Section 1–8.

except at $y_1 = 0$, where the solution $x_2 = y_2/y_1$ is not finite. It is of interest to examine the marginal distribution for y_1, which is the ratio of two standardized normal deviates. We have

$$\phi^M(y_1) = \frac{1}{2\pi y_1{}^2} \int_{-\infty}^{+\infty} |y_2| \exp\left[-\frac{1}{2} y_2{}^2 \left(1 + \frac{1}{y_1{}^2}\right)\right] dy_2$$

$$= \frac{1}{\pi(1 + y_1{}^2)} \quad \text{for} \quad y_1 \neq 0$$

$$= 0 \qquad\qquad \text{for} \quad y_1 = 0.$$

1–6. EXPECTED VALUES AND MOMENTS

Consider a sample space, a random variable x defined over this sample space, and some function of x: $f(x)$. We define the *expected value* of $f(x)$ as

$$\mathcal{E}\{f(x)\} = \sum_S f(x)P(x) \text{ *} \tag{1}$$

if the sample space is discrete, with probability measure $P(x)$; the sum is over all points of the sample space S. If the sample space is continuous with probability density function $\phi(x)$, the expected value is defined as

$$\mathcal{E}\{f(x)\} = \int_{-\infty}^{+\infty} f(x)\phi(x)\, dx. \tag{2}$$

In either case, the expected value is defined only if the sum or integral exists. In most of the following discussion, we shall use the notation appropriate to the continuous case, but the results for the discrete case are completely analogous.

The expected value of the random variable itself

$$\mathcal{E}\{x\} \equiv \mu'_1 = \int_{-\infty}^{+\infty} x\phi(x)\, dx = \mu \tag{3}$$

is called the *mean* value of x or the mean of the distribution.

$$\mathcal{E}\{x^2\} \equiv \mu'_2 = \int_{-\infty}^{+\infty} x^2\phi(x)\, dx \tag{4}$$

is the *second moment* of the distribution, and in general

$$\mathcal{E}\{x^n\} \equiv \mu'_n = \int_{-\infty}^{+\infty} x^n\phi(x)\, dx \tag{5}$$

is called the nth moment of the distribution. The moment is said to exist only if the integral exists, i.e., has a finite value,† or in the case of a discrete

---

* The notation $\bar{f}$ and $\langle f \rangle$, sometimes seen in the scientific literature for expected values of observables over a probability distribution function, have rather special meanings in the statistical literature and should *not* be used to denote statistical expectation.

† For most of the distributions with which we will be concerned, it is sufficient that the integral exist in the ordinary (Riemann) sense. It is shown in most advanced texts on probability theory that this condition is more restrictive than necessary and that a more general definition of integration (Lebesgue) is sufficient. This refinement need not concern the user of this book.

distribution, if the sum converges absolutely. If the nth moment exists, so do all moments of lower order.

The second moment is of particular importance in statistical problems. If it exists, so does the mean μ. It will be convenient in many of our applications to fix our attention on the deviation from the mean, $(x - \mu)$. Of particular importance is the expected value of $(x - \mu)^2$. We have

$$\mathcal{E}\{(x - \mu)^2\} = \mathcal{E}\{x^2\} - 2\mathcal{E}\{x\mu\} + \mathcal{E}\{\mu^2\} \; * \tag{6}$$
$$= \mathcal{E}\{x^2\} - (\mathcal{E}\{x\})^2.$$

This quantity is known as the *variance* of x:

$$\sigma^2(x) \equiv \text{var } (x) \equiv \mathcal{E}\{(x - \mu)^2\} = \mathcal{E}\{x^2\} - \mu^2, \tag{7}$$

and its positive square root σ is called the *standard deviation* of x.

The standard deviation is by far the most commonly used measure of the dispersion of a probability distribution. The *mean deviation*,

$$\mathcal{E}\{|x - \mu|\},$$

although occasionally cited along with experimental results, is in general not such a convenient quantity as the standard deviation. The relationship between the two can be determined only if the probability distribution function is known.

In general,

$$\mu_n \equiv \mathcal{E}\{(x - \mu)^n\} \tag{8}$$

is called the nth *central moment* or the nth moment about the mean. The variance is thus the second central moment.

Moment Generating Functions. A useful concept in the theory of probability distributions is that of the moment generating function, defined formally as

$$M(q) \equiv \mathcal{E}\{e^{qx}\}, \tag{9}$$

where q is a dummy variable. Thus

$$M(q) = \int_{-\infty}^{+\infty} e^{qx}\phi(x) \, dx. \tag{10}$$

Expanding the exponential in (10), we obtain

$$M(q) = \int_{-\infty}^{+\infty} \left(1 + qx + \frac{(qx)^2}{2!} + \cdots\right) \phi(x) \, dx$$

$$= 1 + \mu'_1 q + \mu'_2 \frac{q^2}{2!} + \cdots, \tag{11}$$

where we have again written μ'_n for the nth moment of $\phi(x)$. $M(q)$ can be recognized as a Taylor's series in which the coefficients are the moments of the distribution, and since the Taylor expansion is unique, we have

---

* From the definition of expected value, it is clear that $\mathcal{E}\{A + B\} = \mathcal{E}\{A\} + \mathcal{E}\{B\}$.

$$\mu'_n = \left[\frac{d^n M(q)}{dq^n}\right]_{q=0}.$$ (12)

If the moment generating function for a probability distribution is known, the nth moment of the distribution may be obtained by evaluating the nth derivative of the moment generating function at $q = 0$.

A distribution is completely specified by a complete set of moments, and hence by its moment generating function. Thus, experimental determination of the moments of an unknown population may be useful in obtaining an approximation to the form of the probability density function.

An important property of the moment generating function is that if $z = x + y$, where x and y are *independent* random variables, then

$$M_z(q) = M_x(q) \times M_y(q),$$ (13)

where M_z, M_x, and M_y are the moment generating functions for the probability distributions of z, x, and y.

Example 1-6-1

The moment generating function for the normal distribution is

$$M(q) = \exp\left(\mu q + \tfrac{1}{2}\sigma^2 q^2\right).$$

$M(0) = 1$, since the zeroth moment is simply the total probability. Also,

$$M'(q) \equiv \frac{dM}{dq} = M(q)[\mu + \sigma^2 q]; \; M'(0) = \mu$$

$$M''(q) \equiv \frac{d^2 M}{dq^2} = (\mu + \sigma^2 q)\frac{dM}{dq} + \sigma^2 M(q); \; M''(0) = \mu^2 + \sigma^2.$$

For the special case of $\mu = 0$, we have

$$M(q) = \exp\left(\tfrac{1}{2}\sigma^2 q^2\right); \; M(0) = 1$$
$$M'(q) = \sigma^2 q M(q); \; M'(0) = 0$$
$$M''(q) = [M'(q) + M(q)]\sigma^2; \; M''(0) = \sigma^2$$

. . . .

$$M^{(n)}(q) = [M^{(n-1)}(q) + (n-1)M^{(n-2)}(q)]\sigma^2;$$

$$M^{(n)}(0) \equiv \mu'_n \equiv \mu_n = \begin{cases} 0 \text{ for } n \text{ odd} \\ 1 \cdot 3 \cdot 5 \cdots (n-1)\sigma^n \text{ for } n \text{ even.} \end{cases}$$

Example 1-6-2

Consider two independent random variables x and y, each normally distributed; then

$$M_x(q) = \exp\left[\mu_x q + \tfrac{1}{2}\sigma_x^2 q^2\right]$$
$$M_y(q) = \exp\left[\mu_y q + \tfrac{1}{2}\sigma_y^2 q^2\right].$$

The random variable $z = x + y$ has the moment generating function

$$M_z(q) = M_x(q) \times M_y(q)$$
$$= \exp\left[(\mu_x + \mu_y)q + \tfrac{1}{2}(\sigma_x^2 + \sigma_y^2)q^2\right]$$

which is again the moment generating function for a normally distributed random variable. Thus, we have shown that the distribution function for the sum of two independent normally distributed random variables is a normally distributed random variable with mean

$$\mu_z = \mu_x + \mu_y$$

and variance

$$\sigma_z^2 = \sigma_x^2 + \sigma_y^2.$$

Characteristic Functions. An extension of the moment generating function is the *characteristic function*, which exists under more general conditions than does the moment generating function. This function is defined as

$$\Phi_x(q) = \mathcal{E}\{e^{iqx}\}$$
$$= \int_{-\infty}^{+\infty} e^{iqx}\phi(x)\, dx. \tag{14}$$

It follows that the moments of the distribution in this case are given by

$$\mu'_n = \left(\frac{1}{i^n}\frac{d^n\Phi}{dq^n}\right)_{q=0}. \tag{15}$$

Cumulants. It is sometimes more convenient to consider the logarithm of the moment generating function or the characteristic function. The coefficients of the Taylor expansion for the resulting function are known as the *cumulants* or *semi-invariants* of the distribution:

$$\log M_x(q) = \kappa_1 q + \kappa_2 \frac{q^2}{2!} + \cdots, \tag{16}$$

where κ_n is the nth cumulant. One of the most important properties of the cumulants is that they are rather simply related to the *central* moments of the distribution. In particular, we have

$$\begin{aligned}
\kappa_1 &= \mu'_1 = \mu \\
\kappa_2 &= \mu_2 \\
\kappa_3 &= \mu_3 \\
\kappa_4 &= \mu_4 - 3\mu_2^2.*
\end{aligned} \tag{17}$$

Example 1–6–3

Consider the binomial distribution (Example 1–2–13). What is the expected number of successes in n trials?

* The corresponding quantities for a sample are the k-statistics of Fisher, defined in such a way that

$$\mathcal{E}\{k_n\} = \kappa_n.$$

$$\mathcal{E}\{s\} = \sum_{s=0}^{n} s \binom{n}{s} p^s q^{n-s} \equiv \sum_{s=0}^{n} s B_n(s).$$

Making the substitutions $n' = n - 1$ and $s' = s - 1$, and noting that the first term in the sum is zero, we obtain

$$\mathcal{E}\{s\} = \sum_{s'=0}^{n'} (s' + 1) \binom{n' + 1}{s' + 1} p^{s'+1} q^{n'-s'}$$

$$= (n' + 1) p \sum_{s'=0}^{n'} \binom{n'}{s'} p^{s'} q^{n'-s'}$$

$$= np \sum_{s'=0}^{n'} B_{n'}(s').$$

The latter summation is equal to unity since the probability function is normalized. Thus

$$\mathcal{E}\{s\} = np.$$

A similar technique can be used to show that

$$\sigma^2(s) \equiv \mathcal{E}\{s^2\} - (np)^2 = npq.$$

Example 1-6-4

A fair coin is tossed 20 times. What are the mean and standard deviation of the random variable which is equal to the number of heads in 20 tosses?

$$p = q = \tfrac{1}{2}.$$

Hence

$$\mathcal{E}\{k\} = 20 \cdot \tfrac{1}{2} = 10$$
$$\sigma^2(k) = 20 \cdot \tfrac{1}{2} \cdot \tfrac{1}{2} = 5$$
$$\sigma(k) = 2.24.$$

Example 1-6-5

What are the mean and variance of the Poisson distribution?

$$\mathcal{E}(k) = \sum_{k=0}^{\infty} \frac{k e^{-\lambda} \lambda^k}{k!} = \lambda$$

$$\sigma^2(k) = \mathcal{E}\{k^2\} - \lambda^2 = \lambda.$$

Note that the mean and the variance of the Poisson distribution are numerically equal.

Example 1-6-6

For the normal distribution

$$\mathcal{E}\{x\} = \frac{1}{\sigma(2\pi)^{1/2}} \int_{-\infty}^{+\infty} x \exp\left[-\frac{(x - \mu)^2}{2\sigma^2}\right] dx = \mu$$

$$\text{var}(x) = \frac{1}{\sigma(2\pi)^{1/2}} \int_{-\infty}^{+\infty} x^2 \exp\left[-\frac{(x - \mu)^2}{2\sigma^2}\right] dx - \mu^2 = \sigma^2.$$

The notation μ and σ for the parameters of the normal distribution are thus justified. As noted in previous examples, the normal distribution is often standardized to a distribution with zero mean and unit variance.

Example 1–6–7

For the uniform distribution (Example 1–4–1) where $\phi(x) = 1/2a$ for $-a \leqslant x \leqslant a$,

$$\mu = \int_{-a}^{a} \frac{x \, dx}{2a} = 0$$

$$\sigma^2 = \int_{-a}^{a} \frac{x^2 \, dx}{2a} = \frac{a^2}{3}.$$

In general,

$$\mu_n = \frac{a^n}{n+1} \quad \text{for } n \text{ even}$$

$$\mu_n = 0 \qquad \text{for } n \text{ odd.}$$

Example 1–6–8

The δ-function familiar to chemists and physicists may be looked upon as the limit of the uniform density function as $a \to 0$; i.e.,

$$\phi(x) \, dx \to \delta(x) \, dx$$

and

$$\mathcal{E}\{f(x)\} = \int_{-\infty}^{+\infty} f(x)\phi(x) \, dx$$

$$= \int_{-\infty}^{+\infty} f(x)\delta(x) \, dx$$

$$= f(0).$$

Thus $\delta(x)$ is the probability density function for x when x takes on the value 0 with probability 1.

Example 1–6–9

Consider the probability density function obtained in Example 1–5–7 as the density function for the ratio of two standardized normal deviates:

$$\phi(y) = \frac{1}{\pi(1 + y^2)}; \quad y \neq 0.$$

The integral

$$\sigma^2 = \int_{-\infty}^{+\infty} \frac{y^2 \, dy}{\pi(1 + y^2)}$$

does not have a finite value, so that the variance is not finite, or may be said not to exist. The mean of the distribution is equal to zero provided that the integral is defined as its principal value:

$$\mu = \lim_{A \to \infty} \int_{-A}^{A} \frac{y \, dy}{\pi(1 + y^2)}.$$

Example 1–6–10

Consider the probability density function

$$\phi(x) = \begin{cases} \dfrac{na^n}{x^{n+1}} & \text{for } x \geqslant a \\ 0 & \text{for } x < a, \end{cases}$$

where $a > 0$. Let us calculate the rth moment of this function:

$$\mu'_r = \int_a^{\infty} \frac{na^n}{x^{n+1-r}} \, dx.$$

This integral diverges for $n \leqslant r$; thus the nth and higher moments do not exist. An interesting case is obtained for $n = 1$; i.e.,

$$\phi(x) = \begin{cases} \dfrac{a}{x^2} & \text{for } x \geqslant a \\ 0 & \text{for } x < a. \end{cases}$$

The mean of this distribution

$$\mu = \int_a^{\infty} \frac{a}{x} \, dx$$

does not exist. We have a valid probability density function with an undefined mean value.

Moments of a Multivariate Distribution. For a multivariate distribution, we define the means and second moments as follows

$$\mu_i = \mathcal{E}\{x_i\} = \int_{-\infty}^{+\infty} \phi(x_1, \ldots, x_n) x_i \, dx_1 \cdots dx_n$$

$$m_{ij} = \mathcal{E}\{x_i x_j\} = \int_{-\infty}^{+\infty} \phi(x_1, \ldots, x_n) x_i x_j \, dx_1 \cdots dx_n. \tag{18}$$

Higher moments may be defined in an obvious way, but as they will not be of any further use to us here, we will not go into the details of the notation.

Corresponding to the definition of the variance of x_i as

$$\text{var}(x_i) = \mathcal{E}\{(x_i - \mu_i)^2\} = \mathcal{E}\{x_i^2\} - (\mathcal{E}\{x_i\})^2, \tag{19}$$

we define the *covariance* of x_i and x_j:

$$\text{cov}(x_i, x_j) = \mathcal{E}\{(x_i - \mu_i)(x_j - \mu_j)\}$$
$$= \mathcal{E}\{x_i x_j\} - \mathcal{E}\{x_i\}\mathcal{E}\{x_j\}. \tag{20}$$

If x_i and x_j are independent, i.e.,

$$\phi(x_i x_j) = \phi_1(x_i)\phi_2(x_j), \tag{21}$$

then

$$\mathcal{E}\{x_i x_j\} = \mathcal{E}\{x_i\}\mathcal{E}\{x_j\}, \tag{22}$$

and the covariance vanishes. The converse is not true; a zero covariance does not in general imply statistical independence.*

It is convenient for multivariate distributions to define a quantity known as the *correlation coefficient*:

$$\rho(x_i, x_j) = \frac{\text{cov } (x_i, x_j)}{\sigma(x_i)\sigma(x_j)} \tag{23}$$

The quantity $\rho(x_i, x_j)$ is then always less than or equal to 1 and, in a way to be discussed in more detail later, describes the *linear* dependence of x_i on x_j. Again it is important to note that a correlation coefficient of zero does not imply complete independence, as shown in the following example.

Example 1–6–11

Consider the function $y = x^2$; then

$$\text{cov } (x, y) = \mathcal{E}\{x^3\} - \mathcal{E}\{x^2\}\mathcal{E}\{x\}.$$

If $\phi(x)$ is symmetric about $x = 0$, then

$$\mathcal{E}\{x^3\} = \mathcal{E}\{x\} = 0,$$

and the covariance and correlation coefficient vanish, even though there is a functional relationship between x and y.

Expectation of Functions. The scient'st is occasionally interested in the expected values of functions of more than one random variable. In general, to find these values, the multivariate distribution function must be known; for

$$\mathcal{E}\{f(x_1, x_2, \ldots, x_n)\}$$
$$= \int_{-\infty}^{+\infty} \cdots \int_{-\infty}^{+\infty} f(x_1, \ldots, x_n)\phi(x_1, \ldots, x_n) \, dx_1 \cdots dx_n. \tag{24}$$

Alternatively, one can obtain the probability density function for f as described in an earlier section and evaluate its mean value.

There are a few special cases where knowledge of the density function is not necessary. Linear functions of random variables are rather special in this regard:

$$\mathcal{E}\{ax + by\} = a\mathcal{E}\{x\} + b\mathcal{E}\{y\}$$
$$\text{var } (ax + by) = a^2 \text{ var } (x) + b^2 \text{ var } (y) + 2ab \text{ cov } (x, y). \tag{25}$$

Or more generally,

* However, a zero covariance for a multivariate *normal* distribution is a sufficient condition for independence.

$$\mathcal{E}\left\{\sum_{i=1}^{n} a_i x_i\right\} = \sum_{i=1}^{n} a_i \mathcal{E}\{x_i\}$$

(26)

$$\text{var}\left(\sum_{i=1}^{n} a_i x_i\right) = \sum_{i=1}^{n} a_i^2 \, \text{var}\,(x_i) + \sum_{i=1}^{n}\sum_{\substack{j=1 \\ i\neq j}}^{n} a_i x_j \, \text{cov}\,(x_i, x_j).$$

Also, if

$$y_1 = \sum_i a_i x_i$$

$$y_2 = \sum_i b_i x_i,$$

(27)

it may be shown that

$$\text{cov}\,(y_1, y_2) \equiv \mathcal{E}\{y_1 y_2\} - \mathcal{E}\{y_1\}\mathcal{E}\{y_2\}$$

(28)

$$= \sum_{i=1}^{n} a_i b_i \, \text{var}\,(x_i) + \sum\sum_{i\neq j} a_i b_j \, \text{cov}\,(x_i, x_j).$$

For the general non-linear case, it is always true that

$$\mathcal{E}\{xy\} = \mathcal{E}\{x\}\mathcal{E}\{y\} + \text{cov}\,(x, y).$$

(29)

If $\text{cov}\,(x, y)$ and $\text{cov}\,(x^2, y^2)$ are both zero, a condition that is true if x and y are statistically independent, then

$$\text{var}\,(xy) = \text{var}\,(x)\,\text{var}\,(y) + \mu_y^2\,\text{var}\,(x) + \mu_x^2\,\text{var}\,(y).$$

(30)

An approximation which can be useful for a function of a random variable is that obtained by using only the first two terms of its Taylor expansion:

$$f(x) \approx f(a) + f'(a)(x - a),$$

(31)

where a is the point around which f is expanded. Then

$$\mathcal{E}\{f(x)\} \approx f(a) + f'(a)[\mathcal{E}\{x\} - a]$$
$$\sigma^2(f(x)) \approx (f'(a))^2 \sigma^2(x).$$

(32)

In particular, if we choose to expand about the mean,

$$\mu = \mathcal{E}\{x\},$$
$$\mathcal{E}\{f\} \equiv \mu_f \approx f(\mu)$$

(33)

and

$$\sigma^2(f) \approx (f'(\mu))^2 \sigma^2(x).$$

(34)

For example, if we consider the function

$$f = \frac{1}{x}$$

(35)

we have

$$\mu_f \approx \frac{1}{\mu_x}$$

$$\sigma^2(f) \approx \frac{\sigma^2(x)}{\mu_x^4}.$$

(36)

Any such approximation demands that the two-term series approximation is valid everywhere that there is an appreciable probability density.

Example 1–6–12

Now consider the ratio of two independent random variables

$$r = \frac{y}{x}.$$

If f is defined as before as $1/x$, we have

$$r = yf.$$

Then

$$\mu_r = \mu_y \mu_f$$

and

$$\sigma^2(r) = \sigma^2(y)\sigma^2(f) + \mu_y^2\sigma^2(f) + \mu_f^2\sigma^2(y).$$

If the Taylor expansion above is used for f, then

$$\mu_r \approx \frac{\mu_y}{\mu_x}$$

and

$$\sigma^2(r) \approx \frac{\sigma^2(x)\sigma^2(y) + \sigma^2(x)\mu_y^2 + \sigma^2(y)\mu_x^2}{\mu_x^4}.$$

If we divide by μ_r^2, we obtain

$$\frac{\sigma^2(r)}{\mu_r^2} \approx \frac{\sigma^2(x)\sigma^2(y)}{\mu_x^2\mu_y^2} + \frac{\sigma^2(x)}{\mu_x^2} + \frac{\sigma^2(y)}{\mu_y^2}.$$

If the Taylor expansion is to be at all valid, $\sigma^2(x) \ll \mu_x^2$, the first term is negligible compared to the third, and we obtain the often-quoted *approximation*

$$\left(\frac{\sigma(r)}{\mu_r}\right)^2 \approx \left(\frac{\sigma(x)}{\mu_x}\right)^2 + \left(\frac{\sigma(y)}{\mu_y}\right)^2.$$

That is, the square of the relative error of a ratio is approximately equal to the sum of the squares of the relative errors of numerator and denominator. Care must be used in applying this formula. In particular, there must be virtually no probability that either x or y is near zero; for common density functions this restriction implies that $\sigma^2(x) \ll \mu_x^2$.

It has been shown in Example 1–6–9 that the ratio of two normally distributed random variables with zero mean does not have a finite variance. It can be shown that this statement is true of the ratio of two such variables with arbitrary means, a somewhat surprising result.

Example 1–6–13

Consider a normally distributed random variable x with density function

$$\phi(x) = \frac{1}{\sigma(2\pi)^{1/2}} \exp\left[-\frac{(x-\mu)^2}{2\sigma^2}\right].$$

We wish to determine the variance of the function $y = x^2$.

$$\begin{aligned}
\sigma^2(y) &= \mathcal{E}\{y^2\} - (\mathcal{E}\{y\})^2 = \mathcal{E}\{x^4\} - (\mathcal{E}\{x^2\})^2 \\
&= [\mu_x^4 + 6\mu_x^2\sigma^2(x) + 3\sigma^4(x)] - [\mu_x^2 + \sigma^2(x)]^2 \\
&= 4\mu_x^2\sigma^2(x) + 2\sigma^2(x) \\
&= 4\mu_x^2\sigma^2(x)\left[1 + \frac{1}{2}\frac{\sigma^2(x)}{\mu_x^2}\right].
\end{aligned}$$

The Taylor series approximation gives

$$\sigma^2(y) \approx 4\mu_x^2\sigma^2(x),$$

which agrees with the exact expression only if $|\sigma(x)/\mu_x| \ll 1$, i.e., if the mean of the distribution is well removed from the origin in units of σ.

Example 1–6–14

Suppose that observation has given rise to quantities

$$T, x_1, x_2, \ldots, x_{n-1}$$

with means μ_T and μ_i and variances σ_T^2 and σ_i^2. Consider the functions

$$I_i = x_i T; \quad i = 1, \ldots, n$$

where $x_n = 1 - \sum_{i=1}^{n-1} x_i$. It is assumed that all pairs of x_i and T are statistically independent. (This model has been useful in the least-squares treatment of overlapping x-ray diffraction reflections in the powder method. T is the total intensity in some angular range; the x_i are the fractions of the intensity to be ascribed to particular reflections. I_i is thus the intensity of the ith reflection.) The following may be demonstrated:

$$\begin{aligned}
\mathcal{E}\{I_i\} &= \mu_i\mu_T \\
\sigma^2(I_i) &= \sigma_T^2\mu_i^2 + \sigma_i^2\mu_T^2 + \sigma_i^2\sigma_T^2 \\
\text{cov}(I_i, I_j) &= \mu_i\mu_j\sigma_T^2 \\
\text{cov}(I_i, T) &= \mu_i\sigma_T^2.
\end{aligned}$$

These results hold for I_n, with

$$\mu_n = 1 - \sum_{j \neq n} \mu_j$$

and

$$\sigma_n^2 = \sum_{j \neq n} \sigma_j^2$$

except that

$$\text{cov}\,(I_j, I_n) = \sigma_T{}^2(\mu_j{}^2 + \mu_j\mu_n) - \sigma^2(I_j)$$
$$= \mu_j\mu_n\sigma_T{}^2 - \sigma_j{}^2(\mu_T{}^2 + \sigma_T{}^2).$$

In any practical application, the various standard deviations could be estimated, and the adequacy of the model might well depend upon the method of estimation of the means and variances.

1–7. ESTIMATION OF PARAMETERS, CONFIDENCE INTERVALS, AND HYPOTHESIS-TESTING

We are now prepared to discuss the essential problem to which the ideas of probability theory can be applied: the estimation of physical quantities. We assume that a set of experimental conditions has associated with it a sample space of outcomes with an associated probability function. We will generally assume that the probability function has a given form, but with undetermined parameters, and that we are to use the outcome of an experiment to estimate the parameters of the probability function. The specification of the form of the probability function may vary from the very general to the very specific. As an example of the latter, we may specify that the probability function has the normal distribution with variance 1; in this case, we are to use the outcome of the experiment to estimate the mean. As an example of a more general problem, we may only specify that the distribution has a mean value and finite variance and that the values of these parameters are to be estimated from the experimental outcome.

The sample space corresponding to all possible experimental outcomes is frequently called the *population*, and the parameters of the associated probability function are called *population parameters*. It is not necessary that the population exist in any concrete way, as the name perhaps implies and as is actually the case in many sociological and biological problems. The population here is to be thought of as a set of hypothetical repetitions of the experiment.

It is perhaps not even necessary that it be physically possible to repeat the experiment at all, if one has some justification for assuming a particular probability model for the repetitions if they could be carried out. In making such a statement as this, however, one begins to be involved with incompletely solved—or perhaps incompletely defined—problems in the philosophy of scientific inference.

Example 1–7–1

We have a single sample of a chemical compound. The sample is large enough to make but a single determination of the percentage of iron in the compound. We make this determination and find a value of 25%. Although we are unable to repeat the observation, it seems reasonable that the population of all possible results has a mean, and we take the single measurement as an estimate of this mean.

A further point to be made—or restated—is that, in the present context, the terms *experiment, outcome,* and *sample point* may refer to an entire complex of data, which in many cases will consist of many repetitions of a single measurement. As indicated in Example 1–2–4 this entire series of repetitions may be thought of as a single experiment. Thus a sample point may consist of many single observations of some experimental quantity. The elementary sample space may indeed have the individual measurements as points, but there will be a definite relationship between the elementary sample space and the sample space for the compound experiment.

Example 1–7–2

We have already discussed the composition of a compound sample space from the simpler ones in the example of the derivation of the binomial distribution as the probability function for a sequence of n Bernoulli trials. In general, if the sample space for the single measurement consists of n points,

$$x_1, x_2, \ldots, x_n,$$

with probability functions

$$p_1, p_2, \ldots, p_n,$$

and we repeat the experiment m times, the sample space for the compound experiment will consist of the n^m points, each of which is characterized by a sequence of m numbers

$$\{X\} \equiv \{x_i^1, x_j^2, \ldots, x_k^m\},$$

where i, j, and k can take on any of the values 1 to n, and the probability of this point is given by

$$P\{X\} = p_i p_j \cdots p_k.$$

It is assumed that the successive repetitions are independent.

The wealth of numerical information contained in such an extended sample may be too cumbersome to handle in the form in which it is taken. Furthermore, in the estimation of population parameters, the values of all the individual measurements contained in a sample may not be important; rather, certain simple functions of the individual measurements may suffice. It is thus convenient to abstract the information contained in a sample and define certain functions which are known as *statistics*. A statistic is a function of observations on a sample and is generally chosen to provide an estimate of a population parameter.

Example 1–7–3

Consider a sample of n observations of a single quantity x:

$$x_i, \; i = 1, \ldots, n.$$

Some statistics commonly used are

$$\text{Sample mean:} \quad \bar{x} = \frac{1}{n} \sum_{i=1}^{n} x_i$$

$$\text{Sample variance:} \; s^2 = \frac{1}{n-1} \sum_{i=1}^{n} (x_i - \bar{x})^2 \; *$$

$$\text{Range:} \quad \mathcal{R} = \max (x_i) - \min (x_i).$$

Each of these statistics has a probability distribution which depends upon the parent population and may be derived from it.

There are three different statistical procedures used in the attempt to deduce something from a sample about the nature of the parent population. Although these procedures are not entirely distinct, it will be useful to consider them separately, in the order: point estimation, interval estimation, and hypothesis testing.

Point Estimation. If we say that a certain value x is an estimate of the population mean, or that the value y is an estimate of the population variance, we have made point estimates of these population parameters. We have selected a particular number as our best guess as to the value of the population parameter in question. If the value of a sample statistic is used for this estimate, we call the statistic an *estimator* for the population parameter and the value for the sample an *estimate*. For example, the sample mean is the statistic most commonly used as the estimator for the population mean. The value of the sample mean is said to be a (point) estimate of the population mean.

Let us now examine some of the properties which it is desirable for a statistic to have in order to make it a useful estimator. First of all, we would like the value of the estimator to be on the average a better estimate of the population parameter as the size of the sample increases. Let us make this idea more precise: If $\hat{\theta}_n$, based on a sample of size n, is an estimator for a population parameter θ, we want there to be some number N, such that for arbitrarily small ϵ and δ

$$P(|\hat{\theta}_n - \theta| < \epsilon) > 1 - \delta \text{ for all } n > N. \tag{1}$$

---

* The definition of the sample variance changes from author to author, one using $n - 1$ in the denominator, another n. The use of $n - 1$ is more common, as well as convenient, and we will adhere to this usage.

If this condition is satisfied, $\hat{\theta}_n$ is known as a *consistent* estimator of θ and is said to *converge in probability* to θ.

Consistency is clearly a desirable property for an estimator. It unfortunately says nothing about the relation of the estimate to the population parameter for small values of n, which often is the range of most interest to us. A stronger property of an estimator is that of unbiasedness. An estimator t_n of a population parameter θ is said to be *unbiased* if

$$\mathcal{E}\{\hat{\theta}_n\} = \theta. \tag{2}$$

In choosing an estimator, we will generally prefer an unbiased estimator. There is nothing wrong with using a biased estimator, if the nature of the bias is known, and it is occasionally convenient to do so. Perhaps for a given distribution the unbiased estimates of certain parameters are difficult to calculate, or perhaps the distributions for these estimators are not tabulated. In such a case, we might well settle for the use of a biased estimator which is easier to use. If

$$\mathcal{E}\{\hat{\theta}\} = \theta + \delta, \tag{3}$$

then δ is called the bias of the estimator $\hat{\theta}$.

The *variance of an estimator* is defined in the usual way as

$$\text{var}\,(\hat{\theta}) = \mathcal{E}\{\hat{\theta}^2\} - (\mathcal{E}\{\hat{\theta}\})^2. \tag{4}$$

Note that for a biased estimator the *mean square error* is related to the variance and bias by

$$\mathcal{E}(\hat{\theta} - \theta)^2 = \text{var}\,(\hat{\theta}) + \delta^2. \tag{5}$$

Among the possible estimators for a population parameter θ, an estimator $\hat{\theta}_1$ is said to be better than an estimator $\hat{\theta}_2$ if $\text{var}\,(\hat{\theta}_1) < \text{var}\,(\hat{\theta}_2)$. For most of the distributions in common use there exists a best or *minimum variance estimator* for each of the population parameters of interest. A minimum variance estimator for which $n^{1/2}(\hat{\theta}_n - \theta)$ is asymptotically normal with zero mean is said to be *efficient*.

The derivation of the distributions of sample statistics, given a population distribution function, is the concern of the professional statistician and is beyond the scope of this book. Similarly, we shall not attempt to derive or prove the properties of all the statistics with which we deal. One important method for deriving statistics with optimum properties should however be briefly outlined; this is the principle of maximum likelihood. Consider a sample of size n,

$$x_1, x_2, \ldots, x_n, \tag{6}$$

drawn from a population with parameter θ. If the probability density function for x_i is given by $f(x_i, \theta)$, and if the x_i are independent, as they will usually be, we define the *likelihood function* as follows:

$$L = f(x_1, \theta)f(x_2, \theta) \cdots f(x_n, \theta). \tag{7}$$

If there is a value $\hat{\theta}$ of θ for which L has a maximum as a function of θ, this value $\hat{\theta}(x_1, x_2, \ldots, x_n)$ is said to be a maximum-likelihood estimator for θ. Such an estimator may sometimes, but not always, be obtained by finding $\hat{\theta}$ for which

$$\left(\frac{\partial L}{\partial \theta}\right)_{\hat{\theta}} = 0; \quad \left(\frac{\partial^2 L}{\partial \theta^2}\right)_{\hat{\theta}} < 0. \tag{8}$$

The importance of maximum-likelihood estimators is that they can be shown to be consistent and—more importantly—normally distributed as the size of the sample increases. This fact has the important implication that, if we restrict our attention to members of this class of estimators, for large samples we need only consult tables of the normal distribution when making our statistical tests. Most of the statistics which we will use are maximum-likelihood estimators of population parameters and, in addition, are unbiased.

Example 1–7–4

Consider a sample of n independent observations of a single quantity x. The sample mean

$$\bar{x} \equiv \frac{1}{n} \sum_{i=1}^{n} x_i$$

is an unbiased estimate of the population mean μ, since

$$\mathcal{E}\{\bar{x}\} = \frac{1}{n} \sum_{i=1}^{n} \mathcal{E}\{x_i\} = \frac{1}{n} \sum_{i=1}^{n} \mu = \mu.$$

The variance of this estimate is

$$\mathcal{E}\{(\bar{x} - \mu)^2\} = \mathcal{E}\left\{\left(\frac{1}{n}\sum_i x_i - \mu\right)^2\right\}$$

$$= \frac{1}{n^2} \mathcal{E}\left\{\left(\sum_i x_i - n\mu\right)^2\right\}$$

$$= \frac{1}{n^2} \sum_{i=1}^{n}\sum_{j=1}^{n} \mathcal{E}\{(x_i - n\mu)(x_j - n\mu)\}$$

$$= \frac{1}{n^2}\left[\sum_i \text{var } x_i + \sum_{i \neq j} \text{cov } (x_i, x_j)\right]$$

$$= \frac{\sigma^2}{n},$$

since cov $(x_i, x_j) = 0$ for $i \neq j$. σ^2 here is the population variance. σ^2/n, the variance of the estimate of the mean, may be made as small as desired by choosing n large enough.

Example 1–7–5

Consider the sample variance

$$s^2 = \frac{1}{n-1} \sum_i (x_i - \bar{x})^2.$$

We have

$$\mathcal{E}\{s^2\} = \frac{1}{n-1} \sum_i \mathcal{E}\{(x_i - \bar{x})^2\}$$

$$= \frac{1}{n-1} \sum_i (\mathcal{E}\{x_i^2\} - 2\mathcal{E}\{x_i\bar{x}\} + \mathcal{E}\{\bar{x}^2\}).$$

Now

$$\mathcal{E}\{x_i^2\} = \sigma^2 + \mu^2,$$

$$\mathcal{E}\{\bar{x}^2\} = \frac{\sigma^2}{n} + \mu^2$$

and

$$\mathcal{E}\{x_i\bar{x}\} = \mathcal{E}\left\{\frac{1}{n} \sum_j x_i x_j\right\} = \frac{1}{n}\mathcal{E}\{x_i^2\} + \frac{1}{n} \sum_{j \neq i} \mathcal{E}\{x_i x_j\}.$$

Thus

$$\mathcal{E}\{s^2\} = \frac{1}{n-1} \sum_i \left[\sigma^2 + \mu^2 - \frac{\sigma^2}{n} - \mu^2\right]$$

$$= \sigma^2.$$

Thus the sample variance as defined in an unbiased estimate of the population variance. The desirability of the definition of s^2 with $n-1$ in the denominator is thus illustrated.

Note however that the alternative definition of the sample variance

$$\frac{n-1}{n} s^2 = \frac{\sum_i (x_i - \bar{x})^2}{n}$$

is a *consistent* estimator of σ^2 with bias

$$\delta = -\frac{1}{n}\sigma^2.$$

The bias thus approaches zero as the sample size increases without limit.

Example 1–7–6

Suppose that we have drawn samples from n populations with the same mean but different variances. Let the sample means be denoted by $\bar{x}_i$ with corresponding variances $\sigma_i^2 \equiv \sigma^2(\bar{x}_i)$. We wish to pool the samples to obtain a combined estimate of the population mean μ. Since each of the estimates $\bar{x}_i$ is an unbiased estimate of μ, the quantity

$$\bar{x} = \sum_i a_i \bar{x}_i \quad \text{with} \quad \sum_i a_i = 1$$

is also an unbiased estimate, *regardless of the values* of the a_i. How should the a_i be chosen to obtain in some sense a best unbiased estimate?

A possible procedure is to choose the a_i such that the estimate $\bar{x}$ has minimum variance. Now

$$\text{var}(\bar{x}) = \text{var}\left[\sum_i a_i \bar{x}_i\right] = \sum_i a_i^2 \, \text{var}(\bar{x}_i) = \sum_i a_i^2 \sigma_i^2.$$

Let us minimize this quantity subject to the condition that $\sum_i a_i = 1$. Let

$$F = \sum_i a_i^2 \sigma_i^2 + \lambda \left(\sum_i a_i - 1\right),$$

where we have introduced the Lagrange multiplier λ. We have

$$\frac{\partial F}{\partial a_i} = 0 = 2 a_i \sigma_i^2 + \lambda$$

or

$$a_i = -\frac{\lambda}{2\sigma_i^2}; \quad i = 1, \ldots, n.$$

Since $\sum_j a_j = 1$, $\sum_j (-\lambda/2\sigma_j^2) = 1$, so that

$$\lambda = -\frac{2}{\sum_j (1/\sigma_j^2)}$$

or

$$a_i = \frac{1/\sigma_i^2}{\sum_j (1/\sigma_j^2)}.$$

for the set of a_i which makes $\bar{x}$ a minimum variance estimate.

It is convenient to define the *weight* of the ith mean as

$$w_i = \frac{1}{\sigma_i^2}.$$

We then have

$$a_i = \frac{w_i}{\sum_i w_i}$$

and consequently

$$\bar{x} = \frac{\sum\limits_i w_i \bar{x}_i}{\sum\limits_i w_i}$$

$$\mathrm{var}\,(\bar{x}) = \frac{1}{\sum\limits_i w_i}.$$

If the population variances and hence the weights are unknown, it is not unreasonable to define the weights as

$$w_i = \frac{1}{s_i{}^2},$$

where $s_i{}^2$ is an unbiased estimate of the ith population variance. We cannot know whether this truly gives rise to the minimum variance estimate unless the population variances are indeed known.

This problem can also be approached by using the principle of maximum likelihood. Let us consider the special case where each of the populations has a normal distribution. Then the likelihood function is

$$L = \frac{1}{\sigma_1 \cdots \sigma_n (2\pi)^{n/2}} \exp\left[-\frac{(\bar{x}_1 - \mu)^2}{2\sigma_1{}^2} \right] \cdots \exp\left[-\frac{(\bar{x}_n - \mu)^2}{2\sigma_n{}^2} \right]$$

$$\equiv \frac{1}{\sigma_1 \cdots \sigma_n (2\pi)^{n/2}} \exp\left[-\sum_i \frac{(\bar{x}_i - \mu)^2}{2\sigma_i{}^2} \right].$$

Then

$$\left(\frac{\partial L}{\partial \mu}\right)_{\hat{\mu}} = 0 = \frac{1}{\sigma_1 \cdots \sigma_n (2\pi)^{n/2}} \exp\left[-\sum_i \frac{(\bar{x}_i - \hat{\mu})^2}{2\sigma_i{}^2} \right] \sum_i \frac{\bar{x}_i - \hat{\mu}}{\sigma_i{}^2}$$

$$0 = L \sum_i \frac{x_i - \hat{\mu}}{\sigma_i{}^2}$$

$$\sum_i \frac{\bar{x}_i}{\sigma_i{}^2} = \hat{\mu} \sum_i \frac{1}{\sigma_i{}^2}$$

$$\hat{\mu} = \sum_i \frac{(\bar{x}_i/\sigma_i{}^2)}{(1/\sigma_i{}^2)},$$

which is identical with the result obtained by the minimum-variance method. Thus for samples from normal distributions, the maximum-likelihood estimate of the mean is identical with the minimum-variance estimate. *This is not necessarily true for non-normal distributions.* Note that, if all the σ_i are equal to a common value σ, then

$$\mathrm{var}\,\bar{x} = \frac{1}{\sum\limits_i (1/\sigma_i{}^2)} = \frac{\sigma^2}{n}.$$

Example 1–7–7

Palenik and Donahue* quote a number of P—C bond lengths, each with an estimated σ. Accepting for the moment these estimates of the σ's as the true σ's, we have

x	σ	σ^2
1.867	0.014	0.000196
1.837	0.012	0.000144
1.847	0.003	0.000009
1.853	0.003	0.000009
1.858	0.003	0.000009
1.906	0.020	0.000400

Assuming that these measurements are from populations with identical means, but with variances as given in the table, we can calculate the "best value" for the P—C bond distance as

$$\bar{x} = \frac{\displaystyle\sum_i (x_i/\sigma_i^2)}{\displaystyle\sum_i (1/\sigma_i^2)} = \frac{6.446 \times 10^5}{3.479 \times 10^5} = 1.853$$

$$\sigma^2(\bar{x}) = \frac{1}{3.479 \times 10^5} = 2.874 \times 10^{-6}$$

$$\sigma(\bar{x}) = 0.0017.$$

If we estimate the mean and variance from the three measurements of high weight, we obtain essentially the same results:

$$\bar{x} = \tfrac{1}{3}(1.853 + 1.847 + 1.858) = 1.853$$
$$\sigma^2(\bar{x}) = 9 \times 10^{-6}/3 = 3 \times 10^{-6}.$$

If we had not known the individual variances, we might have calculated an estimate of the mean as

$$\bar{x} = \tfrac{1}{6} \sum_i x_i = 1.861.$$

This is an unbiased estimate, as is any linear combination of the individual numbers. The estimated variance of an individual sample point in this case is

$$s^2 = \tfrac{1}{5} \sum_i (x_i - \bar{x})^2 = 0.000581$$

$$s = 0.024.$$

An unbiased estimate of the variance of $\bar{x}$ is

$$\frac{s^2}{n} = 0.000097,$$

* G. J. Palenik and J. Donahue, *Acta Cryst. 15*, 564 (1962).

and the estimate of the standard deviation of $\bar{x}$ is $s/n^{1/2} = 0.0099$. Although such a result is sometimes written in the scientific literature as

$$\bar{x} = 1.861 \pm 0.010,$$

this practice is to be deplored. First of all, it is incorrect: the value of $\bar{x}$ is 1.861, not $1.861 \pm$ something. Furthermore, when a range is indicated in this way, it is not always clear whether reference is being made to the standard deviation, some kind of limit of error, range in the statistical sense, or confidence interval. Examples of each of these possibilities may be found in the literature of experimental science. It is far better to cite such a result as

$$\bar{x} = 1.861$$
$$\hat{\sigma}(\bar{x}) = s/n^{1/2} = 0.010,$$

or simply as

$$\bar{x} = 1.861; \quad \hat{\sigma}(\bar{x}) = 0.010.$$

This is a clear statement and is not subject to the ambiguities inherent in the $\pm$ notation.

Interval Estimation. A point estimate, although it may represent our best estimate of the value of a population parameter, tells us nothing about how good our estimate is likely to be. For this purpose, it is convenient to introduce the concept of *interval estimation*. Rather than merely stating that our estimate of the population parameter is x_0, we may specify an interval

$$x_1 \leqslant x_0 \leqslant x_2 \tag{9}$$

such that the probability that this interval includes the population parameter is high. If the estimate is of a population parameter μ, and if

$$P(x_1 \leqslant \mu \leqslant x_2) = 1 - \alpha, \tag{10}$$

we say that we have established a $100(1 - \alpha)\%$ *confidence interval* for μ.

Example 1-7-8

Suppose that we make two observations x_1 and x_2 on a quantity which is assumed to be distributed with unknown mean μ but known variance σ^2. We will show in the next chapter that

$$P\left(\bar{x} - \frac{1.96\sigma}{\sqrt{2}} \leqslant \mu \leqslant \bar{x} + \frac{1.96\sigma}{\sqrt{2}}\right) = 0.95.$$

Thus a 95% confidence interval for μ might correctly be written

$$\bar{x} \pm \frac{1.96\sigma}{\sqrt{2}},$$

but it would be better to write the interval as

$$\bar{x} - \frac{1.96\sigma}{\sqrt{2}} \leqslant \mu \leqslant \bar{x} + \frac{1.96\sigma}{\sqrt{2}}.$$

Note that the confidence interval depends both on the sample statistic $\bar{x}$ and the population parameter σ^2.* On the other hand, if the two observations are made from a normal population with unknown variance, we find (again from the more detailed considerations in Chapter 2) that

$$P(\bar{x} - 6.353\Re \leqslant \mu \leqslant \bar{x} + 6.353\Re) = 0.95,$$

where $\Re = x_2 - x_1$ is the *range*.

Example 1–7–9 (The Chebychev Inequality)

A result of great generality and theoretical usefulness is the following: For a random variable x with mean μ and variance σ^2,

$$P(|x - \mu| \geqslant \delta) \leqslant \frac{\sigma^2}{\delta^2}.$$

The truth of this statement is independent of the form of the distribution. All that is required is that the variance be finite. Thus a 95% confidence interval for the worst possible type of distribution with finite variance is that which gives $\sigma^2/\delta^2 = 0.05$, so that $\delta = 2\sqrt{5}\,\sigma$, and the 95% confidence interval for μ based on a single observation is

$$\bar{x} - 4.472\sigma \leqslant \mu \leqslant \bar{x} + 4.472\sigma.$$

Thus for any distribution with finite variance, we may say that the probability that μ lies in this range is 95% or greater. Note that this confidence interval is considerably larger than that for a single observation from a normal distribution

$$\bar{x} - 1.96\sigma \leqslant \mu \leqslant \bar{x} + 1.96\sigma.$$

Hypothesis Tests. Rather than estimate the value of a population parameter or determine an interval which probably includes the parameter, we may frequently wish to ascertain on the basis of a sample whether or not a population parameter has a particular value. That is, we ask whether the value of some statistic for the sample is consistent with the hypothesis that the sample was drawn from a population with specified parameter values. This problem may arise, for example, when we wish to compare the results of two experimental determinations of what is supposed to be one quantity. Or perhaps the experiment has been designed to determine

---

* These well-known confidence limits for the normal distribution with known variance are frequently applied to situations to which they are totally inapplicable.

whether or not a particular theory is valid; we perform the experiment and then, on the basis of the results, would like to state whether or not the experiment is consistent with the theory. The general theory of hypothesis-testing has been developed to handle such questions.

A hypothesis is a statement about the population. If it specifies the population distribution function completely, it is known as a *simple hypothesis*. If it specifies less than the number of parameters necessary to describe the distribution function for the population completely, it is known as a *composite hypothesis*.

Example 1–7–10

Of the following hypotheses, the first is simple; the remainder are composite:

a. The population is normal with mean μ and variance σ^2.
b. The population is normal with mean μ.
c. The population is normal.
d. The population is continuous with finite variance.

The general procedure for handling hypotheses specifying population parameters is as follows:

Step A. We state the hypothesis: The population parameters $\theta_1, \theta_2, \ldots, \theta_n$ have the values $\theta_1^0, \theta_2^0, \ldots, \theta_n^0$. This is generally known as the *null hypothesis, H_0*. For every null hypothesis, there will be an alternative hypothesis H_1 which states that the population parameters do not have the specified values. Thus, within the class of all possible hypotheses, the alternative hypothesis H_1 will be the complement of H_0. The class of possible hypotheses may be restricted or very general, so that the alternative hypothesis H_1 may be either simple or composite.

Step B. We draw a sample from the population and compute values for one or more sample statistics. Based upon the values of these statistics, a decision is made to accept or reject the hypothesis H_0. Unless the sample is the whole population, we cannot say whether H_0 *is true*.

This procedure is known as a *test of the hypothesis*. There are four possible situations to be distinguished:

a. H_0 is true, and the test tells us to accept H_0.
b. H_0 is true, and the test tells us to reject H_0.
c. H_0 is false, and the test tells us to reject H_0.
d. H_0 is false, and the test tells us to accept H_0.

If situation (a) or (c) results, we have made no error; the test of the hypothesis has given the correct result.

If situation (b) holds, we have made what is known in the statistical literature as a *Type I error*; we have rejected a true hypothesis. For a particular test, the probability of a Type I error can often be determined from the sampling distribution. If we write

$$P(b) = P(H_0 \text{ true, but test has rejected it}) = \alpha,$$

the number $100\alpha\%$ is known as the *significance level* of the test.* For a useful test, α should of course be small. The number α is the probability that a random sample from the population specified will have values for the sample statistics which cause us to believe that the sample is from a population having parameters other than those specified.

Another type of error occurs if we accept the hypothesis when it is actually false: situation (d) above. This is known as a *Type II error*. If we write

$$P(d) = P(H_0 \text{ false, but test has accepted it}) = \beta,$$

the number $(1 - \beta)$ is known as the *power* of the test.

Now in general there will be many possible tests at a given significance level that can be performed. One test is said to be more powerful than another if, for the same significance level α, the first test has the smaller probability of a Type II error. In certain situations, there may be one test which has greater power than any other. This is for obvious reasons called the *most powerful test*. If H_1 is a simple hypothesis, the power of the test can be computed, and a most powerful test will in the general case exist. On the other hand, if H_1 is composite, but can be broken down into a set of simple alternative hypotheses

$$H_1{}^1, H_1{}^2, \ldots, \tag{11}$$

the power of the test will almost always depend upon which of the simple alternatives is true, since the probability of a Type II error is a probability calculated on the basis of the truth of the alternative hypothesis. Thus for one alternative hypothesis $H_1{}^1$ a test T_1 might be most powerful, for another alternative hypothesis $H_1{}^2$ another test T_2 might be most powerful. In general, then, a most powerful test does not exist. In certain simple cases, however, the power of a test may be a maximum for all allowable alternative hypotheses. Such a test is known as a *uniformly most powerful test*.

A particularly important class of hypotheses is that whose members are *linear hypotheses*. Suppose that n functions ω_i are defined in terms of m population parameters θ_j by

$$\omega_i = \sum_{j=1}^{n} a_{ij}\theta_j; \quad i = 1, 2, \ldots, n. \tag{12}$$

A hypothesis which assigns values to the ω_i rather than to the θ_j separately is known as a linear hypothesis and will prove to be of extreme importance

---

* Significance levels are sometimes referred to in terms of probabilities and sometimes in terms of percentages. Thus, "a significance level of α" means the same thing as "a significance level of $100\alpha\%$" e.g., 0.05 significance level and 5% significance level are equivalent.

in the analysis of the results of least-squares treatments of experimental data.

Although it should be obvious, it is worthwhile emphasizing that *failure to reject the hypothesis does not mean that the hypothesis is true.* On the other hand, if we are able, on the basis of the test, to reject the hypothesis, we *can* make the statement that there is experimental evidence that the hypothesis is not true. This point should be borne in mind.

Although the exact significance level should always be quoted in connection with a statement regarding the acceptance or rejection of a hypothesis, the following usage has been recommended sometimes in the scientific literature:

Rejection at a significance level greater than 5% is "not significant."
Rejection at a significance level of 5% is "significant."
Rejection at a significance level of 1% is "highly significant."

This usage is largely a matter of taste, and the specification of the level of rejection or the actual probability of the sample's being consistent with the hypothesis is to be strongly encouraged.

Another practical point is that of reaching a compromise between the significance level and the power of a test, for often a test may be made more powerful by increasing α. The decision must be made by the experimenter, who is in a position to assess the relative importance of the two types of error. There are cases where a high power is of considerably greater importance than a small value of α.

Example 1–7–11

Consider the hypothesis

$$H_0: \mu = \mu_0$$

for an unspecified distribution with known σ. Now the Chebychev inequality tells us that, for a single observation x,

$$P\left(-\frac{\sigma}{\alpha^{1/2}} < x - \mu_0 < \frac{\sigma}{\alpha^{1/2}}\right) \geqslant (1 - \alpha).$$

Hence, we can reject H_0 at some unknown significance level which is in any case less than or equal to α if

$$|x - \mu_0| > \frac{\sigma}{\alpha^{1/2}}.$$

That is, the probability of a Type I error is at most α.

An examination of Figure 1–4 will perhaps help in an understanding of the two types of error. Suppose that we are to decide between the null hypothesis H_0 and a single alternative hypothesis H_1 by examination of the sample statistic t. The curve labeled A in the figure is the probability

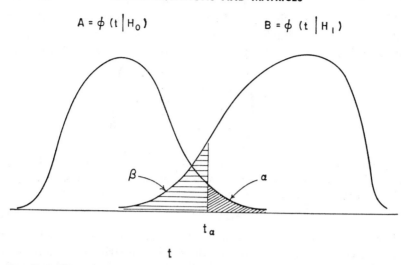

$$A = \phi\,(t\,|\,H_0) \qquad\qquad B = \phi\,(t\,|\,H_1)$$

Fig. 1–4. Illustration of Type I error (α) and Type II error (β) when the null hypothesis H_0 is tested against the simple alternative hypothesis H_1 by examination of the sample statistic t. A is the density function for t when H_0 is true; B is the density function for t when H_1 is true. See text.

density function for t when H_0 is true; the curve labeled B is the probability density function for t when H_1 is true. We will choose to reject H_0 and accept H_1 if $t > t_\alpha$ and to accept H_0 and reject H_1 if $t < t_\alpha$. The area under curve A to the right of t_α is equal to α, the significance level of the test; it is the probability that the sample statistic will exceed t_α and that, hence, the hypothesis will be rejected when it is true. On the contrary, it will be seen that the area under curve B to the left of t_α is equal to the probability of accepting H_0 when H_1 is true. The power of the test with respect to the alternative hypothesis H_1 is equal to $1 - \beta$, the area under curve B and to the right of t_α. It is obvious in this example that as the value of α decreases, so does the power of the test, $1 - \beta$.

As a closing remark to this section, we note that statistical significance does not imply physical significance, although it is clearly possible for the two to be related.

1–8. LINEAR EQUATIONS AND MATRIX THEORY

In the discussion of least-squares adjustments and the associated linear equations, we will find it extremely useful to use matrix notation. We present here a brief introduction to this notation, in the hope that it will be read and digested. Although the reading of this section is not essential to the understanding of most of the book, the assimilation of the material is highly recommended.

A matrix is a two-dimensional array of numbers,* represented in this text by a boldface capital letter, occasionally with two subscripts indicating the dimensions of the matrix; $\mathbf{A}_{m,n}$ is a matrix of m rows and n columns:

$$\mathbf{A}_{m,n} \equiv \begin{pmatrix} a_{11} & a_{12} & \cdots & a_{1n} \\ a_{21} & a_{22} & \cdots & a_{2n} \\ \cdot & \cdot & \cdots & \cdot \\ \cdot & \cdot & \cdots & \cdot \\ \cdot & \cdot & \cdots & \cdot \\ a_{m1} & a_{m2} & \cdots & a_{mn} \end{pmatrix}. \tag{1}$$

The general element, i.e., the element in the ith row and jth column, of $\mathbf{A}_{m,n}$ will be denoted by a_{ij}, and we will frequently define a matrix in terms of its general element as follows:

$$\mathbf{A}_{m,n} \equiv \{a_{ij}\}. \tag{2}$$

The *transpose* of a matrix is defined as the matrix obtained by interchanging the rows and columns of the original matrix. The transpose of an $n \times m$ matrix is an $m \times n$ matrix. The transpose is denoted by placing a prime mark as a superscript on the original matrix. Thus, if the matrix $\mathbf{A}_{m,n}$ is defined as in (1), the transpose of $\mathbf{A}$ is written and defined as

$$\mathbf{A}'_{n,m} \equiv \begin{pmatrix} a_{11} & a_{21} & \cdots & a_{m1} \\ a_{12} & a_{22} & \cdots & a_{m2} \\ \cdot & \cdot & \cdots & \cdot \\ \cdot & \cdot & \cdots & \cdot \\ \cdot & \cdot & \cdots & \cdot \\ a_{1n} & a_{2n} & \cdots & a_{mn} \end{pmatrix}. \tag{3}$$

It may be shown that

$$(\mathbf{A}')' = \mathbf{A}. \tag{4}$$

Example 1–8–1 (Some Typical Matrices)

$$\mathbf{A}_{2,4} \equiv \begin{pmatrix} 13 & 1 & -5 & 6 \\ 21 & 0 & 49 & 14 \end{pmatrix}.$$

$$\mathbf{A}'_{4,2} \equiv \begin{pmatrix} 13 & 21 \\ 1 & 0 \\ -5 & 49 \\ 6 & 14 \end{pmatrix}.$$

$$\mathbf{B}_{1,3} \equiv (b_1 \quad b_2 \quad b_3).$$

$$\mathbf{C}_{3,1} \equiv \begin{pmatrix} c_1 \\ c_2 \\ c_3 \end{pmatrix}.$$

* These numbers may be real or complex, but as the matrices to be used in this book have only real elements, we shall restrict ourselves to such *real matrices* in this section.

Matrices of the types $\mathbf{B}_{1,3}$ and $\mathbf{C}_{3,1}$ are frequently called row and column vectors, respectively. A matrix containing only one row and one column is called a *scalar*.

Manipulation of Matrices. Two or more matrices may be added if they contain the same number of rows and columns. The sum is obtained simply by adding the corresponding elements in all the matrices, i.e., if

$$\mathbf{B} + \mathbf{C} + \cdots + \mathbf{D} = \mathbf{A}, \tag{5}$$

then

$$b_{ij} + c_{ij} + \cdots + d_{ij} = a_{ij}. \tag{6}$$

Addition is commutative:

$$\mathbf{B} + \mathbf{C} = \mathbf{C} + \mathbf{B} \tag{7}$$

and associative:

$$\mathbf{A} + (\mathbf{B} + \mathbf{C}) = (\mathbf{A} + \mathbf{B}) + \mathbf{C}. \tag{8}$$

From the definition of addition, we see also that if a matrix is multiplied by a scalar, each element of the matrix is so multiplied, i.e., if

$$\mathbf{A} = c\mathbf{B} \tag{9}$$

where c is a scalar, then

$$a_{ij} = cb_{ij}. \tag{10}$$

Example 1–8–2

$$\begin{pmatrix} 3 & 1 & 2 \\ 4 & 3 & -1 \end{pmatrix} + \begin{pmatrix} 4 & 2 & 1 \\ 5 & -3 & 2 \end{pmatrix} = \begin{pmatrix} 7 & 3 & 3 \\ 9 & 0 & 1 \end{pmatrix}.$$

$$3\begin{pmatrix} 1 & 2 & 3 \\ 0 & 1 & 4 \end{pmatrix} = \begin{pmatrix} 3 & 6 & 9 \\ 0 & 3 & 12 \end{pmatrix}.$$

$$\begin{pmatrix} 2 & 3 \\ 1 & 6 \end{pmatrix} a = \begin{pmatrix} 2a & 3a \\ a & 6a \end{pmatrix}.$$

The product of two matrices is defined only if the number of columns in the first matrix is equal to the number of rows in the second. Let us consider the matrix product

$$\mathbf{A}_{m,k}\mathbf{B}_{k,n}. \tag{11}$$

We may write

$$\mathbf{C}_{m,n} = \mathbf{AB} \tag{12}$$

with

$$c_{ij} = \sum_{p=1}^{k} a_{ip}b_{pj}. \tag{13}$$

That is, the element in the ith row and jth column of the product is the sum of the products of the elements in the ith row of $\mathbf{A}$ and the jth column of $\mathbf{B}$, taken term by term. Note that matrix multiplication is not generally commutative, i.e.,

$$\mathbf{AB} \neq \mathbf{BA}, \tag{14}$$

even when both products are defined. Multiplication is, however, associative:

$$\mathbf{A(BC)} = \mathbf{(AB)C}, \tag{15}$$

and distributive with respect to addition:

$$\mathbf{A(B + C)} = \mathbf{AB} + \mathbf{AC}. \tag{16}$$

Example 1–8–3

$$\begin{pmatrix} 3 & 2 & 1 \\ 1 & 2 & 3 \end{pmatrix} \begin{pmatrix} 4 & 1 \\ 0 & 1 \\ 2 & 1 \end{pmatrix} = \begin{pmatrix} 14 & 4 \\ 10 & 6 \end{pmatrix}.$$

$$\begin{pmatrix} 4 & 1 \\ 0 & 1 \\ 2 & 1 \end{pmatrix} \begin{pmatrix} 3 & 2 & 1 \\ 1 & 2 & 3 \end{pmatrix} = \begin{pmatrix} 13 & 10 & 7 \\ 1 & 2 & 3 \\ 7 & 6 & 5 \end{pmatrix}.$$

$$\begin{pmatrix} 1 & 2 \\ 1 & 1 \end{pmatrix} \begin{pmatrix} 1 & 4 \\ 2 & 3 \end{pmatrix} = \begin{pmatrix} 5 & 10 \\ 3 & 7 \end{pmatrix}.$$

$$\begin{pmatrix} 1 & 4 \\ 2 & 3 \end{pmatrix} \begin{pmatrix} 1 & 2 \\ 1 & 1 \end{pmatrix} = \begin{pmatrix} 5 & 6 \\ 5 & 7 \end{pmatrix}.$$

Square matrices have some special properties which are extremely useful. First of all, the *determinant* of a square matrix $\mathbf{A}_{n,n}$ is defined as follows:

$$\det \mathbf{A} = \sum (\pm a_{1i} a_{2j} \cdots a_{nk}), \tag{17}$$

where the summation is over all permutations of $i, j, \ldots, k$, where $i, j, \ldots, k$ are the integers 1 to n. The term is given a positive sign if the permutation involves an even number of interchanges and a minus sign if the permutation is odd. We thus form the sum all possible products formed by multiplying together one and only one element from each row of the matrix; thus there are

$$n(n - 1)(n - 2) \cdots 1 = n! \tag{18}$$

terms in the sum. For example, if $n = 3$, we have the even permutations (123), (231), and (312), and the odd permutations (213), (132), and (321). Therefore the determinant may be written

$$\det \mathbf{A}_{3,3} = a_{11}a_{22}a_{33} + a_{12}a_{23}a_{31} + a_{13}a_{21}a_{32}$$
$$- a_{12}a_{21}a_{33} - a_{11}a_{23}a_{32} - a_{13}a_{22}a_{31}. \tag{19}$$

Determinants are rarely evaluated by appealing to the definition, as there are usually more convenient and systematic ways of performing the evaluation. Some of these will be familiar to those with experience in numerical methods.* A general method, again not necessarily the best adapted to computation, is given in the following paragraph.

We define the *cofactor* of the element a_{ij} as $(-1)^{i+j}$ times the determinant of the $(n - 1) \times (n - 1)$ matrix obtained when the ith row and the jth column of **A** are deleted. This is occasionally denoted by

$$\text{cof } a_{ij} = A_{ij}. \tag{20}$$

It can be shown that the determinant of a matrix may be evaluated as

$$\det \mathbf{A} = \sum_j a_{ij} A_{ij} \quad \text{for any } i \tag{21}$$

$$= \sum_i a_{ij} A_{ij} \quad \text{for any } j.$$

The matrix

$$\mathbf{A}^{\dagger} \equiv \{A_{ji}\} \tag{22}$$

obtained by replacing each element a_{ij} in the matrix by the cofactor of the element a_{ji} is known as the *adjoint* of the matrix **A** and will be denoted here by the superscript dagger (†).

Example 1–8–4

If

$$\mathbf{A} = \begin{pmatrix} 13 & 10 & 7 \\ 1 & 2 & 3 \\ 7 & 6 & 5 \end{pmatrix},$$

$$\det \mathbf{A} = 13 \det \begin{pmatrix} 2 & 3 \\ 6 & 5 \end{pmatrix} - 1 \det \begin{pmatrix} 10 & 7 \\ 6 & 5 \end{pmatrix} + 7 \det \begin{pmatrix} 10 & 7 \\ 2 & 3 \end{pmatrix}$$

$$= 13 \times (-8) - 1 \times 8 + 7 \times 16$$
$$= 0$$

If we form all possible square submatrices of the (not necessarily square) matrix **A** and find that at least one determinant of order r † is non-zero but that all determinants of order $r + 1$ vanish, then the matrix is said to be of *rank* r. A square matrix $\mathbf{A}_{n,n}$ is said to be singular if its rank is less than n, that is, if its determinant vanishes. The rank of the product of two matrices is never greater than the rank of either factor. Furthermore, if a matrix of rank r is multiplied by a non-singular square matrix, the rank of the product is also r. The rank of a matrix is never greater than the number of rows or columns, whichever is less.

Example 1–8–5

The matrix **A** in Example 1–8–4 is of rank 2. The 3×3 determinant vanishes, and the matrix is thus singular. There are however

---

* See the Bibliography.
† The order of a square matrix is the number of rows or columns.

a number of non-vanishing 2×2 cofactors. We could have predicted that the rank would be no greater than 2 by observing that **A** is the product of two matrices of rank 2. (See Example 1–8–3.)

A square matrix is said to be *symmetric* if $a_{ij} = a_{ji}$.
In the theory of matrices, the unit matrix

$$\mathbf{I}_{n,n} = \delta_{ij},$$

where

$$\delta_{ij} = \begin{cases} 1 \text{ if } i = j \\ 0 \text{ if } i \neq j. \end{cases}$$

is of particular importance.

If a square matrix $\mathbf{A}_{n,n}$ is non-singular, there exists a matrix $\mathbf{A}^{-1}$, known as the *inverse* of **A**, such that

$$\mathbf{AA}^{-1} = \mathbf{A}^{-1}\mathbf{A} = \mathbf{I}. \tag{23}$$

One way of evaluating the inverse (not generally the most convenient) is by the equation

$$\mathbf{A}^{-1} = \frac{\mathbf{A}^{\dagger}}{\det \mathbf{A}}. \tag{24}$$

If the inverse of a matrix is equal to its transpose,

$$\mathbf{A}^{-1} = \mathbf{A}', \tag{25}$$

the matrix is said to be orthogonal, and since

$$\det \mathbf{A} = \det \mathbf{A}', \tag{26}$$

it follows that

$$(\det \mathbf{A})^2 = 1 \tag{27}$$

for an orthogonal matrix **A**.

Other useful theorems of matrix algebra include the following:
If B and A are square non-singular matrices, then

$$(\mathbf{AB})^{-1} = \mathbf{B}^{-1}\mathbf{A}^{-1}. \tag{28}$$

For any two matrices,

$$(\mathbf{AB})' = \mathbf{B}'\mathbf{A}'. \tag{29}$$

Multiplication by the unit matrix has the property that

$$\mathbf{A}_{m,n}\mathbf{I}_{n,n} = \mathbf{I}_{m,m}\mathbf{A}_{m,n} = \mathbf{A}_{m,n}. \tag{30}$$

Example 1–8–6

The matrix $\mathbf{A} = \begin{pmatrix} 3 & 0 & 2 \\ 0 & 1 & 1 \\ 2 & 1 & 2 \end{pmatrix}$ is symmetric.

Its adjoint is

$$\mathbf{A}^\dagger = \begin{pmatrix} 1 & 2 & -2 \\ 2 & 2 & -3 \\ -2 & -3 & 3 \end{pmatrix}.$$

Since $\det \mathbf{A} = -1$, the inverse of $\mathbf{A}$ is given by

$$\mathbf{A}^{-1} = \begin{pmatrix} -1 & -2 & 2 \\ -2 & -2 & 3 \\ 2 & 3 & -3 \end{pmatrix}.$$

Linear Equations. The set of m linear equations in n unknowns x_j,

$$\sum_{j=1}^{n} a_{ij}x_j = b_i, \quad i = 1, \ldots, m, \tag{31}$$

may be more conveniently written

$$\mathbf{A}_{m,n}\mathbf{X}_{n,1} = \mathbf{B}_{m,1} \tag{32}$$

$\mathbf{A}$ and $\mathbf{B}$ are assumed to be given quantities, and we are required to solve the equations for $\mathbf{X}$. There are three possibilities:

(i) There is no solution, i.e., the equations are inconsistent.
(ii) There is one and only one solution.
(iii) There is more than one solution. If this is the case, the number of solutions is infinite.

Let us form the augmented matrix

$$\mathbf{D} \equiv (\mathbf{A} \quad \mathbf{B}) \equiv \begin{pmatrix} a_{11} & a_{12} & \cdots & a_{1n} & b_1 \\ a_{21} & a_{22} & \cdots & a_{2n} & b_2 \\ \vdots & \vdots & \cdots & \vdots & \vdots \\ & & \cdots & & \\ a_{m1} & a_{m2} & \cdots & a_{mn} & b_m \end{pmatrix}. \tag{33}$$

If the rank of $\mathbf{D}$ is equal to the rank of $\mathbf{A}$, at least one solution exists. If the rank of $\mathbf{A}$ is less than the rank of $\mathbf{D}$, there is no solution. (The rank of $\mathbf{D}$ cannot be less than the rank of $\mathbf{A}$.) Furthermore, if the ranks of $\mathbf{A}$ and $\mathbf{D}$ are both equal to r, then $n - r$ of the unknowns may be assigned any values whatsoever, and the remaining r unknowns are uniquely determined. A unique solution to the original set of equations (32) is possible then only if $r = n$.

If m is less than n, the rank of $\mathbf{A}$ is also necessarily less than n, and the set of equations cannot possess a unique solution.

If $\mathbf{A}$ is a square matrix, the statement $r = n$ implies that $\mathbf{A}$ is non-singular. Thus we may multiply the equations on the left by $\mathbf{A}^{-1}$ to obtain

$$\mathbf{X}_{n,1} = \mathbf{A}_{n,n}^{-1}\mathbf{B}_{n,1}. \tag{34}$$

If m is greater than n and if the equations possess a unique solution, i.e., $r = n$, this solution may be found either by solving any subset of rank r of the equations or else by multiplying on the left by $\mathbf{A}'$ and then by $(\mathbf{A}'\mathbf{A})^{-1}$ to obtain

$$\mathbf{X} = (\mathbf{A}'\mathbf{A})^{-1}\mathbf{A}'\mathbf{B}. \tag{35}$$

Even if the equations are not consistent, the preceding expression gives a solution which is in a sense a best average solution, as will be seen when the theory of least squares is discussed.

Example 1–8–7

Consider the equation $\mathbf{AX} = \mathbf{B}$:

$$\begin{pmatrix} 3 & 2 \\ 1 & 1 \\ 2 & 2 \end{pmatrix} \begin{pmatrix} x_1 \\ x_2 \end{pmatrix} = \begin{pmatrix} 4 \\ 2 \\ 3 \end{pmatrix}.$$

The rank of $\mathbf{A}$, the matrix of coefficients, is 2. The augmented matrix

$$\mathbf{D} = \begin{pmatrix} 3 & 2 & 4 \\ 1 & 1 & 2 \\ 2 & 2 & 3 \end{pmatrix}$$

is non-singular and hence is of rank 3. Therefore no solution exists. On the other hand, if the vector $\mathbf{B}$ is changed to

$$\mathbf{B} \equiv \begin{pmatrix} 4 \\ 2 \\ 4 \end{pmatrix},$$

the equations have a unique solution, since both the matrix $\mathbf{A}$ and the augmented matrix $\mathbf{D}$ have rank 2. The solution can be found as

$$\begin{pmatrix} x_1 \\ x_2 \end{pmatrix} = \begin{pmatrix} 3 & 2 \\ 1 & 1 \end{pmatrix}^{-1} \begin{pmatrix} 4 \\ 2 \end{pmatrix} = \begin{pmatrix} 1 & -2 \\ -1 & 3 \end{pmatrix} \begin{pmatrix} 4 \\ 2 \end{pmatrix} = \begin{pmatrix} 0 \\ 2 \end{pmatrix}.$$

Homogeneous Equations. If $\mathbf{B} = \mathbf{O}$ in the system $\mathbf{AX} = \mathbf{B}$, the equations are said to be homogeneous. Since the augmented matrix $\mathbf{D} = (\mathbf{A}\ \mathbf{O})$ has the same rank as $\mathbf{A}$, at least one solution exists. If $r = n$, one solution only exists, and this is the trivial solution

$$x_1 = x_2 = \cdots = x_n = 0. \tag{36}$$

Only if r is less than n is there a non-trivial solution. As is the case with non-homogeneous equations, the values of $n - r$ of the variables may be assigned at will, and the remainder will be uniquely determined. For a square matrix, the condition that r be less than n implies that a non-trivial solution to the set of homogeneous equations exists only if

$$\det \mathbf{A} = 0. \tag{37}$$

Linear Transformations. If a vector $\mathbf{X}_{n,1}$ is related to a vector $\mathbf{Y}_{n,1}$ by the relationship

$$\mathbf{X} = \mathbf{B}_{n,n}\mathbf{Y}, \tag{38}$$

$\mathbf{X}$ is said to have been obtained from $\mathbf{Y}$ by the linear transformation $\mathbf{B}$. If $\mathbf{B'B} = \mathbf{I}$, the transformation is said to be *orthogonal* (or *unitary* if the elements of $\mathbf{B}$ are complex).

Example 1–8–8

The matrix

$$\mathbf{B} = \begin{pmatrix} 0.6 & 0.8 \\ -0.8 & 0.6 \end{pmatrix}$$

is the matrix of an orthogonal linear transformation which transforms the variables y into the variables x in the following way:

$$\begin{aligned} x_1 &= 0.6y_1 + 0.8y_2 \\ x_2 &= -0.8y_1 + 0.6y_2. \end{aligned}$$

Quadratic Forms. The scalar quantity

$$Q \equiv \mathbf{X'}_{1,n}\mathbf{A}_{n,n}\mathbf{X}_{n,1} \equiv \sum_{i=1}^{n}\sum_{j=1}^{n} x_i x_j a_{ij} \equiv a_{11}x_1^2 + a_{12}x_1x_2 + \cdots + a_{1n}x_1x_n$$
$$+ a_{21}x_2x_1 + a_{22}x_2^2 + \cdots + a_{2n}x_2x_n + \cdots$$
$$+ a_{n1}x_nx_1 + a_{n2}x_nx_2 + \cdots + a_{nn}x_n^2 \tag{39}$$

is known as a *quadratic form*, and $\mathbf{A}$ is the matrix of the quadratic form. The *rank* of a quadratic form is equal to the rank of $\mathbf{A}$.

If $\mathbf{X}$ is subjected to an orthogonal transformation

$$\mathbf{Y} = \mathbf{TX}, \tag{40}$$

we then have

$$\mathbf{X'AX} = \mathbf{Y'TAT'Y} \equiv \mathbf{Y'CY}. \tag{41}$$

The matrices $\mathbf{A}$ and $\mathbf{C}$ are said to be similar.

Eigenvalues and Eigenvectors. It may be shown that every real *symmetric* ($\mathbf{A'} \equiv \mathbf{A}$) square matrix $\mathbf{A}$ can be subjected to an orthogonal transformation (or in general, unitary transformation if the symmetric matrix is complex)

$$\mathbf{T'AT} = \Lambda \tag{42}$$

where Λ is a diagonal matrix, i.e., $\lambda_{ij} = 0$ for $i \neq j$. Let us determine $\mathbf{T}$. Multiplying on the left by $(\mathbf{T'})^{-1} = \mathbf{T}$ (since $\mathbf{T}$ is orthogonal), we find

$$\mathbf{AT} = \mathbf{T}\Lambda. \tag{43}$$

If we now consider $\mathbf{T}$ to be partitioned into column vectors $\mathbf{T}_{n,1}^{(t)}$:

$$\mathbf{T} \equiv (\mathbf{T}^{(1)} \, \mathbf{T}^{(2)} \, \cdots \, \mathbf{T}^{(n)}) \tag{44}$$

then

$$\mathbf{A}\mathbf{T}^{(i)} = \mathbf{T}^{(i)}\lambda_{ii}, \quad i = 1, \ldots, n. \tag{45}$$

We thus have

$$(\mathbf{A} - \lambda_{ii}\mathbf{I})\mathbf{T}^{(i)} = 0, \tag{46}$$

a set of homogeneous linear equations which, as we have seen, has a solution $\mathbf{T}^{(i)}$ only if the determinant of the coefficients vanishes:

$$\det (\mathbf{A} - \lambda\mathbf{I}) = 0. \tag{47}$$

Written out in its entirety, this equation is

$$\det \begin{pmatrix} a_{11} - \lambda & a_{12} & \cdots & a_{1n} \\ a_{21} & a_{22} - \lambda & \cdots & a_{2n} \\ \cdot & \cdot & \cdots & \cdot \\ \cdot & \cdot & \cdots & \cdot \\ \cdot & \cdot & \cdots & \cdot \\ a_{n1} & a_{n2} & \cdots & a_{nn} - \lambda \end{pmatrix} = 0 \tag{48}$$

This equation of the nth degree in λ is known as the characteristic equation of the matrix $\mathbf{A}$, and the n roots are called the characteristic values, eigenvalues, or latent roots of the matrix. To each of the n eigenvalues λ_{ii} corresponds a characteristic vector or eigenvector $\mathbf{T}^{(i)}$, all n of which constitute the matrix $\mathbf{T}$ which diagonalizes $\mathbf{A}$.

It is interesting (and important) to note that the same eigenvalue equation arises from consideration of the following problem:

Find the vector $\mathbf{X}$ such that the quadratic form $\mathbf{X}'\mathbf{A}\mathbf{X}$ is a maximum, subject to the restriction $\mathbf{X}'\mathbf{X} = 1$.

Introducing a variation function F and Lagrange multipliers λ, we have

$$F \equiv \mathbf{X}'\mathbf{A}\mathbf{X} - \lambda(\mathbf{X}'\mathbf{X} - 1)$$
$$\delta F = (2\mathbf{A}\mathbf{X} - 2\lambda\mathbf{X})\delta x = 0. \tag{49}$$

Since the latter equation must be satisfied for arbitrary variations δx, it follows that

$$(\mathbf{A} - \lambda\mathbf{I})\mathbf{X} = 0 \tag{50}$$

and

$$\det (\mathbf{A} - \lambda\mathbf{I}) = 0 \tag{51}$$

for a non-trivial solution. The vectors $\mathbf{X}$ correspond to the $\mathbf{T}^{(i)}$ in the previous derivation.

Example 1-8-9

Find the eigenvalues and eigenvectors of the matrix

$$\mathbf{A} = \begin{pmatrix} 3 & 1 \\ 1 & 1 \end{pmatrix}.$$

We have

$$\det (\mathbf{A} - \lambda \mathbf{I}) = \det \begin{pmatrix} 3 - \lambda & 1 \\ 1 & 1 - \lambda \end{pmatrix} = \lambda^2 - 4\lambda + 2 = 0$$

$$\lambda_{11} = 3.4142$$
$$\lambda_{22} = 0.5858.$$

To obtain the eigenvectors, we substitute the two values of λ, one at a time, into the defining equations:

$$(3 - \lambda_{ii})t_{1i} + t_{2i} = 0$$
$$t_{1i} + (1 - \lambda_{ii})t_{2i} = 0$$

to obtain

$$\mathbf{T}^{(1)} = \begin{pmatrix} 0.9239 \\ 0.3826 \end{pmatrix}$$

and

$$\mathbf{T}^{(2)} = \begin{pmatrix} -0.3826 \\ 0.9239 \end{pmatrix}.$$

To check the diagonalization, we perform the transformation

$$\mathbf{T}'\mathbf{A}\mathbf{T} = \begin{pmatrix} 0.9239 & 0.3826 \\ -0.3826 & 0.9239 \end{pmatrix}\begin{pmatrix} 3 & 1 \\ 1 & 1 \end{pmatrix}\begin{pmatrix} 0.9239 & -0.3826 \\ 0.3826 & 0.9239 \end{pmatrix}$$

to obtain

$$\Lambda = \begin{pmatrix} 3.4141 & 0.0002 \\ 0.0002 & 0.5858 \end{pmatrix},$$

where it will be noted that there are rounding errors causing slight deviations from the ideal values in

$$\Lambda = \begin{pmatrix} \lambda_{11} & 0 \\ 0 & \lambda_{22} \end{pmatrix}.$$

Note that the eigenvalues and eigenvectors are defined for any square matrix. It is only for symmetric matrices, however, that the matrix of the eigenvectors will diagonalize the original matrix.

Example 1–8–10

Given the non-symmetric square matrix

$$\mathbf{B} = \begin{pmatrix} 0.01994 & 0.00000 & 0.00000 \\ 0.15600 & 0.33169 & -0.04075 \\ -0.31471 & -0.62943 & 0.30028 \end{pmatrix},$$

find the eigenvalues and eigenvectors, and show that the matrix of eigenvectors does not diagonalize $\mathbf{B}$. The eigenvalues are found to be

$$\lambda_{11} = 0.01994$$
$$\lambda_{22} = 0.15506$$
$$\lambda_{33} = 0.47691$$

with corresponding eigenvectors

$$\mathbf{T} \equiv (\mathbf{T}^{(1)} \ \mathbf{T}^{(2)} \ \mathbf{T}^{(3)}) = \begin{pmatrix} 1.00000 & 0.00000 & 0.00000 \\ 0.00000 & 0.96280 & -0.27017 \\ 0.00000 & 0.27017 & 0.96280 \end{pmatrix}.$$

Application of the transformation to **B** results in

$$\mathbf{T'BT} = \begin{pmatrix} 0.01994 & 0.00000 & 0.00000 \\ 0.06517 & 0.15506 & 0.00000 \\ -0.34515 & -0.58867 & 0.47689 \end{pmatrix}.$$

The matrix cannot be diagonalized, but the diagonal terms of the transformed matrix are equal to the eigenvalues.

EXERCISES

1–1. A sample space contains twenty points:

$$S \equiv \{x_i : i = 1, 2, \ldots, 20\}.$$

The events A, B, and C are defined by

$$A \equiv \{x_i : i = 5, 6, \ldots, 10\}$$
$$B \equiv \{x_7, x_{12}, x_{15}\}$$
$$C \equiv \{x_i : i = 1, 12\}.$$

Which points are included in the following events?

(a) $A \cup B$ (e) $\overline{A} \cap C$
(b) $A \cup C$ (f) $\overline{A} \cap (C \cup B)$
(c) $A \cap C$ (g) $(\overline{A} \cap C) \cup B$
(d) $\overline{A}$

If each sample point has associated with it a probability measure 1/20, what is the probability of each of the events (a) through (g)? Suppose S is a set of scientists consisting of archeologists (A), biologists (B), and chemists (C). A scientist chosen at random from the set walks through the door. What is the probability that he is a biochemical archeologist? How is the event described in the notation of this problem?

1–2. An experiment is carried out to determine the wavelengths at which the first five strong absorptions occur in the infrared spectrum of a polyatomic molecule. Devise a sample space which might be used to describe the possible results of the experiment.

1–3. Consider the experiment of Exercise 1–2, but suppose that measurements are not only of wavelength but also of intensity. How would you modify your description of the sample space? Are there any points in your sample space to which you would be willing to ascribe an *a priori* probability of zero?

1–4. Take some experiment with which you are familiar, and set up a hypothetical sample space which includes all possible results of the experiment. Assign to each point of the sample space a probability measure based on your experience.

1–5. A rocket which is intended to hit the moon is fired. Assume that such an experiment has been carried out twice previously, once with success and once with failure as the result. Would you be willing to say that the probability of success on the present shot is 0.50? Give several reasons for your answer.

1–6. Toss five coins together ten times and record the number of heads in each of the ten trials. Compare your results with those calculated by assuming a binomial distribution with $p = q = \frac{1}{2}$.

1–7. Compare the binomial probabilities $b_{10}(k)$ for $p = 0.5$ and $p = 0.4$.

1–8. Consider Poisson distributions with parameters $\lambda = 1, 2, 10,$ and 100. For each of these distributions, compute (a) the probability of having exactly λ events in unit time and (b) the probability that the number of events in unit time lies between 0.95λ and 1.05λ.

1–9. A qualitative test for chemical element A gives a positive result 90% of the time when A is present. It gives the same result 50% of the time when B is present. Assume that the *a priori* probabilities of having A or B present are each equal to $\frac{1}{2}$, and compute the probability that A is present, given that a positive result is obtained. Suppose that the experiment is repeated on the same sample and a positive result is again obtained. What is the probability that two positive results indicate the presence of A rather than B? (Assume that the results of the two tests are independent.)

1–10. Consider the probability density function

$$\phi(x) = \frac{C}{(1 + |x|)^2} \text{ for } -\infty \leqslant x \leqslant +\infty.$$

What is the value of the normalization constant C? What is the probability that x lies between 1 and 2?

1–11. Consider the bivariate probability density function

$$\phi(x, y) = Cx(x + 4y)$$

defined for

$$0 < x < 1$$
$$0 < y < 1.$$

Determine the value of the normalization constant C. Determine the marginal distributions $\phi_x{}^M(x)$ and $\phi_y{}^M(y)$. Determine the conditional distributions $\phi_x{}^C(x|y)$ and $\phi_y{}^C(y|x)$. If $x = \frac{1}{2}$, what is the probability that y lies between 0 and $\frac{1}{4}$?

1–12. If $\phi(x) = \frac{1}{2}$ for $-1 < x < +1$ and is otherwise zero, determine the probability density functions for

$$f_1 = \frac{1}{x}$$

$$f_2 = x^2$$
$$f_3 = \sin^{-1} x.$$

1–13. If $\phi(x, y)$ is as defined in Exercise 1–11, determine the probability density function for $f = xy$.

1–14. If $\phi(x) = 1/2a$ for $-a \leqslant x \leqslant +a$ and $\phi(y) = 1/2b$ for $-b \leqslant y \leqslant +b$, and if x and y are independent, determine the probability density function for $f = x/y$.

1-15. For the bivariate density function in Exercise 1–11, find $\varepsilon\{x\}$, $\varepsilon\{y\}$, $\varepsilon\{x^2\}$, $\varepsilon\{y^2\}$, $\varepsilon\{xy\}$, $\sigma^2(x)$, $\sigma^2(y)$, and cov (x, y).

1-16. For an arbitrary distribution with finite second moment, show that $\varepsilon(x - \alpha)^2$ is a minimum when α is the mean.

1-17. The *median* of a probability distribution is defined as that value β for which

$$\int_{-\infty}^{\beta} \phi(x)\, dx = \int_{\beta}^{\infty} \phi(x)\, dx = 0.50.$$

Show that β is the value for which the mean deviation

$$\varepsilon\{|x - \beta|\}$$

is a minimum.

1-18. Derive the moment generating function for the sample mean of a sample of size n from a normal distribution. What is the behavior of this function as n increases without limit?

1-19. Derive the moments of the distribution defined by

$$\phi(x) = (1 - x^2)^{1/2} \quad \text{for } -1 \leqslant x \leqslant 1$$
$$= 0 \qquad\qquad \text{otherwise.}$$

Compare with the moments of the normal distribution which has the same variance.

1-20. Derive an expression for the moments of the Poisson distribution.

1-21. Derive an approximate expression for the standard deviation of an angle, given the standard deviations in each of the three lengths determining the angle. Assume that the errors in the lengths are uncorrelated.

1-22. Derive an approximate expression for the length of a vector, given the standard deviation in each of the components, which are presumed to be statistically independent.

1-23. It was shown in Example 1–6–10 that the probability density function

$$\phi(x) = \frac{a}{x^2} \quad \text{for } x \geqslant a$$

$$= 0 \quad \text{otherwise}$$

where $a > 0$, has no mean. Find the value of the median.

1-24. Consider a bivariate normal distribution written in the form

$$\phi(x, y) = N \exp\left[-(ax^2 + by^2 + cxy)\right].$$

Express the standard deviations and the correlation coefficient in terms of the constants a, b, and c.

1-25. The random variables x and y are distributed according to the bivariate normal distribution. What is the density function for the product xy.

1-26. If $\phi(x) = 2x/a^2$ for $0 < x < a$ and is otherwise zero, show that the maximum-likelihood estimator for the mean is

$$\hat{\mu} = \tfrac{2}{3} x_{\max}$$

where $x_{\max}$ is the maximum value of x observed in a sample. Is this an unbiased estimator? Is it consistent?

1-27. Find the expected value of the range in a sample of two from a normal population.

1-28. Suppose that we have drawn a sample of size one from a normal population. Discuss the meaning of a test of the hypothesis

$$H_0: \sigma^2 = \sigma_0{}^2.$$

Does your discussion suggest why it is closer to the truth to say that a hypothesis is not rejected rather than to say it is accepted?

1-29. Indicate a method for deriving the distribution of the maximum x_{max} in a sample of n from a population with density function $\phi(x)$.

1-30. Consider a sample with mean $\bar{x}$ from a population with mean μ. Discuss the difference between the statements:

i. There is a 95% probability that the mean μ lies between $\bar{x} - 1.96\sigma$ and $\bar{x} + 1.96\sigma$.

ii. There is a 95% probability that the statement

$$\bar{x} - 1.96 < \mu < \bar{x} + 1.96$$

is true.

1-31. Find a density function for which the Chebychev inequality becomes an equality, and suggest a method for the proof of the Chebychev inequality.

1-32. What are the moments of the density function which has characteristic function $\cos\theta$? What is this density function?

1-33. Is it possible to devise a density function with zero first and second moments but non-zero third moment?

1-34. Give examples of matrices of the following dimensions: 6×6, 3×1, 1×3, 4×5, 1×1. Write down the transposes of these matrices. Determine the inverses of those matrices which possess inverses. Find the rank of each matrix you have written.

1-35. Find the 3×3 product of the 3×1 and 1×3 matrices you have written in Exercise 1-34. Find the eigenvalues and eigenvectors of this matrix.

1-36. Given matrices $\mathbf{X}_{1,n}$ and $\mathbf{M}_{n,n}$, show that

$$\mathbf{XMX'} = \text{Trace}\ (\mathbf{X'XM}).$$

The trace of a square matrix is the sum of the diagonal elements.

1-37. If x is normally distributed with mean μ and variance σ^2, find the mean and variance of the function $y = x^{1/2}$. Frequently a physically observable quantity is the square of the parameter of fundamental interest.

2

Estimation When a Single Random Variable Is Involved

2-1. INTRODUCTION

We present in this chapter a brief survey of the methods used for the estimation of the mean and variance of population distribution functions involving a single random variable. We further present the more commonly used hypothesis tests used for making statistical statements about these quantities. The concepts and sampling distributions introduced here, aside from being useful in themselves, serve as a convenient introduction to estimation and hypothesis-testing for multivariate distributions, with which the experimental chemical physicist is more often concerned.

The importance of the normal distribution function is revealed, and most of the tests used are based on it. A discussion of tests for non-normality and the effects of non-normality on the hypothesis tests is deferred until Chapter 5.

2-2. POINT ESTIMATION

As we have noted previously, unbiased estimates for the population mean and variance from a sample of size n are given respectively by

$$\bar{x} = \frac{1}{n} \sum_{i=1}^{n} x_i \tag{1}$$

and

$$s^2 = \frac{1}{n-1} \sum_{i=1}^{n} (x_i - \bar{x})^2 \tag{2}$$

These results are valid for any population with finite variance. On the other hand, these may not be the best estimates for the population parameters, although for most commonly encountered distributions they are.

These are point estimates. To obtain interval estimates and to test hypotheses, the usual methods require that we know the form of the population distribution. This is not absolutely necessary, as there are methods independent of the distribution which have been extensively developed in recent years. A simple example is the Chebychev inequality (Example 1–7–9), which is independent of the form of the distribution. However, most of the commonly applied interval estimates and hypothesis tests do indeed specify the form of the distribution, and we will devote most of our attention to such methods.

2–3. NORMAL DISTRIBUTION

The *normal density function* with mean μ and variance σ^2 is defined as

$$\phi(x) = \frac{1}{\sigma(2\pi)^{1/2}} \exp\left[-\frac{(x-\mu)^2}{2\sigma^2}\right] \quad \text{for} \quad -\infty < x < \infty, \tag{1}$$

and its integral, the *cumulative normal distribution function*, may be written

$$F(x) = \frac{1}{\sigma(2\pi)^{1/2}} \int_{-\infty}^{x} \exp\left[-\frac{(y-\mu)^2}{2\sigma^2}\right] dy. \tag{2}$$

All the odd central moments of the distribution vanish, a consequence of the symmetry around $x = \mu$, and the even central moments are given by the recursion formula

$$\mu_n = (n-1)\sigma^2 \mu_{n-2}. \tag{3}$$

For example,

$$\mu_4 = 3\sigma^2 \mu_2 = 3\mu_2^2. \tag{4}$$

The quantity

$$\frac{\kappa_4}{\kappa_2^2} = \frac{\mu_4}{\mu_2^2} - 3 \tag{5}$$

which is thus zero for the normal distribution is called the *kurtosis* of a distribution, and the corresponding sample statistic is frequently used as a test of normality. Departures of μ_3 from zero measure the asymmetry or *skewness* of the distribution.

Example 2–3–1

That $\mu_4 = 3\mu_2^2$ may also be seen by examination of the cumulant generating function for the normal distribution:

$$\log M(q) = \mu q + \tfrac{1}{2}\sigma^2 q^2$$

$$= \kappa_1 q + \frac{\kappa_2 q^2}{2!} + \frac{\kappa_3 q^3}{3!} + \cdots.$$

Thus

$$\kappa_1 = \mu$$
$$\kappa_2 = \sigma^2$$
$$\kappa_i = 0, \quad i = 3, 4, 5, \ldots.$$

In particular,

$$\kappa_4 = \mu_4 - 3\sigma^2 = 0.$$

Any distribution whose higher cumulants are small in comparison with σ^2 is thus approximately normal.

For the purpose of compiling tables, the transformation to the standard normal deviate

$$w = \frac{x - \mu}{\sigma} \tag{6}$$

is usually made. The resulting density function is

$$\phi(w) = \frac{1}{(2\pi)^{1/2}} e^{-w^2/2}, \tag{7}$$

and the distribution function is

$$F(w) = \frac{1}{(2\pi)^{1/2}} \int_{-\infty}^{w} e^{-y^2/2} \, dy. \tag{8}$$

It is values of these and related functions which usually appear in tables of the normal distribution. Since the transformed distribution has zero mean and unit variance, it is frequently called the *unit normal distribution*. Values are given in Table I in the Appendix.

An important characteristic of the normal distribution is that the sum

$$y = \sum_{i=1}^{n} x_i \tag{9}$$

of n independent normally distributed variables

$$x_1, x_2, \ldots, x_n \tag{10}$$

with means

$$\mu_1, \mu_2, \ldots, \mu_n \tag{11}$$

and variances

$$\sigma_1^2, \sigma_2^2, \ldots, \sigma_n^2 \tag{12}$$

is also normally distributed with

$$\mu(y) = \sum_{i=1}^{n} \mu_i = \mu_1 + \mu_2 + \cdots + \mu_n \tag{13}$$

and variance

$$\sigma^2(y) = \sum_{i=1}^{n} \sigma_i^2 = \sigma_1^2 + \sigma_2^2 + \cdots + \sigma_n^2. \tag{14}$$

Now that we have introduced the normal distribution, we should perhaps present some justification for its use in the remaining sections in this chapter. First of all, it has been observed that the values of variables describing many naturally occurring phenomena do indeed, over the range of the variable where the density function is large, follow a normal distribution closely. Consequently a large body of literature concerning the normal distribution and others based on it has been developed. This is of course not a sufficient reason for using it in every case, particularly if there are sound reasons for believing that the parent distribution is non-normal. However, it can be shown that many conclusions drawn from tests based on the normal distribution are not too seriously affected by departures from normality, provided that the density function is almost any kind of a unimodal or bell-shaped curve. The behavior in the tails, where the probability is low, is relatively unimportant for many tests concerning the population.

2–4. CENTRAL LIMIT THEOREM

One of the most remarkable theorems of statistics, the one which leads to the unique importance of the normal distribution function in statistical analysis, is the *central limit theorem*, which we state without proof:

Given a set of n *independent* random variables

$$x_1, x_2, \ldots, x_n, \tag{1}$$

each with an arbitrary probability distribution function with finite mean μ_i and second moment σ_i^2, consider the sum

$$y = \sum_{i=1}^{n} a_i x_i. \tag{2}$$

We know that it is true then that

$$\mu_y = \sum_{i=1}^{n} a_i \mu_i \tag{3}$$

and that

$$\sigma^2(y) = \sum_{i=1}^{n} a_i^2 \sigma_i^2. \tag{4}$$

The central limit theorem states that, as n increases, the distribution of y approaches the normal distribution with mean μ_y and variance $\sigma^2(y)$.

The central limit theorem is most easily proved for the case where all the x_i have the same non-normal distribution. Under rather general conditions, it can be extended to the sum of various random variables, each of which has a different type of distribution.

One important consequence of the central limit theorem is that the distribution of the sample mean for samples from a population having any distribution with finite variance tends to the normal distribution as the size of the sample increases. In view of this remarkable fact, we often use tables of the normal distribution for testing hypotheses concerning sample means when the distribution of the individual sample points is unknown; we must only take care that the sample is large enough.

The validity of the central limit theorem is responsible for the fact that many of the distributions observed in the measurement of naturally occurring phenomena are normal. If we assume that the variation in a particular measurement is the result of many independent sources of error which are additive, the central limit theorem tells us that we may expect the total error to be approximately normally distributed, regardless of the distributions of the individual error components. Thus the height of a man is determined by many factors, some genetic, some not. Each of these factors acting alone would perhaps give rise to a small range of heights. The sum of all the factors, each of which may be far from being normally distributed, will by the central limit theorem be approximately normally distributed, so that when we measure the heights of a large number of men, we are not surprised to find the distribution to be normal.

Example 2–4–1

The binomial distribution, being a sum of independent Bernoulli trials (Example 1–2–13), has the normal distribution as its limit when the number of trials becomes large. By the use of Stirling's formula for $n!$, one can show that

$$\lim_{n \to \infty} b_n(k, p) = N(np, npq),$$

where we have used the notation $N(\mu, \sigma^2)$ to represent the density function of the normal distribution with mean μ and variance σ^2. That this is a fair approximation for a value of n as low as 5 can be seen from an examination of Figure 2–1, where both the cumulative distribution functions and the density functions have been plotted for $p = \frac{1}{2}$ and for $p = \frac{1}{4}$.

Example 2–4–2

Consider the mean of a sample from the rectangular or uniform distribution

$$\phi(x) = 1 \quad \text{for} \quad 0 < x < 1$$
$$\phi(x) = 0 \quad \text{otherwise.}$$

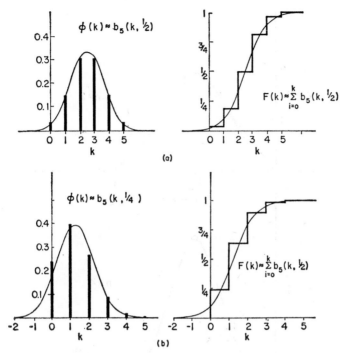

Fig. 2–1. Discrete binomial distributions $b_5(k, \frac{1}{2})$ and $b_5(k, \frac{1}{4})$ compared with the normal approximations $N(\frac{5}{2}, \frac{5}{4})$ and $N(\frac{5}{4}, \frac{15}{16})$. The density functions $\phi(k)$ are on the left and the cumulative distribution functions $F(k)$ are on the right.

It can be shown that the mean of a sample of size n has the density function

$$\phi(\bar{x}) = \frac{n}{(n-1)!} \sum_{j=0}^{[n\bar{x}]} (-1)^j \binom{n}{j} (n\bar{x} - j)^{n-1} \quad \text{for} \ \ 0 < \bar{x} < 1$$

$$\phi(\bar{x}) = 0 \quad \text{otherwise.}$$

In this definition, $[z]$ is the greatest integer less than or equal to z. According to the central limit theorem, $\phi(\bar{x})$ should approach the normal distribution with mean $\mu = 1/2$ and variance $\sigma^2 = 1/12n$: $N(1/2, 1/12n)$. That the limit is approached rapidly may be seen by an examination of Figure 2–2, where the true density functions and the normal approximations are plotted for sample sizes 2 and 4.

A further comparison of the two distributions is afforded by the kurtosis. The moment generating function for a single observation from a rectangular distribution with half-width a and mean 0 is

$$M(q) = \frac{\sinh{(aq)}}{aq}.$$

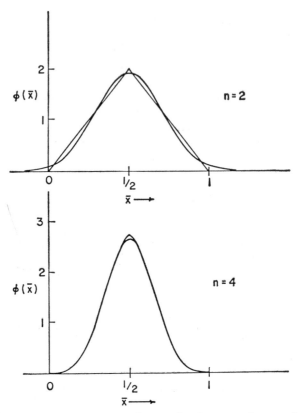

Fig. 2–2. Comparison of the density function for the mean of a sample from a uniform population and the normal density function having the same mean and variance. The upper curves are for the case $n = 2$; the density function for the mean of the sample is triangular. The lower curves are for a sample of size 4; the peak of the normal density function is the lower of the two.

The cumulant generating function is hence

$$\log \frac{\sinh (aq)}{aq} = \frac{(aq)^2}{6} - \frac{(aq)^4}{180} + \cdots.$$

The cumulant generating function for the sum of n observations being n times that for a single observation, we have

$$\frac{\kappa_2}{2!} = \frac{na^2}{6}; \qquad \frac{\kappa_4}{4!} = -\frac{na^4}{180}.$$

For $a = \frac{1}{2}$ in the present example, we thus have

$$\kappa_2 = \frac{n}{12}; \qquad \kappa_4 = \frac{n}{120}$$

for the cumulants of the sum.

The rth cumulant for the mean is $1/n^r$ times that for the sum of n observations. Hence for the mean,

$$\kappa_2 = \frac{1}{12n}; \qquad \kappa_4 = \frac{1}{120n^3},$$

and the kurtosis is

$$\frac{\kappa_4}{\kappa_2^2} = \frac{144n^2}{120n^3} = \frac{1.2}{n}.$$

The kurtosis is, accordingly, 0.6 and 0.3 for the two cases considered and approaches 0, the value for the normal distribution, as n increases without limit.

2–5. DISTRIBUTION OF A SINGLE OBSERVATION FROM A NORMAL POPULATION

Given a normal population with mean μ and variance σ^2, we take as our sample a single observation. The mean and the variance of this observation are again μ and σ^2. If the value of the observation is x, we know that

$$w = \frac{x - \mu}{\sigma} \tag{1}$$

is distributed as a unit normal deviate, i.e., as $N(0, 1)$. What is the probability that the magnitude of w calculated from the sample exceeds some specified value, i.e.,

$$P(|w| > w_\gamma) \tag{2}$$

where w_γ is defined as the value of w to the right of which lies an area γ under the probability density curve:

$$P(w > w_\gamma) = \gamma. \tag{3}$$

We have

$$P(|w| > w_\gamma) = \frac{1}{(2\pi)^{1/2}} \left[\int_{-\infty}^{-w_\gamma} e^{-y^2/2} \, dy + \int_{w_\gamma}^{\infty} e^{-y^2/2} \, dy \right]$$

$$= 2F(-w_\gamma)$$
$$= 2[1 - F(w_\gamma)]$$
$$= 2\gamma. \tag{4}$$

The value of $F(w_\gamma)$ may be found by consulting a table of the cumulative normal distribution function (Table I). Thus, for $w_\gamma = 1.96$, we have

$$P(|w| > 1.96) = 2(1 - 0.975) = 0.05. \tag{5}$$

We may rewrite (4) as

$$P\left(\left| \frac{x - \mu}{\sigma} \right| > w_\gamma \right) = 2[1 - F(w_\gamma)] \tag{6}$$

or

$$P(\mu - \sigma w_\gamma < x < \mu + \sigma w_\gamma) = 1 - 2[1 - F(w_\gamma)]$$
$$= 2F(w_\gamma) - 1.$$

and for the particular numerical values in (5) as

$$P(\mu - 1.96\sigma < x < \mu + 1.96\sigma) = 0.95. \tag{7}$$

The probability that a single observation from the given population will lie within 1.96σ of the mean is 0.95.

The inequalities (6) and (7) may be looked upon either as establishing a confidence interval for the mean of the population or as forming the basis for a test of the hypothesis

$$H_0: \mu = \mu_0; \quad \phi = N(\mu, \sigma^2) \tag{8}$$

against the alternative

$$H_1: \mu \neq \mu_0; \quad \phi = N(\mu, \sigma^2). \tag{9}$$

The unit normal deviate is calculated as

$$w = \frac{x - \mu_0}{\sigma}, \tag{10}$$

and if we reject the hypothesis H_0 when $|w| > 1.96$, we subject ourselves to the possibility of rejecting the hypothesis when it is true 5% of the time. We have tested the hypothesis at the 5% significance level. The test we have performed is a typical example of a *two-tailed test*, for the value

$$\alpha \equiv 2\gamma = 0.05 \tag{11}$$

is the sum of the areas in the two tails of the normal distribution. The test has been formulated so that we reject the hypothesis for values of w that are either much greater or much less than zero. We reject the hypothesis either if

$$w > 1.96 \tag{12}$$

or if

$$w < -1.96. \tag{13}$$

Suppose that we are carrying out an experiment where we know that $\mu = \mu_0$ or, if not, that $\mu > \mu_0$. In this case, we wish to test the hypothesis

$$H_0: \mu = \mu_0; \quad \phi = N(\mu, \sigma^2) \tag{14}$$

against the alternative

$$H_1: \mu > \mu_0; \quad \phi = N(\mu, \sigma^2). \tag{15}$$

We will specify that H_0 is to be rejected only if $w > w_\gamma$. The probability of a Type I error (rejection of the hypothesis when true) in this case is the area under only one tail of the normal distribution, and the significance level of the test is thus

$$\gamma \equiv \alpha. \tag{16}$$

A hypothesis test based on the probability in either extreme of the distribution is known as a *one-tailed test*, and it should be noted that for the normal distribution (or any distribution for which $\phi(x) = \phi(-x)$) a one-tailed test at the $100\alpha\%$ significance level is equivalent to a two-tailed test at the $100(2\alpha)\%$ significance level in the sense that the same critical value of w applies to the two cases (see Figure 2–3).

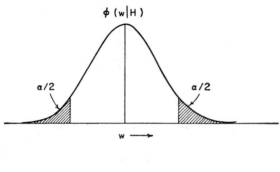

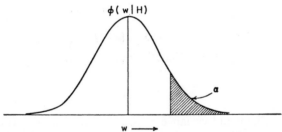

Fig. 2–3. Two-tailed test (upper) and one-tailed test (lower) of the hypothesis H. For the two-tailed test, we are testing against the alternative hypothesis $\mu \neq \mu_0$. For the one-tailed test, we are testing against the alternative hypothesis $\mu > \mu_0$.

An analogous one-tailed test for the low end of the distribution is obtained when we test

$$H_0: \mu = \mu_0; \quad \phi = N(\mu, \sigma^2) \tag{17}$$

against the alternative

$$H_1: \mu < \mu_0; \quad \phi = N(\mu, \sigma^2). \tag{18}$$

H_0 is rejected only if

$$w < -w_\gamma. \tag{19}$$

Example 2–5–1

A measurement of a C—C bond length in an organic compound results in a value of 1.52 A. Let us test the hypothesis that this observation is from a normal population with mean 1.54 A and $\sigma = 0.01$ A. We compute

$$|w| = \left| \frac{x - \mu_0}{\sigma} \right| = \left| \frac{1.52 - 1.54}{0.01} \right| = 2.0.$$

This value of w exceeds the value 1.96; hence we can reject the hypothesis at the 5% significance level. If the hypothesis is true, we may write

$$P(1.54 - 0.0196 < x < 1.54 + 0.0196)$$
$$\equiv P(1.5204 < x < 1.5596) = 0.95,$$

meaning that if the true C—C bond length is 1.54, we would rarely (less than 5% of the time) obtain a value of w lying outside the limits given. We thus have some evidence to support the statement that the mean is not 1.54 A.

Example 2–5–2

What is the probability that a single measurement from a normal population with mean 1.54 and standard deviation 0.01 will exceed 1.56 A? Again we have $w = 2$, and

$$P(w > 2) = 0.0227.$$

2–6. DISTRIBUTION OF THE SAMPLE MEAN

We have previously shown that the sample mean

$$\bar{x} = \frac{1}{n} \sum_{i=1}^{n} x_i \tag{1}$$

has expected value μ and variance σ^2/n. Since the sum of normally distributed random variables is again normally distributed, we have for the density function of $\bar{x}$,

$$\phi(\bar{x}) = \frac{1}{\sigma} \left(\frac{n}{2\pi} \right)^{1/2} \exp \left[-\frac{n(\bar{x} - \mu)^2}{2\sigma^2} \right]. \tag{2}$$

Making the transformation to the standardized variable

$$w = \frac{(\bar{x} - \mu)n^{1/2}}{\sigma} \tag{3}$$

we may follow the method of the Section 2–5 to calculate the probability that the deviation of the sample mean from the population mean exceeds a specified value. Thus

$$P \left(\mu - \frac{\sigma w_\gamma}{n^{1/2}} < \bar{x} < \mu + \frac{\sigma w_\gamma}{n^{1/2}} \right) = 2F(w_\gamma) - 1. \tag{4}$$

For example, for a sample of size 4 from a normal population with mean μ and variance σ^2, we have

$$P(\mu - 0.98\sigma < \bar{x} < \mu + 0.98\sigma) = 0.95. \tag{5}$$

Thus, if we wish to test, on the basis of a sample of n observations with sample mean $\bar{x}$, the hypothesis

$$H_0: \mu = \mu_0; \quad \phi = N(\mu, \sigma^2) \tag{6}$$

against the alternative

$$H_1: \mu \neq \mu_0; \quad \phi = N(\mu, \sigma^2), \tag{7}$$

we compute

$$w = \frac{(\bar{x} - \mu_0)n^{1/2}}{\sigma} \tag{8}$$

and reject the hypothesis at the $100\alpha\%$ significance level if

$$|w| > w_{\alpha/2} \tag{9}$$

where $w_{\alpha/2}$ is the value of w for which

$$2[1 - F(w_{\alpha/2})] = \alpha. \tag{10}$$

The following probability statement places a $100(1 - \alpha)\%$ confidence interval on the mean μ:

$$P\left(\bar{x} - \frac{\sigma w_{\alpha/2}}{n^{1/2}} < \mu < \bar{x} + \frac{\sigma w_{\alpha/2}}{n^{1/2}}\right) = (1 - \alpha). \tag{11}$$

Example 2–6–1

Five measurements of the H—O—H bond angle in water molecules bound to metal atoms in crystals gave the following results:

$$108°, \ 109°, \ 110°, \ 103°, \ 111°.$$

Given that all five measurements are from the same normal population with an assumed variance of 4 degrees², let us inquire whether it is likely that the population mean is 106°. We first compute

$$\bar{x} = 108.2°$$

$$|w| = \left|\frac{108.2 - 106.0}{2}\right| 5^{1/2} = 2.46.$$

Thus the hypothesis

H_0: The sample was drawn from a normal population
with variance 4 degrees² and mean 106.0°.

can be rejected at the 5% level of significance since the statistic $|w|$ computed from the sample above exceeds the value of $w_{\alpha/2} = 1.96$. A 95% confidence interval for the mean is

$$106.45 < \mu < 109.95.$$

Let us now examine in more detail the hypothesis test concerning the mean μ of a normal population with known variance σ^2. We assume in each case that we have a sample of size n with sample mean $\bar{x}$. Let us test the hypothesis

$$H_0: \mu = \mu_0 \tag{12}$$

where μ_0 is a hypothesized value of the mean. We calculate

$$w_0 = \frac{\bar{x} - \mu_0}{\sigma} n^{1/2}. \tag{13}$$

If $|w_0| > w_{\alpha/2}$, we reject the hypothesis and stand a $100\alpha\%$ risk of rejecting a true hypothesis. That is, the probability of Type I error is α.

On the other hand, the probability β of a Type II error, that of accepting (not rejecting) the hypothesis when it is false, depends upon the specific alternative hypothesis presumed to be true:

$$H_1: \mu = \mu_1. \tag{14}$$

We want to determine

$$\beta = P(-w_{\alpha/2} < w_0 < w_{\alpha/2}) \tag{15}$$

when H_1 is true. Let

$$w_1 = \frac{(\bar{x} - \mu_1)n^{1/2}}{\sigma}. \tag{16}$$

Now w_1 is distributed as a unit normal deviate if the alternative hypothesis (14) is true:

$$w_1 = \frac{n^{1/2}}{\sigma} (\bar{x} - \mu_0 + \mu_0 - \mu_1)$$

$$= w_0 + \frac{(\mu_0 - \mu_1)n^{1/2}}{\sigma}. \tag{17}$$

Thus

$$w_0 = w_1 + \frac{(\mu_1 - \mu_0)n^{1/2}}{\sigma} \tag{18}$$

and

$$\beta = P(-w_{\alpha/2} < w_0 < w_{\alpha/2})$$

$$= P\left(-w_{\alpha/2} < w_1 + \frac{(\mu_1 - \mu_0)n^{1/2}}{\sigma} < w_{\alpha/2}\right)$$

$$= P\left(-w_{\alpha/2} - \frac{(\mu_1 - \mu_0)n^{1/2}}{\sigma} < w_1 < w_{\alpha/2} - \frac{(\mu_1 - \mu_0)n^{1/2}}{\sigma}\right). \tag{19}$$

If $\mu_1 - \mu_0$ is small, the probability of not rejecting the hypothesis if it is false is nearly as great as that of not rejecting it when it is true. Thus the power of the test $1 - \beta$ increases as $(\mu_1 - \mu_0)/\sigma$ becomes large or as the size of the sample increases. This is in agreement with our intuitive feeling that it is easier to distinguish two alternative means either if they are very different or if we make the measurement many times. Figure 2–4 illustrates the power of the test for $\alpha = 0.01$ and $\alpha = 0.05$ as a function of the quantity

$$\delta = \frac{(\mu_1 - \mu_0)n^{1/2}}{\sigma}. \qquad (20)$$

Note again that the power increases with an increase in α.

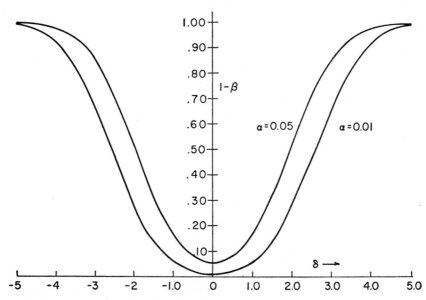

Fig. 2–4. Power $(1 - \beta)$ of the hypothesis test on the mean of a normal population with known variance plotted against the quantity

$$\delta = (\mu_1 - \mu_0)\, n^{1/2}/\sigma$$

for values of $\alpha = 0.05$ and 0.01. The null hypothesis is $\mu = \mu_0$. The alternative hypothesis is $\mu = \mu_1$, and the significance levels α are for the two-tailed test.

Example 2–6–2

In Example 2–6–1, suppose that we had wished to determine the power of the test of the null hypothesis against the specific alternative $H_1\colon \mu = 108°$. We compute

$$\delta = \frac{108 - 106}{2} (5)^{1/2} = 2.236$$

and find, applying (19), that for a significance level $\alpha = 0.05$, $\beta = 0.4$ and the power $(1 - \beta) = 0.6$. If the theory governing these measurements had been such that the only possible hypotheses were H_0 and H_1 and, if the test has told us to accept H_0, then our probability of having made an incorrect decision if H_1 were correct would be 0.40. This example illustrates well the fact that non-rejection of a hypothesis should not lead us to believe that it is true. Furthermore, the basic asymmetry in the two types of error in the usual type of hypothesis test is made clear.

The fact that the power of the test increases with the sample size n is important from a practical point of view. For any given alternative hypothesis, we see that we may make the power as near to unity as we like by increasing the sample size. For any simple hypothesis, there is some sample size which will permit us to reject the hypothesis unless it is *exactly* true. These concepts are widely used in the design of experiments and sampling procedures. We decide the significance level of the test and the required power relative to some alternative hypothesis, and choose a sample size sufficient to meet these requirements.

2–7. HYPOTHESIS TESTS WHEN THE VARIANCE IS UNKNOWN

Although the tests discussed in Section 2–6 are interesting and instructive, we will more frequently wish to test hypotheses concerning the mean when both the mean and the variance are unknown; this is almost always the case in experimental physical science. The tests described above using the tabulated percentage points of the normal distribution are thus inadequate, since a knowledge of the variance is required for transformation to the unit normal deviate.

When the size of the sample is large, we can safely use the sample variance in place of the unknown population variance in the formulas of Section 2–6 and proceed in exactly the same way. For small samples, however, such a procedure will be grossly in error. It is a remarkable fact that we can in such cases test hypotheses about the mean, even though the variance is unknown. The necessary distribution was derived by W. S. Gossett, writing under the name of "Student." If we define

$$t = \frac{(\overline{x} - \mu_0)n^{1/2}}{s}, \tag{1}$$

where s is the square root of the *sample* variance defined by

$$s^2 = \frac{1}{n-1} \sum_{i=1}^{n} (x_i - \overline{x})^2, \tag{2}$$

then the quantity t so defined may be shown to have the probability density function

$$\phi(t) = \frac{\Gamma([\nu + 1]/2)}{(\nu\pi)^{1/2}\Gamma(\nu/2)} \left(1 + \frac{t^2}{\nu}\right)^{-(\nu+1)/2} \tag{3}$$

for $-\infty < t < +\infty$, where $\nu = n - 1$ if the sample size is n. $\Gamma(x)$ denotes the ordinary gamma function. The distribution with density function (3) is known as *Student's t distribution* for ν degrees of freedom. Note that as ν increases

$$\phi(t) \to N(0, 1).$$

Values of $t_{\nu,\alpha}$ such that

$$P(|t| > t_{\nu,\alpha}) = \alpha \tag{4}$$

are presented in Table II in the Appendix. (Note that this is the two-tailed probability usually tabulated.)

We obtain confidence limits for the mean exactly as in the preceding section, but we use the tabulated percentage points of the t distribution rather than of the normal distribution. Thus the statement

$$P\left(\bar{x} - \frac{st_{n-1,\alpha}}{n^{1/2}} < \mu < \bar{x} + \frac{st_{n-1,\alpha}}{n^{1/2}}\right) = 1 - \alpha \tag{5}$$

defines a $100(1 - \alpha)\%$ confidence interval for the mean. Let us examine the use of this result in testing the hypothesis

$$H_0: \mu = \mu_0 \tag{6}$$

against the alternative

$$H_1: \mu \neq \mu_0 \tag{7}$$

We compute

$$t = \frac{(\bar{x} - \mu_0)n^{1/2}}{s} \tag{8}$$

and reject the hypothesis at the α significance level if

$$|t| > t_{n-1,\alpha} \tag{9}$$

Example 2–7–1

Consider the bond angles given in Example 2–6–1, but assume now that our only knowledge of the variance comes from the sample. The sample mean is $108.2°$ as before, and the variance is computed in the usual way to be

$$s^2 = 9.70 \text{ deg}^2; \quad s = 3.115°.$$

Let us again test the hypothesis that $\mu = 106°$. We have

$$t = \frac{108.2 - 106}{3.115} \times 2.236 = 1.58$$

From Table II, we find that a significant value of t for 4 degrees of freedom is 2.78 at the 0.05 significance level. The hypothesis cannot be rejected at this level. 95% confidence limits for the mean can be established as follows:

$$\frac{st_{n-1,\alpha}}{n^{1/2}} = \frac{3.115 \times 2.78}{2.236} = 3.87.$$

Thus a 95% confidence interval for the mean is

$$104.3 < \mu < 112.1.$$

The power of the Student t test or the complement of the power, the probability of Type II error, depends again on the particular alternative hypothesis to be tested and on the *population* variance as well. These are combined as before into the *non-centrality parameter*

$$\delta = \frac{n^{1/2}|\mu_0 - \mu_1|}{\sigma}. \tag{10}$$

Under the condition that the alternative hypothesis H_1 is true, t no longer has the distribution given in Equation (3) but rather has the *non-central t distribution*, depending on δ and having density function

$$\phi(t) = \frac{2^{-(\nu-1)/2}}{\Gamma(\nu/2)(\nu\pi)^{1/2}} \left(1 + \frac{t^2}{\nu}\right)^{-(\nu+1)/2} \exp\left[-\frac{1}{2}\frac{\delta^2}{1 + t^2/\nu}\right]$$

$$\times \int_0^\infty x^\nu \exp\left[-\frac{1}{2}\left(x - \frac{t\nu}{\sqrt{\nu + t^2}}\right)\right] dx \tag{11}$$

for $-\infty < t < +\infty$.

Thus the power depends on the quantity δ, which we do not know. However, the test may be used to answer the question of the probability of a Type II error under the alternative hypothesis of a specified standardized deviation, $|\mu_0 - \mu_1|/\sigma$. To obtain an approximation to the power for an actual deviation $|\mu_0 - \mu_1|$, the estimate s of σ may be used in the non-centrality parameter for what, it must be realized, is only an estimate of the power. This will, however, be sufficient for many practical purposes.

The non-central t distribution is typical of the distributions that arise when we wish to consider the power of a test, i.e., the distribution of the statistic in question when the null hypothesis is not true. These non-central distributions will in general be functions of a non-centrality parameter that depends both on the particular alternative hypothesis and on the value of a population statistic which will generally be unknown. Tables of non-central t are readily available.*

As another example of a one-tailed hypothesis test, let us test the hypothesis

$$H_0: \mu \leqslant \mu_0 \tag{12}$$

against the alternative hypothesis

$$H_1: \mu > \mu_0. \tag{13}$$

We compute

$$t = \frac{(\bar{x} - \mu_0)\, n^{1/2}}{s} \tag{14}$$

* For example, Resnikoff and Lieberman (see Bibliography).

and reject the hypothesis H_0 if

$$t > t_{n-1,2}; \tag{15}$$

for, if $\mu = \mu_0$ is true, we know that

$$P(t > t_{n-1,2}) = \alpha. \tag{16}$$

Also, if $\mu < \mu_0$, then

$$P(t > t_{n-1,2}) < \alpha, \tag{17}$$

so that the size of the critical region is smaller than if $\mu = \mu_0$. The probability of Type I error thus depends on the true μ but is at most α.

2–8. DISTRIBUTION OF THE ESTIMATE OF THE VARIANCE IN A NORMAL POPULATION

The density function for the estimate s^2 based on a sample of size n of the population variance σ^2 in a normal population can be shown to be

$$\phi(s^2) = \frac{1}{\Gamma(\nu/2)} \left(\frac{\nu}{2\sigma^2}\right)^{\nu/2} \exp\left[-\frac{\nu s^2}{2\sigma^2}\right](s^2)^{\nu/2-1} \quad \text{for} \quad s^2 > 0 \tag{1}$$

$$= 0 \quad \text{otherwise,}$$

where $\nu = n - 1$ is the number of degrees of freedom. The distribution of s^2 is a special case of the very important χ^2 (*chi-square*) distribution which is defined by the density function

$$\phi(\chi^2) = \frac{1}{2^{\nu/2}\Gamma(\nu/2)} e^{-\chi^2/2} (\chi^2)^{\nu/2-1} \quad \text{for} \quad \chi^2 \geqslant 0 \tag{2}$$

$$= 0 \quad \text{otherwise.}$$

Setting $\chi^2 = \nu s^2/\sigma^2$, we see that the two density functions are identical.

If k observations are made from a normal population with zero mean and unit variance, the sum of the squares of the observations is distributed as χ^2 with k degrees of freedom. The sum of two independent random variables distributed as χ^2 is again a χ^2-distributed random variable:

$$\chi^2_{\nu_1} + \chi^2_{\nu_2} = \chi^2_{\nu_1+\nu_2} \tag{3}$$

Table III in the Appendix gives values of $\chi^2_{\nu,\alpha}$ such that

$$P(\chi^2_\nu > \chi^2_{\nu,\alpha}) = \alpha. \tag{4}$$

Confidence Intervals for the Variance. If we wish to establish a 95% confidence interval for the variance by the statement

$$P(\sigma_1^2 < \sigma^2 < \sigma_2^2) = 0.95 \tag{5}$$

and wish the probabilities in each tail of the distribution to be equal,* i.e.,

$$P(\sigma^2 < \sigma_1^2) = P(\sigma^2 > \sigma_2^2) = 0.025, \tag{6}$$

* Note that the χ^2 density function is not symmetrical about its mean.

we calculate

$$\nu s^2 = \sigma^2 \chi^2 \tag{7}$$

for the sample. From

$$P(\chi^2_{4,0.025} > \chi^2 > \chi^2_{4,0.975}) = 0.95, \tag{8}$$

we have

$$P\left(\chi^2_{4,0.025} > \frac{\nu s^2}{\sigma^2} > \chi^2_{4,0.975}\right) = 0.95, \tag{9}$$

or

$$P\left(\frac{\nu s^2}{\chi^2_{4,0.025}} < \sigma^2 < \frac{\nu s^2}{\chi^2_{4,0.975}}\right) = 0.95. \tag{10}$$

Example 2–8–1

From the data of Examples 2–6–1 and 2–7–1, we calculated s^2 to be 9.70. Table III gives the following values for the pertinent χ^2:

$$\chi^2_{4,0.025} = 11.14; \quad \chi^2_{4,0.975} = 0.48.$$

We have then

$$P\left(\frac{4 \times 9.70}{11.14} < \sigma^2 < \frac{4 \times 9.70}{0.48}\right) = 0.95$$

$$P(3.48 < \sigma^2 < 80.4) = 0.95$$

$$P(1.82 < \sigma < 9.0) = 0.95.$$

The value of $2°$ assumed for the standard deviation in Example 2–6–1 was thus not unreasonable.

Hypothesis Tests on the Variance. The establishment of a 95% confidence interval for the variance is equivalent to the test of the hypothesis

$$H_0: \sigma^2 = \sigma_0^2 \tag{11}$$

against the alternative

$$H_1: \sigma^2 \neq \sigma_0^2 \tag{12}$$

at the 5% significance level. We calculate the statistic

$$\chi^2 = \frac{\nu s^2}{\sigma_0^2} \tag{13}$$

and reject the hypothesis if

$$\chi^2 < \chi^2_{\nu,1-\alpha/2} \tag{14}$$

or if

$$\chi^2 > \chi^2_{\nu,\alpha/2}. \tag{15}$$

In Example 2–8–1, the hypothesis

$$H_0: \sigma^2 = 4 \tag{16}$$

would be accepted at the significance level of 5%, since the sample χ^2 is equal to 9.70 if the null hypothesis is true, and the critical values of χ^2 are 11.14 and 0.48.

A corresponding one-tailed test for the hypothesis

$$H_0: \sigma^2 = \sigma_0^2 \tag{17}$$

against the alternative

$$H_1: \sigma^2 > \sigma_0^2 \tag{17a}$$

is obtained in the following way: We again calculate χ^2 for the sample. If

$$\chi^2 > \chi^2_{\nu,\alpha}, \tag{18}$$

we reject H_0. The test for H_0 (17) against the alternative

$$H_1: \sigma^2 < \sigma_0^2 \tag{18a}$$

is carried out similarly.

Power of the χ^2 Test on the Variance. We would like to ask now for the probability of a Type II error when χ^2 is used to test hypotheses concerning the variance of a normal population. We wish to find the value of

$$\beta = P\left(\chi^2_{\nu,\alpha/2} > \frac{\nu s^2}{\sigma_0^2} > \chi^2_{\nu,1-\alpha/2}\right) \tag{19}$$

when σ_1^2 is the true variance. If σ_1^2 is the true variance, the quantity $\nu s^2/\sigma_1^2$ will be distributed as χ^2_ν. Therefore

$$\beta = P\left(\chi^2_{\nu,\alpha/2}\frac{\sigma_0^2}{\sigma_1^2} > \frac{\nu s^2}{\sigma_1^2} > \chi^2_{\nu,1-\alpha/2}\frac{\sigma_0^2}{\sigma_1^2}\right). \tag{20}$$

We consult Table III to determine the probability that a chi-square variate with ν degrees of freedom lies between

$$\chi^2_{\nu,\alpha/2}\frac{\sigma_0^2}{\sigma_1^2} \quad \text{and} \quad \chi^2_{\nu,1-\alpha/2}\frac{\sigma_0^2}{\sigma_1^2}. \tag{21}$$

Example 2–8–2

Suppose that we wish to distinguish between the two hypotheses

$$H_0: \sigma^2 = 4$$
$$H_1: \sigma^2 = 10.$$

In Example 2–8–1, H_0 was accepted at the 5% significance level. We are interested in the probability that we would make a wrong decision in accepting H_0 if the true variance were that given by H_1 in this example. We have

$$\beta = P(0.4 \times 11.14 > \chi^2 > 0.4 \times 0.484).$$

Examination of more extended tables of χ^2 than Table III indicates that

$$\beta \approx 0.64.$$

There is a greater-than-60% chance that we would not reject H_0 when H_1 is really true.

2-9. DISTRIBUTION OF THE RATIO OF TWO ESTIMATES OF THE SAME VARIANCE; THE F DISTRIBUTION

In the present section, we introduce a very versatile and widely used distribution which will be the basis of most of our multivariate hypothesis tests.

If y_1 is distributed as χ^2 with ν_1 degrees of freedom and if y_2, *independent* of y_1, is distributed as χ^2 with ν_2 degrees of freedom, the ratio

$$F_{\nu_1,\nu_2} = \frac{(y_1/\nu_1)}{(y_2/\nu_2)} \tag{1}$$

has the probability density function

$$\phi(F) = \frac{\Gamma([\nu_1 + \nu_2]/2)}{\Gamma(\nu_1/2)\Gamma(\nu_2/2)} \left(\frac{\nu_1}{\nu_2}\right)^{\nu_1/2} F^{(\nu_1-2)/2}\left(1 + \frac{\nu_1}{\nu_2}F\right)^{-(\nu_1+\nu_2)/2} \quad \text{for} \quad F > 0 \tag{2}$$

$$= 0 \quad \text{otherwise.}$$

Table IV in the Appendix gives values of $F_{\nu_1,\nu_2,\alpha}$ such that

$$P(F > F_{\nu_1,\nu_2,\alpha}) = \alpha. \tag{3}$$

In using these tables, it should be noted that they can be extended by using the relation

$$F_{\nu_1,\nu_2,\alpha} = \frac{1}{F_{\nu_2,\nu_1,1-\alpha}}. \tag{4}$$

Care should always be taken to identify correctly the numerator (ν_1) and denominator (ν_2) degrees of freedom, since the function is *not* symmetric in these variables.

A feeling for the location and width of the F distribution may be obtained by noting that

$$\mathcal{E}\{F\} = \frac{\nu_2}{\nu_2 - 2} \quad \text{for} \quad \nu_2 > 2 \tag{5}$$

and

$$\sigma(F) = \frac{\nu_2}{\nu_2 - 2}\sqrt{\frac{2(\nu_1 + \nu_2 - 2)}{\nu_1(\nu_2 - 4)}} \quad \text{for} \quad \nu_2 > 4. \tag{6}$$

Now we have seen above that $\nu_1 s_1^2/\sigma_1^2$ for a sample from a normal population is distributed as $\chi^2_{\nu_1}$. Hence, for two independent samples from two, possibly different, normal populations, we find that s_1^2/s_2^2 is distributed as

$$\frac{\sigma_1^2}{\sigma_2^2} F_{\nu_1,\nu_2}. \tag{7}$$

Let us test at the α significance level the hypothesis

$$H_0: \sigma_1^2 = \sigma_2^2 \tag{8}$$

against the alternative

$$H_1: \sigma_1{}^2 \neq \sigma_2{}^2. \tag{9}$$

The null hypothesis is that the samples were drawn from populations with identical variances. We compute

$$F = \frac{s_1{}^2}{s_2{}^2} \tag{10}$$

and reject the hypothesis if either

$$F < F_{\nu_1,\nu_2,1-\alpha/2} \tag{11}$$

or

$$F > F_{\nu_1,\nu_2,\alpha/2}. \tag{12}$$

Since $\sigma_1{}^2/\sigma_2{}^2 = 1$ under the null hypothesis, the probability that the null hypothesis will be rejected when true is thus α.

What is the probability of a Type II error, that is, the probability that the hypothesis is accepted when it is not true? This probability will depend on the ratio $\sigma_1{}^2/\sigma_2{}^2$. Suppose now that the true value of the ratio is given by

$$\sigma_1{}^2/\sigma_2{}^2 = \gamma; \tag{13}$$

then $s_1{}^2/s_2{}^2$ is distributed as $\gamma F_{\nu_1,\nu_2}$. We seek

$$\beta = P\left(F_{\nu_1,\nu_2,1-\alpha/2} < \frac{s_1{}^2}{s_2{}^2} < F_{\nu_1,\nu_2,\alpha/2}\right) \tag{14}$$

when the alternative hypothesis is true. This is equivalent to

$$\beta = P\left(\frac{F_{\nu_1,\nu_2,1-\alpha/2}}{\gamma} < F < \frac{F_{\nu_1,\nu_2,\alpha/2}}{\gamma}\right). \tag{15}$$

For any value of γ, these limits may be evaluated by consulting tables of F. A plot of $1 - \beta$ against γ for $F_{10,10,0.05}$ is presented in Figure 2–5. For a small number of degrees of freedom, the F test is a test of little power unless the ratio of the true variances is indeed large.

The variance ratio distribution was first introduced by Fisher in the form

$$z = \log_e F^{1/2}. \tag{16}$$

The sometimes useful fact that F_{1,ν_2} is identical with the square of Student's t_{ν_2} should be noted and remembered:

$$t_{\nu,\alpha} = (F_{1,\nu,\alpha})^{1/2}. \tag{17}$$

Statement (17) implies that the values of $t_{\nu,\alpha}$ are defined so that α is the probability in both tails of the t distribution; critical values of t are usually so tabulated. Usual tables of F, however, define α as the probability in a single tail of the distribution. The fact that a single value of F (which is always positive) corresponds to both a negative and positive value of t is in agreement with this practice.

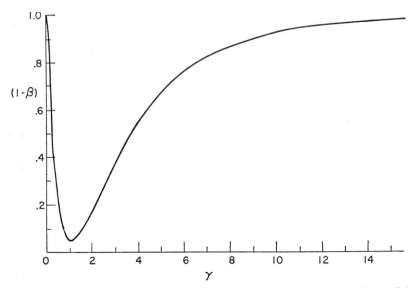

Fig. 2–5. Power $(1 - \beta)$ of the F test for the ratio of two variances. The null hypothesis is $\sigma_1{}^2 = \sigma_2{}^2$. The alternative hypothesis is $\sigma_1{}^2 = \gamma \sigma_2{}^2$. The power is plotted against γ, for $\nu_1 = 10$, $\nu_2 = 10$ and $\alpha = 0.05$.

Example 2–9–1 (An Elementary Analysis-of-Variance Problem)

Suppose n samples of m points each are taken from normal populations with variances σ_i and means μ_i:

$$\begin{aligned}
&\text{sample 1: } x_{11} \quad x_{12} \quad \cdots \quad x_{1m} \\
&\text{sample 2: } x_{21} \quad x_{22} \quad \cdots \quad x_{2m} \\
&\qquad\qquad \cdot \qquad\ \cdot \qquad \cdots \qquad \cdot \\
&\qquad\qquad \cdot \qquad\ \cdot \qquad \cdots \qquad \cdot \\
&\qquad\qquad \cdot \qquad\ \cdot \qquad \cdots \qquad \cdot \\
&\text{sample } n\text{: } x_{n1} \quad x_{n2} \quad \cdots \quad x_{nm}
\end{aligned}$$

The sample means and variances are given by

$$\overline{x}_i = \frac{1}{m} \sum_{j=1}^{m} x_{ij}$$

$$s_i{}^2 = \frac{1}{m-1} \sum_{j=1}^{m} (x_{ij} - \overline{x}_i)^2.$$

We wish to test the hypothesis that all the samples are from the same population with mean μ and variance σ^2. This is a simple and typical example of what are called *analysis-of-variance* techniques, which will be treated more fully in Chapter 3.

The grand mean

$$\bar{x} = \frac{1}{n} \sum_{i=1}^{n} \bar{x}_i = \frac{1}{nm} \sum_{i,j} x_{ij}$$

is an unbiased estimate of the common population mean. If the hypothesis

$$H_0: \sigma_1{}^2 = \sigma_2{}^2 = \cdots = \sigma_n{}^2 = \sigma^2$$

is true, we have

$$\sigma^2(\bar{x}_i) = \frac{1}{m} \sigma^2$$

and

$$\sigma^2(\bar{x}) = \frac{1}{n} \sigma^2(\bar{x}_i) = \frac{1}{mn} \sigma^2.$$

Now each of these $s_i{}^2$ is an unbiased estimate of σ^2, and hence $(1/m)s_i{}^2$ is an unbiased estimate of $\sigma^2(\bar{x}_i)$ and $(1/n^2m) \sum_{i=1}^{n} s_i{}^2$ is an unbiased estimate of $\sigma^2(\bar{x})$. On the other hand

$$\frac{s^2}{n} = \frac{1}{n(n-1)} \sum_{i=1}^{n} (\bar{x}_i - \bar{x})^2$$

is also an unbiased estimate of $\sigma^2(\bar{x})$. A comparison of the two estimates of $\sigma^2(\bar{x})$ is a possible test of the validity of the hypothesis of equal variances in the populations from which the samples are drawn.

Now $(m-1)s_i{}^2/\sigma^2$ is distributed as χ^2 with $m-1$ degrees of freedom; hence

$$\frac{m-1}{\sigma^2} \sum_{i} s_i{}^2$$

is distributed as χ^2 with $n(m-1)$ degrees of freedom. In addition,

$$\frac{(n-1)s^2}{\sigma^2(\bar{x}_i)}$$

is distributed as χ^2 with $n-1$ degrees of freedom. The ratio

$$F_{nm-n,n} = \frac{(1/n\sigma^2) \sum_{i} s_i{}^2}{s^2/\sigma^2(\bar{x}_i)}$$

is hence distributed as F. This ratio may be further simplified:

$$F = \frac{(1/n\sigma^2) \sum_{i} s_i{}^2}{ms^2/\sigma^2} = \frac{\sum_{i} s_i{}^2}{nms^2},$$

which is simply the ratio of the two estimates of the variance of $\bar{x}$. The estimate in the numerator may be called the within-samples estimate, while the one in the denominator may be called the between-samples estimate. The hypothesis is thus tested by consulting a table of critical values of F. This example, in assuming equal sample sizes and equal variances, is somewhat specialized; the more important test for equal means in samples of different sizes from populations with different variances is deferred until Chapter 3.

Without going into great detail, we assert that the hypothesis

$$H_0: \sigma_1^2 > \sigma_2^2 \tag{18}$$

may be tested against the alternative hypothesis

$$H_1: \sigma_1^2 \leqslant \sigma_2^2 \tag{19}$$

in the following way:

If $s_1^2/s_2^2 < F_{\nu_1,\nu_2,1-\alpha}$, we reject H_0.

Under these conditions we can show that the maximum Type I error, i.e., the probability of rejecting H_0 when true, is α, and the maximum Type II error, i.e., the probability of accepting H_0 when H_1 is really true, is $1 - \alpha$. Thus the power of the test is greater than α. Reversing the role of the two hypotheses, we can choose

$$s_1^2/s_2^2 > F_{\nu_1,\nu_2,\alpha}$$

as the condition for rejecting H_1 with a maximum Type I error of α and a maximum Type II error of $1 - \alpha$. We can make statements only about the maximum values of the error, since the ratio s_1^2/s_2^2 is distributed as γF, and γ is unknown. The value of α at which the tests are made will be determined by the relative importance of the two types of error.

Example 2–9–2

The following samples of sizes 10 and 2 were drawn at random from a table reputed to be composed of values drawn from a normal distribution with mean 4000 and variance 1,000,000:

Sample 1		Sample 2
4639	2771	4584
4031	4371	3308
3102	3923	
3545	3583	
3605	3717	

The sample means and variances are

$$\bar{x}_1 = 3728.7, \quad \bar{x}_2 = 3946.0,$$
$$s_1^2 = 305,630, \quad s_2^2 = 814,088.$$

For sample 1, we may compute 95% confidence limits for the mean as

$$\bar{x} - \frac{st_{9,0.05}}{n^{1/2}} \leqslant \mu \leqslant \bar{x} + \frac{st_{9,0.05}}{n^{1/2}}$$

or

$$P(3333.3 < \mu < 4124.1) = 0.95$$

since $t_{9,0.05} = 2.262$. We cannot reject the hypothesis that $\mu = 4000$. For sample 1, confidence limits for the variance may be obtained as

$$P\left(\frac{9s^2}{\chi^2_{9,0.025}} < \sigma^2 < \frac{9s^2}{\chi^2_{9,0.975}}\right) = 0.95.$$

$$P(144,772 < \sigma^2 < 1,018,767) = 0.95,$$

and again at the 5% significance level we cannot reject the hypothesis that the distribution is the one specified.

Let us test the hypothesis

$$H_0: \sigma_1{}^2 = \sigma_2{}^2$$

against the alternative

$$H_1: \sigma_1{}^2 \neq \sigma_2{}^2.$$

We compute

$$\frac{s_2{}^2}{s_1{}^2} = \frac{814,088}{305,630} = 2.66,$$

which we test as a variance ratio with 1 and 9 degrees of freedom. Now from Table IV we determine that

$$F_{1,9,0.025} = 7.2093$$
$$F_{1,9,0.975} = 0.00104,$$

so that the hypothesis cannot be rejected. It is clear, however, that many alternative hypotheses would be equally acceptable. In fact, we can look on a confidence interval as the set of all acceptable hypotheses. Again we emphasize that the acceptance of a hypothesis is no guarantee of its truth, or even of its probability. We must always consider the power relative to alternative hypotheses deemed to be of importance.

2–10. CONFIDENCE INTERVALS FOR THE POISSON DISTRIBUTION

If we consider an experiment giving rise to a distribution of discrete events in time which can be described by the Poisson distribution

$$p(k) = \frac{e^{-\lambda}\lambda^k}{k!} \tag{1}$$

and observe the number of events occurring in unit time intervals,

$$k_1, k_2, \ldots, k_n, \tag{2}$$

then

$$\bar{k} = \frac{1}{n}\sum_i k_i \tag{3}$$

is an unbiased estimate of λ, and the variance of this estimate is

$$\operatorname{var} \bar{k} = \frac{\lambda}{n}. \tag{4}$$

A $100(1 - \alpha)\%$ confidence interval for λ can be set by finding the values of λ for which

$$P(k \leqslant n\bar{k}) = \sum_{k=0}^{n\bar{k}} \frac{e^{-n\lambda}(n\lambda)^k}{k!} \leqslant \frac{\alpha}{2} \tag{5}$$

and

$$P(k \geqslant n\bar{k}) = \sum_{k=n\bar{k}}^{\infty} \frac{e^{-n\lambda}(n\lambda)^k}{k!} \leqslant \frac{\alpha}{2}, \tag{6}$$

where $n\bar{k}$ is the total number of events. These values have been tabulated by Ricker.*

The central limit theorem may be used to show that the Poisson distribution approaches the normal distribution with mean $n\lambda$ and variance $n\lambda$ as n increases without limit. As with the binomial distribution, the approach is rapid, and thus one may obtain confidence limits for λ by considering

$$t = \frac{n\bar{k} - n\lambda}{(n\lambda)^{1/2}} \tag{7}$$

as a standard normal deviate.

Example 2–10–1

Suppose that the total observed number of events is 25. The exact method above gives 95% confidence limits for λ as follows:

$$P(16.2 < n\lambda < 36.8) = 0.95$$

while the normal approximation gives

$$P(25 - 1.96 \times 5 < n\lambda < 25 + 1.96 \times 5) = 0.95$$
$$P(15.2 < n\lambda < 34.8) = 0.95.$$

The latter approximation to the confidence interval would be satisfactory for most practical purposes. It is interesting to note that for $n\bar{k} = 0$, i.e., no events are observed, the 95% confidence interval for λ is given by

$$0 < n\lambda < 3.7.$$

2–11. USE OF χ^2 AS A GOODNESS-OF-FIT TEST

Suppose that we wish to consider the hypothesis that a group of observations have a completely specified distribution of any type whatsoever. By some means, we establish n classes into which we can group the observa-

* W. E. Ricker, *J. Am. Statist. Assoc.* 32, 349 (1937).

tions according to their values. We then compute the number which would be expected in each class on the basis of the hypothetical distribution. Let n_k be the number actually found in the kth class and d_k be the number predicted by the hypothesis. It may then be shown that

$$\chi^2 = \sum_{k=1}^{n} \frac{(n_k - d_k)^2}{d_k} \tag{1}$$

is distributed approximately as χ^2_{n-1}, provided that each d_k is moderately large, say at least 5. The validity of the test improves as d_k increases. If parameters of the distribution are estimated from the data, the number of degrees of freedom for the χ^2 test must be reduced by 1 for each independent parameter so determined.

Example 2–11–1

Suppose that a particular experiment that gives only integral results was repeated 100 times, and it is desired to test whether the results follow a Poisson distribution with $\lambda = 5$. The results are as follows:

Observation	Times Observed	Poisson ($\lambda = 5$)
0	8	0.7
1	11	3.3
2	9	8.3
3	10	14.0
4	12	17.5
5	8	17.5
6	12	14.5
7	10	10.4
8	9	6.5
9	11	3.6
>9	0	3.7

Since the predicted numbers in the lower and higher classes are small, it seems sensible to group the observations as follows (the grouping is arbitrary, and other choices of groups would serve equally well):

Observation	Times Observed	Predicted	Difference
0–2	28	12.3	15.7
3–5	30	49.0	−19.0
6–8	31	31.4	−0.4
⩾9	11	7.3	3.7

χ^2 for the sample is calculated to be

$$\chi^2 = \frac{15.7^2}{12.3} + \frac{19.0^2}{49.0} + \frac{0.4^2}{31.4} + \frac{3.7^2}{7.3} = 29.3.$$

Now $\chi^2_{3,0.005} = 12.8$. It is thus extremely unlikely that the observations were from the specified Poisson distribution.

On the other hand, if we wished to test the hypothesis that the observations were random digits from 0 to 9, we would predict 10 in each class. The sample χ^2 is readily calculated to be 2.0. Examination of the χ^2 table for 9 degrees of freedom indicates that the hypothesis can certainly not be rejected. In fact the agreement with the postulated distribution is so good that one might suspect that the observations are not entirely random. In general an improbably low value of χ^2 should make one look very carefully at the sampling procedures for the possible detection of systematic effects.

2–12. FISHER-BEHRENS PROBLEM

Consider two populations with normal density functions:

$$N(\mu_1, \sigma_1^2) \quad \text{and} \quad N(\mu_2, \sigma_2^2). \tag{1}$$

Samples of sizes n_1 and n_2 with means $\bar{x}_1$ and $\bar{x}_2$ are drawn from the two populations. We desire to test the hypothesis

$$H_0: \mu_1 = \mu_2. \tag{2}$$

If the population variances are equal:

$$\sigma_1^2 = \sigma_2^2 \tag{3}$$

then the statistic

$$u = \frac{(\bar{x}_1 - \bar{x}_2) - (\mu_1 - \mu_2)}{(s^2/n_1 + s^2/n_2)^{1/2}} \tag{4}$$

with

$$s^2 = \frac{\sum_{i=1}^{2}\sum_{j=1}^{n_i}(x_{ij} - \bar{x}_i)^2}{n_1 + n_2 - 2} \tag{5}$$

is distributed as Student's t with $n_1 + n_2 - 2$ degrees of freedom. Thus under the null hypothesis, we compute u for $\mu_1 - \mu_2 = 0$, and compare with the desired percentage points of the t distribution.

In many practical problems, however, it will not be known that the variances of the two populations are equal, and we would like to be able to test hypotheses concerning the means, having available only the sample variances s_1^2 and s_2^2. There is as yet no universal agreement among statisticians as to the best method of handling this problem, which is frequently known as the Fisher-Behrens problem. The most common methods used are based upon the statistic proposed by Behrens:

$$u = \frac{(\bar{x}_1 - \bar{x}_2) - (\mu_1 - \mu_2)}{\left(\dfrac{s_1^2}{n_1} + \dfrac{s_2^2}{n_2}\right)^{1/2}}. \tag{6}$$

It can be shown that u is *approximately* distributed as Student's t with

$$f = \frac{\left(\dfrac{\sigma_1^2}{n_1} + \dfrac{\sigma_2^2}{n_2}\right)^2}{\dfrac{\sigma_1^4}{n_1^2(n_1 - 1)} + \dfrac{\sigma_2^4}{n_2^2(n_2 - 1)}} \tag{7}$$

degrees of freedom. This expression for the number of degrees of freedom of course involves the unknown population variances. A frequent procedure is to substitute the estimates s_1^2 and s_2^2 in Eq. (7). A somewhat better estimate of f is

$$f' = \frac{\left(\dfrac{s_1^2}{n_1} + \dfrac{s_2^2}{n_2}\right)^2}{\dfrac{s_1^4}{n_1^2(n_1 + 1)} + \dfrac{s_2^4}{n_2^2(n_2 + 1)}} - 2. \tag{8}$$

The Fisher-Behrens problem of the comparison of two means is a special case of the more general problem formulated and treated by Welch as follows: We assume that we have k normally distributed random variables x_i with means and variances μ_i and σ_i^2. Let

$$y = \sum_i a_i^{1/2} x_i \tag{9}$$

be a linear function of the x_i such that

$$\mathcal{E}\{y\} = \mu_y = \sum_i a_i^{1/2} \mu_i \tag{10}$$

and

$$\sigma^2(y) = \sum_i a_i \sigma_i^2 \tag{11}$$

where the a_i are known but the σ_i^2 are unknown. We draw a sample of size n_i from each population and compute the sample means $\bar{x}_i$ and variance estimates

$$s_i^2 = \frac{1}{n_i - 1} \sum_j (x_{ij} - \bar{x}_i)^2. \tag{12}$$

We may test the hypothesis

$$H_0: \mu_y = \mu_y^0 \tag{13}$$

against the alternative

$$H_1: \mu_y \neq \mu_y^0 \tag{14}$$

by noting that the statistic

$$v = \frac{(\bar{y} - \mu_y^0)}{\left(\sum_i a_i s_i^2\right)^{1/2}} \tag{15}$$

is distributed approximately as Student's t with

$$f = \frac{\left(\sum_i a_i \sigma_i^2\right)^2}{\sum_i \dfrac{a_i^2 \sigma_i^4}{n_i - 1}} \tag{16}$$

degrees of freedom. If the $\sigma_i{}^2$ are not known, the estimate of f,

$$f' = \frac{\left(\sum\limits_i a_i s_i{}^2\right)^2}{\sum\limits_i \dfrac{a_i s_i{}^4}{n_i + 1}} - 2 \tag{17}$$

may be used.

REFERENCES

ANSCOMBE, F. J. 1960. The rejection of outliers. *Technometrics* 2, 132–147.

ANSCOMBE, F. J., and J. W. TUKEY. 1963. The examination and analysis of residuals. *Technometrics* 5, 141–160.

RAY, W. D., and A. E. N. T. PITMAN. 1961. An exact distribution of the Fisher-Behrens-Welch statistic for testing the difference between the means of two normal populations with unknown variances. *J. Roy. Statist. Soc.* 23B, 377–384.

"STUDENT." 1908. The probable error of a mean. *Biometrika* 6, 1–25.

WELCH, B. L. 1937. The significance of the difference between two means when the population variances are unequal. *Biometrika* 29, 350–362.

WELCH, B. L. 1947. The generalization of Student's problem when several different population variances are involved. *Biometrika* 34, 28–35.

WELCH, B. L. 1951. On the comparison of several mean values—An alternative approach. *Biometrika* 38, 330–336.

EXERCISES

2–1. The following values are found for several determinations of the vapor pressure at a constant temperature of an organic compound: 132.3, 128.0, 125.0, 130.2, 126.6, 128.6, 127.8, 128.4, 128.0, 128.4, 128.0, 128.5, 128.4, 128.7, 127.2. Find the sample mean and variance, and thus estimate the population mean and variance. What is the variance of the sample mean?

2–2. Compare the first four cumulants of the normal distribution, the rectangular distribution, the distribution described by the density function

$$\phi(x) = \tfrac{1}{2}[\delta(x - a) + \delta(x + a)]$$

(where $\delta(x)$ is the Dirac delta function), and the distribution defined by the density function

$$\phi(x) = \frac{2x}{a^2} \quad \text{for} \quad 0 < x < a$$

$$= 0 \quad \text{otherwise.}$$

2–3. Take the mean and variance of the sample in Exercise 2–1, and write down the precise form of the normal density function for these parameters. What transformation must be used to convert this to the unit form?

2–4. Assume that the population variance for the data in Exercise 2–1 is known and is equal to the sample variance, and that the distribution is normal. Give a 95% confidence interval for the mean, and compare this interval with that given by application of Student's t distribution to the same data. What would be the 95% confidence interval for the mean if the distribution were rectangular, with a population variance equal to the sample variance?

2–5. Assuming a normal distribution, find a 95% confidence interval for the population variance from the data of Exercise 2–1.

2–6. Again taking the data of Exercise 2–1 and assuming a normal population, test at the 95% confidence level the following hypotheses:

$$\text{(i) } H_0\colon \mu = 130.0$$
$$\text{(ii) } H_0\colon \mu \geqslant 130.0$$
$$\text{(iii) } H_0\colon \sigma^2 = 9.0$$
$$\text{(iv) } H_0\colon \sigma^2 \geqslant 20.0.$$

2–7. Consider the following two sets of measurements purporting to be measurements of the same physical quantity by identical techniques:

Sample I: 0.806, 0.827, 0.816, 0.809, 0.814
Sample II: 0.813, 0.803, 0.810, 0.807, 0.804.

Assuming normal populations, test the hypotheses of equal variances and equal means. If the hypothesis of equal means is not rejected, obtain the minimum variance estimate of the common mean and the estimate of the variance of this estimate.

2–8. Given a Poisson distribution with parameter λ, formulate the probability that no events are observed in time t.

2–9. Compare the first four cumulants of the Poisson distribution with those for the normal distribution with the same mean and variance.

2–10. Four coins were tossed together 80 times, with the following results:

Event		Times Observed
4 H	0 T	7
3 H	1 T	20
2 H	2 T	25
1 H	3 T	24
0 H	4 T	4

Use a χ^2 goodness-of-fit test of the hypothesis that these observations fit a binomial distribution with parameter $p = \frac{1}{2}$.

2–11. A table claimed to be composed of random numbers lying in the range $1 \leqslant x \leqslant 400$, each number having equal probability, is found to contain numbers in four classes as follows:

Numbers	Frequency
1–100	90
101–200	110
201–300	90
301–400	110

Would you be suspicious of the table? Why? What would be the result of a χ^2 goodness-of-fit test? In what other ways might you test the data? Discuss the dangers of selecting the hypothesis to be tested after you have seen the data.

3

Analysis of Variance

3–1. INTRODUCTION

We are often faced with the situation of having on our hands many samples from different populations, perhaps differing in experimental conditions, and wishing to estimate the differences between the means of these populations or often simply to test whether any differences exist. One of the techniques most frequently used in such problems is that of the so-called analysis of variance (sometimes abbreviated ANOVA). No complete discussion of all the various models which are treated under this heading will be attempted here. For those wishing to pursue the subject, the books by Graybill and Scheffe* are recommended.

The more complex problems which will confront the readers of this book are more easily handled by least-squares techniques. Our treatment of the analysis of variance will thus be limited to a general introduction and illustrations of a few of the simpler models in use. The reader may prefer to read the introduction (Section 3–2) after the sections treating the special cases.

3–2. ANALYSIS OF VARIANCE IN AN r-WAY CLASSIFICATION

The analysis of variance always involves the comparison of sums of squares of deviations of experimental observations from various means, i.e., it compares variance estimates computed in two or more ways. As the following examples will make clear, an analysis-of-variance model is a mathematical expression of the observation which includes all sources of variability that may enter the experimental value. The assumption of a

* See Bibliography.

particular model leads to expressions for the estimation of means and variances, and to the methods and distributions required for testing hypotheses concerning these means and variances. As always, the experimenter must decide whether the physical experiment corresponds to the statistical model. In the ideal situation, he will design the experiment in such a way as to satisfy the assumptions of a preferred model.

Consider an experimental quantity such as a chemical reaction rate y which is measured in the presence of several different catalysts. The rate may be measured several times for each catalyst. We might perhaps write the observed reaction rate for the jth observation with the ith catalyst as

$$y_{ij} = \mu + c_i + \epsilon_{ij} \tag{1}$$

where μ is the reaction rate in the absence of catalyst, c_i is the enhancement of the reaction rate caused by the ith catalyst, and ϵ_{ij} is a random error associated with the measurement y_{ij}. (In many models, the ϵ_{ij} are considered to be identically and independently distributed, often normally.) In this model (1), the experimenter assumes that all factors but the catalyst are constant; the catalyst is the one *factor* which is varied. An analysis of variance based on this model is known as a *one-way* analysis of variance. The *effects* c_i can be associated with the values ascribed to a single variable (the catalyst).

Suppose that we further wish to vary the temperature and measure the reaction rate at several different temperatures T_k for each catalyst. The analysis of variance now requires a two-way model which we may choose to write as

$$y_{ikj} = \mu + c_i + t_k + (ct)_{ik} + \epsilon_{ikj} \tag{2}$$

where y_{ikj} is the *response* (reaction rate) for the ith catalyst at the kth temperature. μ and c_i are defined as before, t_k is the effect of the kth temperature on the reaction rate, and $(ct)_{ik}$ is the added effect of the simultaneous presence of catalyst i and temperature T_k in the experimental situation. The latter may be called an *interaction effect*. The random error associated with the measurement y_{ikj} is denoted now by ϵ_{ikj}.

On adding pressure as an additional experimental variable, we might describe a three-way model by the equation

$$y_{iklj} = \mu + c_i + t_k + p_l + (ct)_{ik} + (cp)_{il} + (tp)_{kl} + (ctp)_{ikl} + \epsilon_{iklj} \tag{3}$$

where the notation is an extension of that for the one- and two-way models. The terms c_i, t_k, and p_l are class effects, $(ct)_{ik}$, $(cp)_{il}$, and $(tp)_{kl}$ are first-order interaction effects, and $(ctp)_{ikl}$ is a second-order interaction effect.

In the models (1), (2), and (3), we may wish to place constraints of some kind on the various terms which enter the equations. For example, in models (2) and (3), where temperature is a factor, it might be convenient to define μ as the reaction rate in the absence of catalyst at 25° C. That is, if the kth temperature is 25° C., we define t_k to be zero. Similarly, if the lth pressure is one atmosphere, we might define p_l to be zero. In any case, μ will always correspond to the expected response when all factors are set to standard values for which the class effects are defined to be zero. It may or may not be possible to establish these standard values in the actual experiment, e.g., if the standard temperature were chosen to be 0° K., we would not be able to measure the reaction rate at this temperature, and hence would not be able to estimate μ.

One can extend these concepts to an *r-way* model, but the notation necessarily becomes extremely clumsy. The following example of an *r-way* model is perhaps as good as any in illustrating the difficulties.

Let us consider r experimental *variables* or *factors* which we will denote by

$$B^1, B^2, \ldots, B^r. \tag{4}$$

Each of these factors B^i can take on an unspecified number of values $B_p{}^i$. We will denote the effects of the factor B^i by $\beta^i(B^i)$ or simply by β^i. β^i may thus take on a number of different values, one for each value of B^i. Thus $\beta_p{}^i$ will denote the effect of the pth value of the ith factor. A first-order interaction effect, denoted by β^{ij} may take on as many values as the product of the number of values of B^i and the number of values of B^j. Higher-order interaction effects may be expressed by an extension of this notation. The general *response* or experimental observation may then be written

$$y_k(B^1, \ldots, B^r) = \mu + \sum_{i=1}^{r} \beta^i + \sum_{i<j} \beta^{ij} + \sum_{i<j<m} \beta^{ijm} + \cdots$$
$$+ \beta^{123\cdots r} + \epsilon_k(B^1, \ldots, B^r). \tag{5}$$

As defined in (5), y_k is the kth observation of an experimental set in which $B^1, \ldots, B^r$ have specified values, i.e., there will be more than one observation for each such set.

Example 3–2–1

A three-way classification in notation (5) would be written

$$y_k(B^1, B^2, B^3) = \mu + \beta^1 + \beta^2 + \beta^3 + \beta^{12} + \beta^{13} + \beta^{23} + \beta^{123}$$
$$+ \epsilon_k(B^1, B^2, B^3).$$

The model of Eq. (3) could thus be written

$$y_j(C, T, P) = \mu + c + t + p + (ct) + (cp)$$
$$+ (tp) + (ctp) + \epsilon_j(C, T, P)$$

if we make the identifications

$$B^1 = C, \quad B^2 = T, \quad B^3 = P$$
$$\beta^1 = c, \quad \beta^2 = t, \quad \beta^3 = p.$$

The class effects c, t, and p take on the values c_i, t_k, and p_l for C, T, and P equal to the ith catalyst, the kth temperature, and the lth pressure, respectively.

Having set up this experimental model, we may wish to test various hypotheses concerning the several class and interaction effects. Examples of such hypotheses are

$$H: \text{All } \beta^{ij} = 0 \quad \text{for } i, j = 1, 2, \ldots, r, \tag{6}$$

i.e., all first-order interactions are zero;

$$H: \text{All } \beta^{i} = 0 \quad \text{for } i = 2, 3, \text{ and } 4, \tag{7}$$

i.e., there are no class effects for the second, third, and fourth classes. These hypotheses are generally tested by computing certain sums of squares and testing the ratios of these sums as F. The reader is referred to more specialized texts for details of the tests for multiple classifications.

The usual analysis-of-variance techniques depend on the assumption that the quantities ϵ are normally distributed, with identical variances, and are independent of the parameters β. If the variances are not identical, but have known ratios, the techniques can still be applied by the use of weighted observations. If the ratios are unknown, we have a generalization of the Fisher-Behrens problem (Section 1–12), and the usual techniques are inapplicable, although they can be used as approximations if unbiased estimates $\hat{\sigma}_i^2$ based on large numbers of degrees of freedom are available for the σ_i^2.

Example 3–2–2

We give here a specific example of a three-way classification with two values for each factor. We consider that the length of the carbon-hydrogen bond has been measured in two compounds, A and B, at each of two laboratories, Podunk (P) and Uptown (U), by both x-ray (X) and neutron (N) diffraction techniques. The different sets of measurements would be

$$\text{y(A, P, X),} \quad \text{y(B, P, X),} \quad \text{y(A, P, N),} \quad \text{y(B, P, N)}$$
$$\text{y(A, U, X),} \quad \text{y(B, U, X),} \quad \text{y(A, U, N),} \quad \text{y(B, U, N).}$$

The value μ would be the over-all average bond length. The three possible class effects to be tested for are

(i) Compound A has a longer bond length than compound B.
(ii) Neutron diffraction gives longer bond lengths than does x-ray diffraction.
(iii) Bond lengths at Uptown are longer than those at Podunk.

A first-order interaction might be of the form:

Neutron diffraction at Uptown and x-ray diffraction at Podunk give longer bond lengths than x-ray diffraction at Uptown and neutron diffraction at Podunk.

3-3. ANALYSIS OF VARIANCE IN A ONE-WAY CLASSIFICATION: EQUAL VARIANCES AND SAMPLE SIZES

Many problems of interest can be treated by a one-way classification scheme. We will treat first the case of samples of equal size from populations of the same variance but possibly different means. For a one-way classification, we may write

$$y_{ij} = \mu + \beta_i + \epsilon_{ij}, \quad i = 1, \ldots, n; j = 1, \ldots, m. \qquad (1)$$

A sample of size m has been drawn from each of the n classes. The ϵ_{ij} are assumed to be independently and normally distributed with mean zero and variance σ^2.

We define

$$\bar{y}_i \equiv \frac{1}{m} \sum_{j=1}^{m} y_{ij}. \qquad (2)$$

Thus

$$\bar{y}_i = \frac{1}{m} \sum_{j=1}^{m} (\mu + \beta_i + \epsilon_{ij}), \qquad (3)$$

and since $\mathcal{E}\{\epsilon_{ij}\} = 0$, $\bar{y}_i$ is an unbiased estimate of $\mu + \beta_i$. Furthermore,

$$s_i^2 \equiv \frac{1}{m-1} \sum_{j=1}^{m} (y_{ij} - \bar{y}_i)^2 \qquad (4)$$

is an unbiased estimate of σ^2, and the quantity

$$\frac{1}{\sigma^2} \sum_{j=1}^{m} (y_{ij} - \bar{y})^2 \qquad (5)$$

is distributed as χ^2_{m-1}. Consequently

$$s^2 \equiv \frac{1}{n} \sum_{i=1}^{n} s_i^2 = \frac{1}{nm-n} \sum_{i=1}^{n} \sum_{j=1}^{m} (y_{ij} - \bar{y})^2 \qquad (6)$$

is also an unbiased estimate of σ^2—a pooled estimate from all the samples—and

$$\frac{1}{\sigma^2} \sum_{i=1}^{n} \sum_{j=1}^{m} (y_{ij} - \bar{y})^2 \qquad (7)$$

is distributed as χ^2 with $N - n$ degrees of freedom, where we have defined $N = nm$ as the total number of observations. The double sum

---

* In the notation of Section 3-2, this would be written

$$y_i(B^1) = \mu + \beta^1 + \epsilon_i(B^1),$$

where i is a subscript that varies as B^1 and hence β^1 take on all possible values; the notation of Eq. (1) will be adhered to in the remainder of the chapter.

$$S_w \equiv \sum_i \sum_j (y_{ij} - \bar{y})^2 \tag{8}$$

is called the *within-classes sum of squares* and, when divided by $N - n$, provides us with an unbiased within-classes estimate of the common variance σ^2.

An over-all sample mean is defined by

$$\bar{y} \equiv \frac{1}{n} \sum_{i=1}^{n} \bar{y}_i = \frac{1}{N} \sum_{i=1}^{n} \sum_{j=1}^{m} y_{ij}$$

$$= \mu + \sum_i \beta_i + \frac{1}{N} \sum_i \sum_j \epsilon_{ij}. \tag{9}$$

If, as is convenient, we define the model in such a way that the sum of the class effects is zero,

$$\sum_{i=1}^{n} \beta_i = 0, \tag{10}$$

then $\bar{y}$ as defined in (9) is an unbiased estimate of μ, the grand mean. We further define

$$S_b = m \sum_{i=1}^{n} (\bar{y}_i - \bar{y})^2 \tag{11}$$

as the *between-classes sum of squares* and with some manipulation can show that

$$\mathcal{E}\left\{ \frac{S_b}{n-1} \right\} = \sigma^2 + \frac{m}{n-1} \sum \beta_i^2. \tag{12}$$

Thus, the between-classes sum of squares can provide us with an unbiased estimate of the sum of the error variance σ^2 and a function of the class effects. S_b/σ^2 is distributed as χ^2_{n-1} if and only if

$$\sum \beta_i^2 = 0. \tag{13}$$

Otherwise S_b/σ^2 can be shown to have the distribution of *non-central* χ^2 with non-centrality parameter

$$\xi^2 = \frac{m}{\sigma^2} \sum_i \beta_i^2. * \tag{14}$$

* Non-central χ^2 for k degrees of freedom may be thought of as the sum of the squares of k independent normal deviates $x_1, \ldots, x_k$ with means $\mu_1, \ldots, \mu_k$ and variances $\sigma_1^2, \ldots, \sigma_k^2$. The non-centrality parameter is defined as

$$\xi^2 = \sum_{j=1}^{k} \left(\frac{\mu_j}{\sigma_j} \right)^2.$$

The density function of non-central χ^2 is given by

$$\phi(\chi^2) = \frac{1}{\chi^2} e^{-(\xi^2 + \chi^2)/2} \sum_{p=0}^{\infty} \frac{1}{p!} \left(\frac{\xi^2}{2} \right)^p \left(\frac{\chi^2}{2} \right)^{k/2+p} \frac{1}{\Gamma(k/2 + p)}$$

and the expected value $\mathcal{E}\{\chi^2\}$ is $k + \xi^2$.

Suppose that we wish to test the null hypothesis

$$H_0: \beta_1 = \beta_2 = \cdots = \beta_n = 0. \tag{15}$$

We may form the ratio

$$F = \frac{S_b/(n-1)}{S_w/(N-n)} \tag{16}$$

which will be distributed as $F_{n-1,N-n}$ if the null hypothesis is true. If

$$F > F_{n-1,N-n,\alpha} \tag{17}$$

we will reject the hypothesis at the α significance level. The power of the test is clearly related to the *non-central F distribution* defined as the ratio of a non-central χ^2 to an independent central χ^2. We will not concern ourselves here with the details of this aspect of the problem but will only remark the fact that the power of the test increases with the non-centrality parameter ξ^2.

Example 3–3–1

Suppose that we have measured C—C bond lengths in two aromatic compounds and find the following values:

Compound A: 1.390, 1.470, 1.455, 1.375, 1.380, 1.470
Compound B: 1.380, 1.400, 1.410, 1.370, 1.430, 1.380.

We hypothesize (perhaps unreasonably from a chemical point of view) that the bond lengths in each group are equal and that the other assumptions for the analysis-of-variance model of this section are valid. We find

$$\bar{y}_A = 1.423$$
$$\bar{y}_B = 1.395$$
$$\bar{y} = \tfrac{1}{2}(\bar{y}_A + \bar{y}_B) = 1.409.$$

These are unbiased estimates of $\mu + \beta_A$, $\mu + \beta_B$, and μ. The class effects are consequently estimated as

$$\hat{\beta}_A = 0.014$$
$$\hat{\beta}_B = -0.014.$$

We further compute $S_w = 0.013234$, and the within-classes estimates of σ^2 and σ are

$$\hat{\sigma}^2 = \frac{S_w}{12 - 2} = 0.0013234$$

and

$$\hat{\sigma} = 0.0364.$$

The between-classes sum of squares is

$$S_b = 6[(0.014)^2 + (-0.014)^2]$$
$$= 0.002352.$$

To test the null hypothesis

$$H_0: \beta_A = \beta_B = 0,$$

we form the ratio

$$\frac{S_b/(2-1)}{S_w/(12-2)} = \frac{0.002352}{0.0013234} = 1.776$$

and test as $F_{1,10}$. The ratio computed from the data is not significant at the 10% significance level, since $F_{1,10,0.10} = 3.285$. We cannot reject the hypothesis that the bond lengths in the two compounds are equal.

For this special case of two classes, the variance ratio is equal to

$$\frac{m(\bar{y}_1 - \bar{y}_2)}{2s^2},$$

and since $F_{1,\nu}$ is identical with t_ν^2, we can test

$$t = \frac{|\bar{y}_1 - \bar{y}_2|}{s} \left(\frac{m}{2}\right)^{1/2}$$

as Student's t with $2(m-1)$ degrees of freedom. In this context, s is the pooled estimate of σ. For the present numerical example, we compute

$$t = \frac{1.423 - 1.395}{0.0364} \left(\frac{6}{2}\right)^{1/2}$$

$$= 1.332.$$

The value of $t_{10,0.10}$ is 1.81, so again we conclude that the null hypothesis cannot be rejected. The two tests are of course identical.

For analyses with more than two classes, Student's t can be used in a similar way to test the significance between any one preselected pair of group means; the quantity

$$t = \frac{|\bar{y}_i - \bar{y}_k|}{s} \left(\frac{m}{2}\right)^{1/2}$$

is tested as Student's t with $N - n$ degrees of freedom. One cannot, however, by repeated application of this test, test the significance of the difference between two or more pairs of means. Suppose that, by use of the t test, we reject the hypothesis $\mu_1 = \mu_2$ at the 5% significance level. Suppose we similarly reject the hypothesis $\mu_2 = \mu_3$. Although the probability that either hypothesis is incorrectly rejected is less than 5%, the probability of error in simultaneously rejecting both may be considerably greater than 5%. If we wish the Type I error per experiment rather than the Type I error per hypothesis to be less than 5%, we must take another approach. (See Section 3–8 on *multiple comparisons*.)

If the hypothesis $\beta_i = 0$, $i = 1, \ldots, n$ is not rejected, the experimenter will have available two estimates of σ^2, an *internal* or *within-classes* estimate (6)

$$\hat{\sigma}^2 = \frac{1}{N - n} S_w \tag{18}$$

and an *external* or *between-classes estimate*

$$\hat{\sigma}^2 = \frac{1}{n - 1} S_b \tag{19}$$

with S_b defined in (11). In reporting the results of a physical experiment, the careful scientist will indicate which of these estimates is used in his tables.

Model II Analysis of Variance in a One-Way Classification. The model we have considered in this section is one in which the β_i are *fixed effects* characteristic of the classes. Such a model is frequently called a Model I analysis of variance. A Model II analysis of variance may also be written

$$y_{ij} = \mu + \beta_i + \epsilon_{ij}, \tag{20}$$

but the β_i are assumed to be drawn at random from a population with mean 0 and variance σ_β^2. We are no longer interested in the identification of the extra variation with individual classes, but only with the estimation of σ_β^2. From the analysis of Model I above, we can see that for Model II

$$\mathcal{E}\left\{ \frac{S_b}{n - 1} \right\} = \mu + m\sigma_\beta^2, \tag{21}$$

and an unbiased estimate of σ^2 is given by

$$\hat{\sigma}_\beta^2 = \frac{1}{m} \left[\frac{S_b}{n - 1} - \frac{S_w}{N - n} \right]. \tag{22}$$

The Model I hypothesis

$$H_0: \beta_1 = \beta_2 = \cdots = \beta_n \tag{23}$$

is analogous to the Model II hypothesis

$$H_0: \sigma_\beta^2 = 0, \tag{24}$$

i.e., there is no additional variation in the measurement because of class effects. The emphasis in most applications of Model II is on the estimation of σ_β^2, not on the testing of hypotheses concerning it.

3–4. ANALYSIS OF VARIANCE IN A ONE-WAY CLASSIFICATION: EQUAL VARIANCES AND UNEQUAL SAMPLE SIZES; MODELS I AND II

The analysis-of-variance scheme outlined in Section 3–3 is easy to apply; part of its simplicity lies in the fact that the sample size m was chosen to be the same for all classes. In the design of an experiment to be used in tests for class effects, it is thus most convenient to take samples of equal size from each class. Frequently, however, the scientist is faced with a situation where it is impossible to arrange the experiment in this way or, even more frequently, where data with unequal sample sizes are presented to him for analysis.

We assume that there are m_i observations in each of n classes for a total of

$$\sum_{i=1}^{n} m_i = N \tag{1}$$

observations. The within-classes sum of squares is computed, as before, as

$$S_w = \sum_{i=1}^{n} \sum_{j=1}^{m_i} (y_{ij} - \bar{y}_i)^2, \tag{2}$$

and $S_w/(N - n)$ is again an unbiased estimate of the common error variance σ^2. The between-classes sum of squares, however, is computed as

$$S_b = \sum_{i=1}^{n} m_i(\bar{y}_i - \bar{y})^2 \tag{3}$$

where

$$\bar{y} = \frac{1}{N} \sum_{i=1}^{n} \sum_{j=1}^{m} y_{ij}. \tag{4}$$

It may be shown that

$$\mathcal{E}\left\{\frac{S_b}{n-1}\right\} = \sigma^2 + \frac{1}{n-1}\left[\sum_{i=1}^{n} m_i\beta_i^2 - \frac{\left(\sum_{i=1}^{n} m_i\beta_i\right)^2}{N}\right] \tag{5}$$

for the case of a Model I (fixed effects) analysis of variance, or

$$\mathcal{E}\left\{\frac{S_b}{n-1}\right\} = \sigma^2 + \sigma_\beta^2\left[\frac{N^2 - \sum_i m_i^2}{N(n-1)}\right] \tag{6}$$

for a Model II (random effects) analysis of variance. Again, S_w/σ^2 is distributed as χ^2_{N-n}, and, if there are no class effects, S_b/σ^2 is distributed as χ^2_{n-1}, so that the ratio

$$F = \frac{S_b/(n-1)}{S_w/(N-n)} \tag{7}$$

is distributed as $F_{n-1, N-n}$. The Model I hypothesis

$$H_0: \beta_1 = \cdots = \beta_n = 0 \tag{8}$$

or the Model II hypothesis

$$H_0: \sigma_\beta^2 = 0 \tag{9}$$

is thus tested by comparing the sample F against $F_{n-1, N-n, \alpha}$. Again

$$\bar{y}_i = \frac{1}{m_i} \sum_{j=1}^{m_i} y_{ij} \tag{10}$$

is an unbiased estimate of $\mu + \beta_i$ with variance σ^2/m_i, and consequently the unweighted average of the $\bar{y}_i$,

$$y' = \frac{1}{n} \sum_i \bar{y}_i, \tag{11}$$

is an unbiased estimate of μ if $\sum_i \beta_i$ is assumed to be zero. The variance of y' is found to be

$$\sigma^2(y') = \frac{\sigma^2}{n} \sum_i \frac{1}{m_i}. \tag{12}$$

It should be noted that in the presence of class effects $\bar{y}$ is not an unbiased estimate of μ since

$$\mathcal{E}\{\bar{y}\} = \mu + \frac{\sum_i m_i\beta_i}{N} \tag{13}$$

and $\sum m_i\beta_i$ is not generally zero, as our model presumes that $\sum \beta_i$ is equal to zero. This result indicates one good reason for preferring a model with equal sample sizes.

The comparison between the means of any two *a priori* selected classes may, as before, be tested as Student's t with $N - n$ degrees of freedom, although again another approach (Section 3–8) is necessary for multiple comparisons. The sample t is computed as

$$t = \frac{|\bar{y}_i - \bar{y}_k|}{s(1/m_i + 1/m_k)^{1/2}} \tag{14}$$

where s is determined from all classes as

$$s^2 = \frac{S_w}{N - n} \tag{15}$$

with S_w defined in (2).

Example 3–4–1

As an example of Model I, consider the following three groups of metal-oxygen bond lengths in an inorganic crystal; the grouping was made on the basis of chemical coordination, not by value:

Group I: 2.19, 2.04, 1.96, 2.20, 2.10, 1.93
Group II: 2.00, 1.94, 2.06, 2.06
Group III: 2.48, 2.71.

We will assume that all conditions for the model of this section are satisfied. We calculate

$$\bar{y}_I = 2.070, \quad \bar{y}_{II} = 2.015, \quad \bar{y}_{III} = 2.595$$
$$\bar{y} = \tfrac{1}{12}(6 \times 2.070 + 4 \times 2.015 + 2 \times 2.595) = 2.139.$$

An unbiased estimate of μ is

$$y' = \tfrac{1}{3}(2.070 + 2.015 + 2.595) = 2.227.$$

An unbiased estimate of σ^2 is

$$\hat{\sigma}^2 = \frac{S_w}{N - n} = \frac{0.10115}{12 - 3} = 0.01124.$$

The between-classes sum of squares may be calculated to be

$$S_b = 6(0.069)^2 + 4(0.124)^2 + 2(0.456)^2 = 0.50594.$$

The variance ratio is thus

$$F = \frac{0.50594/2}{0.01124} = 22.51.$$

This exceeds by far $F_{2,9,0.005} = 10.107$, so that the null hypothesis H_0: $\beta_{\mathrm{I}} = \beta_{\mathrm{II}} = \beta_{\mathrm{III}} = 0$ can be rejected at the 0.5% significance level. We conclude that there are significant differences among the group means.

If we wish to compare two means $\bar{y}_r$ and $\bar{y}_q$, we may compute

$$t = \frac{|\bar{y}_r - \bar{y}_q|}{\hat{\sigma}(1/m_1 + 1/m_2)^{1/2}}$$

and test as Student's t with $12 - 3 = 9$ degrees of freedom. The values for this example are

$$t(\mathrm{I, II}) \quad = \frac{0.055}{0.106 \times 0.646} = 0.803$$

$$t(\mathrm{I, III}) \quad = \frac{0.525}{0.106 \times 0.817} = 6.06$$

$$t(\mathrm{II, III}) = \frac{0.580}{0.106 \times 0.866} = 6.32.$$

Since $t_{9,0.005} = 3.69$, we would be tempted to conclude that the difference between Groups I and II is not significant, but that there are significant differences between the means for Group III and the other groups. This is perhaps a correct conclusion, but because it is a conclusion about a multiple hypothesis, the significance level 0.005 for the single t test does not apply, and methods such as those of Section 3-8 must be used.

3-5. ANALYSIS OF VARIANCE IN A ONE-WAY CLASSIFICATION: UNEQUAL VARIANCES AND SAMPLE SIZES

We now turn to a more general form of the one-way classification for the analysis of variance. We assume that we have n classes of observations with m_i observations in the ith class:

Sample from Class 1: $y_{11}, y_{12}, \ldots, y_{1m_1}$
Sample from Class 2: $y_{21}, y_{22}, \ldots, y_{2m_2}$
. . . .
Sample from Class n: $y_{n1}, y_{n2}, \ldots, y_{nm_n}$.

The y_{ij} are assumed to be drawn from independent normal populations with means $\mu + \beta_i$ and variances σ_i^2, where the ratios σ_i^2/σ_k^2 are known for all pairs i and k. An unbiased estimate for $(\mu + \beta_i)$ is provided by

$$\bar{y}_i = \frac{1}{m_i} \sum_{j=1}^{m_i} y_{ij}. \tag{1}$$

The variance of this estimate is

$$\text{var}(\bar{y}_i) = \frac{\sigma_i^2}{m_i}. \tag{2}$$

The quantity

$$\frac{\sum_{j=1}^{m_i} (y_{ij} - \bar{y}_i)^2}{\sigma_i^2} \tag{3}$$

is distributed as $\chi^2_{m_i-1}$, and

$$\frac{1}{m_i - 1} \sum_{j=1}^{m_i} (y_{ij} - \bar{y}_i)^2 \tag{4}$$

is an unbiased estimate of σ_i^2. Since the sum of independent χ^2 variates is again a χ^2 variate, the quantity

$$A = \sum_{i=1}^{n} \frac{1}{\sigma_i^2} \sum_{j=1}^{m_i} (y_{ij} - \bar{y}_i)^2 \tag{5}$$

is distributed as χ^2_{N-n}, with

$$N = \sum_{i=1}^{n} m_i \tag{6}$$

being the total number of observations.

Let us introduce an unknown constant σ^2 and define the *weight* w_i for an observation from the ith class by

$$w_i \equiv \frac{\sigma^2}{\sigma_i^2}.^* \tag{7}$$

The form of (7) suggests that the constant σ^2 may be called the *variance of an observation of unit weight*. The quantity A defined in (5) becomes

$$A = \frac{1}{\sigma^2} \sum_{i=1}^{n} w_i \sum_{j=1}^{m_i} (y_{ij} - \bar{y}_i)^2, \tag{8}$$

* Although σ^2 is unknown, the ratio σ^2/σ_i^2 is presumed to be known, so that the relative weights are known. This ratio may be arbitrarily chosen, e.g., the weight of the first class may be set equal to unity. The analysis is independent of the scale of the weights.

so that

$$\hat{\sigma}^2 \equiv \frac{S_w}{N-n} = \frac{1}{N-n} \sum_{i=1}^{n} w_i \sum_{j=1}^{m_i} (y_{ij} - \bar{y}_i)^2 \tag{9}$$

is an unbiased estimate of σ^2. Since σ_i^2/σ^2 is known, the variance for each class is estimated by

$$s_i^2 \equiv \hat{\sigma}_i^2 = \frac{\hat{\sigma}^2}{w_i}. \tag{10}$$

We define the weighted over-all sample mean by

$$\bar{y} \equiv \frac{1}{\sum\limits_{i=1}^{n} m_i w_i} \sum_{i=1}^{n} m_i w_i \bar{y}_i$$

$$= \frac{1}{\sum\limits_{i=1}^{n} m_i w_i} \sum_{i=1}^{n} \sum_{j=1}^{m_i} w_i y_{ij}. \tag{11}$$

We have

$$\mathcal{E}\{\bar{y}\} = \frac{1}{\sum\limits_{i=1}^{n} m_i w_i} \sum_{i=1}^{n} m_i w_i \beta_i, \tag{12}$$

so that in the presence of fixed effects the $\bar{y}$ is not in general an unbiased estimate of μ, since $\sum m_i w_i \mu_i$ is not necessarily zero. The variance of $\bar{y}$ as a biased estimate of μ is

$$\sigma^2(\bar{y}) = \frac{\sigma^2}{\sum\limits_{k=1}^{n} m_k w_k}. \tag{13}$$

It may be shown that $\bar{y}$ is a minimum variance estimator.

An unbiased estimate of μ is given by

$$y' = \frac{1}{n} \sum_{i=1}^{n} \bar{y}_i, \tag{14}$$

although the variance of this estimate,

$$\sigma^2(y') = \frac{\sigma^2}{n^2} \sum_{k=1}^{n} \frac{1}{m_k w_k}, \tag{15}$$

is greater than the variance of $\bar{y}$ for all cases except that for which

$$m_i w_i = m_k w_k \tag{16}$$

for all values of i and k.

If the class effects are assumed to be zero, or if the classes are chosen at random from a population of classes with random effects and zero means (randomized design), $\bar{y}$ does provide an unbiased estimate of μ and is to be preferred over y', since $\bar{y}$ is a minimum variance estimate, while y' is not.

The between-classes sum of squares is computed as

$$S_b = \sum_{i=1}^{n} w_i m_i (\bar{y}_i - \bar{y})^2, \tag{17}$$

and it can be shown that

$$\mathcal{E}\{S_b\} = (n - 1)\sigma^2 + \sum_{i=1}^{n} m_i w_i \beta_i^2 - \frac{\left(\sum_i m_i w_i \beta_i\right)^2}{\sum_i m_i w_i} \tag{18}$$

for a Model I with fixed effects μ_i, or

$$\mathcal{E}\{S_b\} = (n - 1)\sigma^2 + \sigma_\beta^2 \left[\frac{\sum_i m_i w_i^2 - \sum_i m_i^2 w_i^2}{\sum_i m_i w_i} \right] \tag{19}$$

for a Model II with random effects with variance σ_β^2. In the latter case, an unbiased estimate for σ_β^2 is obtained by solving (19) for σ_β^2 and substituting the value of S_b computed from the data for $\mathcal{E}\{S_b\}$. To test the Model I null hypothesis,

$$H_0: \beta_1 = \beta_2 = \beta_3 = \cdots = \beta_n = 0, \tag{20}$$

we form the ratio

$$F = \frac{S_b/(n - 1)}{S_w/(N - n)}, \tag{21}$$

where S_w and S_b are obtained from (9) and (17), and test as $F_{n-1, N-n}$ (see Exercise 3–6). If the value F computed from the data exceeds the tabulated value of $F_{n-1, N-n, \alpha}$, the null hypothesis (20) may be rejected at the $100\alpha\%$ level.

The two sample t test becomes in this case a test of

$$t = \frac{|\bar{y}_r - \bar{y}_q|}{\hat{\sigma}(1/w_r m_r + 1/w_q m_q)^{1/2}} \tag{22}$$

with $\hat{\sigma}$ being defined from the within-classes sum of squares S_w by (9). The statistic t defined in (22) is tested as Student's t with $N - n$ degrees of freedom; again multiple tests should be made by a procedure such as that in Section 3–8.

Example 3–5–1

Suppose that in Example 3–4–1, the variances for the three classes are known to be in the ratio $1:1:2$. The values for the $\bar{y}_i$ are of course unchanged. Let us set the weight for the third group equal to 1. The weights for the first and second groups are then 2. We have then

$$S_w = 2 \times 0.0636 + 2 \times 0.0099 + 1 \times 0.02645 = 0.17345,$$

$$s^2 \equiv \hat{\sigma}^2 = \frac{S_w}{N - n} = \frac{0.17345}{12 - 3} = 0.01927.$$

The latter is an unbiased estimate of σ^2, and since $w_i \sigma_i^2$ is equal to σ^2 it follows that unbiased estimates for the σ_i^2 are

$$s_1^2 = s_2^2 = 0.009635 \quad \text{and} \quad s_3^2 = 0.01927.$$

The weighted sample mean is

$$\bar{y} = \frac{46.15}{22} = 2.098$$

with variance

$$(\bar{y}) = \frac{0.01927}{22} = 0.00088.$$

An unbiased estimate of μ is again given by

$$y' = 2.227,$$

now with variance

$$\sigma^2(y') = \frac{0.01927}{9} \left(\frac{1}{12} + \frac{1}{8} + \frac{1}{2} \right) = 0.00152.$$

We compute S_b as follows:

$$S_b = 12(0.028)^2 + 8(0.083)^2 + 2(0.497)^2 = 0.5585.$$

The ratio

$$F = \frac{0.5585/2}{0.01927} = 14.49$$

is again significant at the 1% level, so we reject the hypothesis that there are no class effects.

Although the treatment of this section might appear to be of great generality, it nevertheless demands a knowledge of the relative variances of the various classes, knowledge generally unavailable. Tests for variance homogeneity will be given in Section 3–7. Unless there is strong evidence for heterogeneity in the variances, evidence based either on the data or on a sound model of the physical experiment, it is perhaps simplest to use the methods of Sections 3–3 and 3–4 rather than the computationally more complex results of this section.

If the relative variances of the classes are unknown, one might guess that the variance estimates s_i^2 could be substituted for σ_i^2 in the treatment given above. If the samples are large, this is indeed a satisfactory procedure. For small samples, it may be somewhat dangerous. The problem is a generalization of the Fisher-Behrens problem (Section 2–1), and an analogous approximate procedure can be used. Welch (1951) has shown that if the weights are defined by

$$w_i = \frac{1}{s_i^2} \tag{23}$$

we may test the hypothesis

$$H_0: \mu_i = \mu_j, \quad i,j = 1, \ldots, n$$

by calculating the ratio

$$F = \frac{\sum_{i=1}^{n} w_i m_i (\bar{y}_i - \bar{y})^2/(n-1)}{1 + [2(n-2)/(n^2-1)] \sum_{i=1}^{n} [1/(m_i - 1)]\left(1 - m_i w_i \Big/ \sum_{k=1}^{n} m_k w_k\right)^2} \tag{24}$$

which under the null hypothesis is distributed approximately as the variance ratio F, with

$$\nu_1 = n - 1 \tag{25}$$

and

$$\nu_2 = \left[\frac{3}{n^2-1} \sum_{i=1}^{n} \frac{1}{m_i - 1}\left(1 - \frac{m_i w_i}{\sum_k m_k w_k}\right)^2\right]^{-1} \tag{26}$$

degrees of freedom.

It is worth noting that the effects of unequal variances are less severe if the sizes of all the samples are equal or nearly equal.

Example 3–5–2

Let us apply the test ratio (24) to the data of Example 3–4–1. We have

Sample	w_i	$w_i m_i$	$(\bar{y}_i - \bar{y})^2$
I	$\dfrac{1}{0.01296}$	460.3	0.000225
II	$\dfrac{1}{0.00330}$	1210.0	0.001600
III	$\dfrac{1}{0.02645}$	75.5	0.291600

Thus

$$F = \frac{\frac{1}{2}(460.3 \times 0.000225 + 1210.0 \times 0.001600 + 75.5 \times 0.291600)}{1 + \frac{2}{8}(\frac{1}{5} \times 0.542 + \frac{1}{3} \times 0.094 + \frac{1}{1} \times 0.915)}$$

$$= 9.5$$

This ratio is to be tested as $F_{2,\nu_2,\alpha}$ where

$$\nu_2 = 2.5.$$

Now $F_{2,3,0.05} = 9.55$, so that we can see without interpolation that the hypothesis of equal class means cannot be rejected at the 5% significance level. The effective number of degrees of freedom for the F test has been greatly reduced because of the very small number of degrees of freedom involved in the estimation of the $s_i{}^2$.

3–6. ANALYSIS OF VARIANCE FOR VERY LARGE SAMPLES

The general formalism of the analysis of variance is useful when a number of class means for large samples are to be compared. We consider samples large enough for the sample variances to be highly reliable estimates of the population variances. Suppose that there are n classes, with class means

$$\bar{y}_1, \ldots, \bar{y}_n \tag{1}$$

and *variances of the mean*

$$\sigma^2(\bar{y}_1), \ldots, \sigma^2(\bar{y}_n). \tag{2}$$

We will retain the notation $\sigma_i{}^2$ for the variances of the individual observations which we do not require to be given. Thus

$$\sigma^2(\bar{y}_i) = \frac{\sigma_i{}^2}{m} \tag{3}$$

As before, we define the weights for the individual observations as

$$w_i \equiv \frac{\sigma^2}{\sigma_i{}^2} = \frac{\sigma^2}{m_i \sigma^2(\bar{y}_i)}. \tag{4}$$

The quantity

$$p_i = \frac{1}{\sigma^2(\bar{y}_i)} \tag{5}$$

may then be called the weight for the ith mean, since

$$\bar{y} = \frac{1}{\sum\limits_{k=1}^{n} m_k w_k} \sum_{i=1}^{n} m_i w_i \bar{y}_i \equiv \frac{1}{\sum\limits_{k=1}^{n} p_k} \sum_{i=1}^{n} p_i \bar{y}_i. \tag{6}$$

This minimum variance estimate of μ is again unbiased only in the cases of zero or randomized class effects, since

$$\mathcal{E}\{\bar{y}\} = \mu + \frac{1}{\sum\limits_{k=1}^{n} p_k} \sum_{i=1}^{n} p_i \mu_i. \tag{7}$$

The variance of $\bar{y}$ is

$$\sigma^2(\bar{y}) = \frac{1}{\sum\limits_{k=1}^{n} p_k}. \tag{8}$$

The unbiased estimate of μ,

$$y' = \frac{1}{n} \sum_{i=1}^{n} \bar{y}_i, \tag{9}$$

has variance

$$\sigma^2(y') = \frac{1}{n^2} \sum_{i=1}^{n} \sigma^2(\bar{y}_i) = \frac{1}{n^2} \sum_{k=1}^{n} \frac{1}{p_k}. \tag{10}$$

The within-classes mean sum of squares is

$$\frac{S_w}{N-n} = \frac{1}{N-n} \sum_{i=1}^{n} w_i \sum_{j=1}^{m_i} (\bar{y}_i - y_{ij})^2$$

$$= \frac{1}{N-n} \sum_{i=1}^{n} w_i (m_i - 1)\hat{\sigma}_i^2 \tag{11}$$

$$= \hat{\sigma}^2,$$

since $w_i\hat{\sigma}_i^2 = \hat{\sigma}^2$ by definition. The between-classes mean sum of squares is

$$\frac{S_b}{n-1} = \frac{1}{n-1} \sum_{i=1}^{n} w_i m_i (\bar{y}_i - \bar{y})^2$$

$$= \frac{\sigma^2}{n-1} \sum_{i=1}^{n} p_i (\bar{y}_i - \bar{y})^2. \tag{12}$$

The ratio

$$\frac{S_b/(n-1)}{S_w/(N-n)} \equiv \frac{1}{n-1} \sum_{i=1}^{n} p_i (\bar{y}_i - \bar{y})^2 \tag{13}$$

is distributed as $F_{n-1,N-n}$, but, as we have assumed that each of the m_i is large, $N-n$ is large, and we may make use of the fact that

$$\lim_{\nu_2 \to \infty} F_{\nu_1,\nu_2} = \frac{\chi^2_{\nu_1}}{\nu_1}. \tag{14}$$

Thus the weighted sum of squares

$$\frac{S_b}{\sigma^2} = \sum_i p_i (\bar{y}_i - \bar{y})^2 \tag{15}$$

is distributed as χ^2_{n-1}, and we may thus test the hypothesis

$$H_0: \beta_1 = \beta_2 = \cdots = \beta_n = 0 \tag{16}$$

by consulting a table of χ^2.

The significance of the difference between two *previously chosen* means may, as before, be tested by computing

$$t = \frac{\bar{y}_s - \bar{y}_q}{(\sigma^2(\bar{y}_s) + \sigma^2(\bar{y}_q))^{1/2}} \tag{17}$$

and testing as Student's t with an infinite number of degrees of freedom, i.e., as a unit normal deviate.

Example 3–6–1

A treatment, based on the results of this section, may now be given of the data presented in Example 1–7–7. We assume, for the purposes of this example, that each of the values quoted represents the mean of a sample from a single normal population and that the quoted errors are estimates of standard deviations of the mean based on many degrees of freedom. We have the following relevant values:

$\bar{y}_i$	$\sigma^2(\bar{y}_i)$	p_i	$(\bar{y}_i - \bar{y})^2$
1.867	196×10^{-6}	5,102	196×10^{-6}
1.837	144×10^{-6}	6,944	256×10^{-6}
1.847	9×10^{-6}	111,111	36×10^{-6}
1.853	9×10^{-6}	111,111	0×10^{-6}
1.858	9×10^{-6}	111,111	25×10^{-6}
1.906	400×10^{-6}	2,500	2809×10^{-6}

The computed values are

$$\bar{y} = 1.853 \qquad \sigma^2(\bar{y}) = 2.87 \times 10^{-6}$$
$$y' = 1.861 \qquad \sigma^2(y') = 21.3 \times 10^{-6}$$

$$\frac{S_b}{\sigma^2} = 16.58.$$

We may reject the hypothesis

$$H_0: \mu_1 = \mu_2 = \mu_3 = \mu_4 = \mu_5 = \mu_6$$

at the 1% significance level, since $\chi^2_{5,0.01} = 15.08$. There are probably significant differences among the means.

3–7. TESTS FOR THE HOMOGENEITY OF VARIANCE

As we have seen, the analysis of variance takes on its simplest form when the classes can all be assumed to have the same variance. It thus becomes important to be able to test for the homogeneity of the variances. One such test in common use has been proposed by Bartlett. If the sample variances are

$$s_1^2, s_2^2, \ldots, s_n^2 \tag{1}$$

with

$$\nu_1, \nu_2, \ldots, \nu_n \tag{2}$$

degrees of freedom and

$$s^2 = \frac{\sum_i \nu_i s_i^2}{\sum_i \nu_i} \tag{3}$$

is the pooled variance estimate, then the statistic to be calculated is

$$M = \left(\sum_i \nu_i\right) \log s^2 - \sum_i \nu_i \log s_i^2. \tag{4}$$

The distribution of M is rather complicated, but if all the ν_i are 5 or greater, M is satisfactorily approximated by χ^2_{n-1}. In fact, under the null hypothesis

$$H_0: \sigma_1^2 = \sigma_2^2 = \cdots = \sigma_n^2, \tag{5}$$

the inequality

$$P(M > \chi^2_{n-1,\alpha}) > \alpha \tag{6}$$

is strictly true. If the hypothesis cannot be rejected by using the χ^2 approximation, it cannot be rejected by using the exact form of the distribution of M. On the other hand, care must be taken if the number of degrees of freedom is small and the χ^2 test tells us to reject the null hypothesis; either a low significance level should be used, or the detailed distribution of M should be referred to.

Example 3–7–1

In Example 3–4–1, we had three groups of observations with the following sample variances:

$$s_I^2 = 0.01296 \qquad \nu_I = 5$$
$$s_{II}^2 = 0.00330 \qquad \nu_{II} = 3$$
$$s_{III}^2 = 0.02645 \qquad \nu_{III} = 1.$$

In this case

$$M = 9 \log (0.01124) - 5 \log (0.01296)$$
$$- 3 \log (0.00330) - \log (0.02645) = 2.11.$$

This is to be compared with $\chi^2_{2,0.05} = 5.99$. The hypothesis of equal variances cannot be rejected by using χ^2 as an approximation to M. It could therefore not be rejected by using the exact distribution of M.

A test which is more convenient to apply and which suffers less from deviations from the assumption of normality is the maximum F-ratio test of Hartley. Consider estimates

$$s_1^2, s_2^2, \ldots, s_n^2 \tag{7}$$

for the variances of n normal populations. Let

$$s^2_{max} = \max \{s_i^2 \mid i = 1, \ldots, n\}$$
$$s^2_{min} = \min \{s_i^2 \mid i = 1, \ldots, n\}. \tag{8}$$

Define

$$F_{max} = \frac{s^2_{max}}{s^2_{min}}. \tag{9}$$

This statistic is easily estimated at a glance from a tabulation of the sample variances. Tables of percentage points of $F_{\max}$ are available in the *Biometrika* tables* and elsewhere. The test is limited to the case for which each of the estimates s_i^2 is based on the same number of degrees of freedom ν, and the tables of percentage points are presented as functions of ν and n.

3–8. MULTIPLE COMPARISONS

As pointed out in Section 3–4, the procedure of making more than one comparison of class means by use of a t test is invalid and misleading. In making several such comparisons simultaneously, one is in effect trying to test a multiple hypothesis for which the simple theory is inapplicable. Although the t test does indeed test the hypothesis $\mu_i = \mu_j$ for a pair of means, one can get into serious trouble by testing several such hypotheses at once by the t test.† The conclusion stated at the end of Example 3–4–1, although possibly correct, cannot reliably be based on the three separate t tests cited. An example will help to illustrate one of the difficulties that can arise.

Example 3–8–1

Consider a Model I analysis of variance with equal variances and sample sizes. We draw four samples of size 2 from four populations with the following results:

$$
\begin{array}{ccc}
\text{I} & 2.00 & 2.05 \\
\text{II} & 2.05 & 2.10 \\
\text{III} & 2.10 & 2.15 \\
\text{IV} & 2.15 & 2.20.
\end{array}
$$

Thus, in the notation of Section 3–4, we have $n = 4$, $m = 2$, $N = 8$. The class means are 2.025, 2.075, 2.125, and 2.175, while the over-all mean is $\bar{y} = 2.100$. S_w and S_b may be computed to be 0.005 and 0.025, respectively. The ratio

$$
\frac{0.025/3}{0.005/4} = 6.67
$$

* See Bibliography.

† If k independent hypotheses on the means are tested at the $100\alpha\%$ significance level, the probability that all of the hypotheses will be accepted when they are true is $(1 - \alpha)^k$, which becomes smaller and smaller as k increases. If one is testing many hypotheses, the probability is high that some of these hypotheses will be incorrectly rejected, even though the probability of Type I error for each hypothesis is small. If the means of k samples, each based on the same number of degrees of freedom, from the same population are compared by using separate t tests, the probability that the difference between the largest and the smallest will be declared significant approaches 1 as k increases without limit.

exceeds the value of $F_{3,4,0.05} = 6.59$, so that the hypothesis of equal class means can be rejected at the 5% significance level. On the other hand, the value of

$$|t| = \frac{|\bar{y}_i - \bar{y}_j|}{s} \left(\frac{m}{2}\right)^{1/2}$$

is found to be

$$|t| = \frac{0.050}{(0.00125)^{1/2}} \times 1 = 1.41$$

for each of the comparisons I,II; II,III; and III,IV. We cannot reject at the 5% level the hypotheses

$$\mu_I = \mu_{II},$$
$$\mu_{II} = \mu_{III},$$
or $\mu_{III} = \mu_{IV}$

on the basis of the t tests, for $t_{4,0.05} = 2.78$. Yet we know that it is probable that some differences exist. The reader will notice that the hypotheses

$$\mu_I = \mu_{III}$$
and $\mu_I = \mu_{IV}$

can be rejected at the 5% level, but it is never fair to pick out the hypotheses to be tested on the basis of the results.

The purpose of this section is to indicate one possible way of obtaining valid confidence intervals for a number of simultaneous hypotheses.

Consider a Model I analysis-of-variance problem with equal class variances σ^2 but possibly unequal sample sizes m_i. The population means

$$\mu_i: i = 1, \ldots, n \tag{1}$$

are estimated by

$$\bar{y}_i: i = 1, \ldots, n \tag{2}$$

The variances of the estimates

$$\frac{\sigma^2}{m_i} \tag{3}$$

are estimated by

$$\frac{s^2}{m_i} \tag{4}$$

where s^2 is given by Eq. (15) of Section 3–4.

A linear function of the means

$$\theta = \sum_{i=1}^{n} a_i \mu_i \tag{5}$$

with

$$\sum_{i=1}^{n} a_i = 0 \tag{6}$$

is called a *contrast*. Examples of contrasts are

$$\theta_1 = \mu_1 - \mu_2 \tag{7}$$

and

$$\theta_2 = \mu_1 + \mu_2 - \mu_3 - \mu_4. \tag{8}$$

A contrast is estimated by

$$\hat{\theta} = \sum_i a_i \bar{x}_i \tag{9}$$

with variance

$$\sigma_\theta^2 \equiv \sigma^2(\hat{\theta}) = \sum_{i=1}^{n} \frac{a_i^2 \sigma^2}{m_i}. \tag{10}$$

The variance σ_θ^2 can be estimated by

$$\hat{\sigma}_\theta^2 = s^2 \sum_i \frac{a_i^2}{m_i}. \tag{11}$$

If we define S by

$$S^2 = (n-1)F_{n-1,N-n,\alpha}, \tag{12}$$

the following statement defines simultaneous $100(1 - \alpha)\%$ confidence intervals for all possible contrasts θ:

$$P(\hat{\theta} - S\hat{\sigma}_\theta < \theta < \hat{\theta} + S\hat{\sigma}_\theta) = 1 - \alpha. \tag{13}$$

These are $100(1 - \alpha)\%$ confidence intervals in the sense that, if *many such experiments* are carried out, we may expect that all the confidence statements will be correct $100(1 - \alpha)\%$ of the time, while in $100\alpha\%$ of *the experiments*, one or more statements will be incorrect. The two-sample t test, on the other hand, says that $100\alpha\%$ of the individual statements will be incorrect. Other procedures, which may result in narrower confidence intervals in some cases, have been suggested for handling this problem, but the one which is presented here (Scheffé, 1953) is versatile and easy to apply.

It is worth noting that the same formalism may be applied for establishing confidence limits for any linear function (5) of the means. We drop the condition (6) which defines a contrast, and at the same time change the definition of S:

$$S^2 = nF_{n,N-n,\alpha}. \tag{12a}$$

The confidence intervals (13) are again valid.

Example 3–8–2

Consider the data presented in Example 1–8–1. Let us establish 95% confidence intervals in the sense of this section for the following contrasts:

$$\theta_1 = \mu_1 - \mu_2$$
$$\theta_2 = \mu_1 - \mu_4$$
$$\theta_3 = \mu_4 + \mu_3 - \mu_2 - \mu_1.$$

We have

$$\hat{\theta}_1 = -0.05; \quad \hat{\sigma}_\theta = 0.035$$
$$\hat{\theta}_2 = -0.15; \quad \hat{\sigma}_\theta = 0.035$$
$$\hat{\theta}_3 = \quad 0.20; \quad \hat{\sigma}_\theta = 0.050$$

and

$$S^2 = 3F_{3,4,0.05} = 3 \times 6.59$$
$$S = 4.45.$$

The confidence intervals are thus

$$-0.21 < \theta_1 < 0.11$$
$$-0.31 < \theta_2 < 0.01$$
$$-0.02 < \theta_3 < 0.42,$$

considerably wider intervals than would be given by separate t tests. On the basis of the given samples, then, one is unable to pinpoint the source of the variation. Further sampling is indicated.

Example 3–8–3

We consider again the analysis of variance problem presented in Example 3–4–1. Let us define the following contrasts:

$$\theta_1 = \mu_1 - \mu_2$$
$$\theta_2 = \mu_1 - \mu_3$$
$$\theta_3 = \mu_2 - \mu_3$$

with estimates of the contrasts and their variances

$$\hat{\theta}_1 = \quad 0.055; \quad \hat{\sigma}_\theta^2 = 0.01124(\tfrac{1}{6} + \tfrac{1}{4}) = 0.00469$$
$$\hat{\theta}_2 = -0.525; \quad \hat{\sigma}_\theta^2 = 0.01124(\tfrac{1}{6} + \tfrac{1}{2}) = 0.00751$$
$$\hat{\theta}_3 = -0.580; \quad \hat{\sigma}_\theta^2 = 0.01124(\tfrac{1}{4} + \tfrac{1}{2}) = 0.00845.$$

S is found from

$$S^2 = (3 - 1)F_{2,9,0.05} = 8.52.$$

Performing the rest of the arithmetic, we find the three required 95% confidence statements:

$$P(-0.143 < \theta_1 < \quad 0.253) = 0.95$$
$$P(-0.779 < \theta_2 < -0.271) = 0.95$$
$$P(-0.848 < \theta_3 < -0.312) = 0.95.$$

We reach the same conclusion as previously, that there are probably differences between the mean of Group III and those for Groups I and II. Here, however, the conclusion is soundly based.

Multiple Comparisons for Large Samples. We may combine the results of this section and those of Section 3-6 to arrive at a frequently useful result. We denote the variances of the large-sample means $\bar{y}_i$ by $\sigma^2(\bar{y}_i)$ as in Eq. (2) of Section 3-6, and Eq. (11) of this section becomes

$$\hat{\sigma}^2(\theta) = \sum_i a_i{}^2 \sigma^2(\bar{y}_i). \qquad (14)$$

Also,

$$S^2 = (n - 1)F_{n-1,\infty,\alpha}$$
$$= \chi^2{}_{n-1,\alpha}. \qquad (15)$$

With these definitions, the confidence intervals (13) may be interpreted as before. On the other hand, the narrower limits obtained in the two-sample test of

$$|t| = \frac{|\bar{y}_i - \bar{y}_j|}{[\sigma^2(\bar{y}_i) + \sigma^2(\bar{y}_j)]^{1/2}} \qquad (16)$$

as a unit normal deviate are invalid for multiple comparisons.

Example 3-8-4

The following estimates, based on many degrees of freedom, were obtained for the bond lengths and standard deviations of the mean in the $XeO_6{}^{-4}$ ion:

$\bar{y}_i$	$\sigma^2(\bar{y}_i)$
1.92	0.0009
1.88	0.0009
1.82	0.0009
1.87	0.0004

Let us set up the 95% confidence intervals for the contrasts

$$\theta_1 = \mu_1 + \mu_2 - \mu_3 - \mu_4$$
$$\theta_2 = \mu_1 + \mu_2 + \mu_4 - 3\mu_3$$
$$\theta_3 = \mu_1 - \mu_3$$
$$\theta_4 = \mu_1 - \mu_2$$
$$\theta_5 = \mu_4 - \mu_3$$

and compare these with the confidence intervals which would have been obtained by the two-sample tests. We have

$\hat{\theta}_i$	$\hat{\sigma}(\theta_i)$
0.11	0.056
0.21	0.101
0.10	0.042
0.04	0.042
0.05	0.036

and
$$S^2 = \chi^2_{3,0.05} = 7.81$$
$$S = 2.795.$$

(The two-sample test is obtained by using (13) with $S = 1.96$.) The confidence intervals are

Multiple-Comparison	Two-Sample
$-0.05 \leqslant \theta_1 \leqslant 0.27$	$0.00 \leqslant \theta_1 \leqslant 0.22$
$-0.07 \leqslant \theta_2 \leqslant 0.49$	$0.01 \leqslant \theta_2 \leqslant 0.41$
$-0.02 \leqslant \theta_3 \leqslant 0.22$	$0.02 \leqslant \theta_3 \leqslant 0.18$
$-0.08 \leqslant \theta_4 \leqslant 0.16$	$-0.04 \leqslant \theta_4 \leqslant 0.12$
$-0.05 \leqslant \theta_5 \leqslant 0.15$	$-0.02 \leqslant \theta_5 \leqslant 0.12$

Thus, the two-sample tests would reject, perhaps incorrectly, the hypotheses

$$H_2: \mu_1 + \mu_2 + \mu_4 - 3\mu_3 = 0$$
$$H_3: \mu_1 - \mu_3 = 0.$$

REFERENCES

Box, G. E. P. 1954. Some theorems on quadratic forms applied in the study of analysis of variance problems. I. Effect of inequality of variance in the one-way classification. *Ann. Math. Statist.* 25, 290–302.

Cohen, E. R., J. W. M. duMond, T. W. Layton, and J. S. Rollett. 1955. Analysis of variance of the 1952 data on the atomic constants and a new adjustment. *Rev. Mod. Phys.* 27, 363–380.

Hartley, H. O. 1950. The maximum *F*-ratio as a short-cut test for heterogeneity of variance. *Biometrika* 37, 308–325.

Mikiewicz, J. 1961. The estimate of the common mean from samples from normal populations with different variances. *Zastosowania Mat.* 6, 119–126.

Plackett, R. L. 1960. Models in the analysis of variance. *J. Roy. Statist. Soc.* 22B, 195–217.

Scheffé, H. 1953. A method for judging all contrasts in the analysis of variance. *Biometrika* 40, 87–104.

Tang, P. C. 1938. The power function of the analysis of variance tests with tables and illustrations for their use. *Statist. Res. Mem.* 2, 126–157.

Thompson, G. M., and M. Merrington. 1946. Tables for testing the homogeneity of a set of estimated variances. *Biometrika* 33, 296–304.

Welch, B. L. 1951. On the comparison of several mean values—An alternative approach. *Biometrika* 38, 330–336.

EXERCISES

3–1. The following data are C—C bond lengths in aromatic rings in six different compounds:

$$\text{I: } 1.414, \ 1.384, \ 1.403, \ 1.374, \ 1.409, \ 1.407$$
$$\text{II: } 1.367, \ 1.426, \ 1.363$$
$$\text{III: } 1.415, \ 1.379, \ 1.403, \ 1.405, \ 1.430, \ 1.437$$
$$\text{IV: } 1.400, \ 1.410, \ 1.390, \ 1.410, \ 1.380, \ 1.390$$
$$\text{V: } 1.420, \ 1.430, \ 1.350, \ 1.450, \ 1.440, \ 1.370$$
$$\text{VI: } 1.450, \ 1.420, \ 1.410, \ 1.410, \ 1.430, \ 1.450.$$

Test these groups for homogeneity of variance.

3-2. Assume equal variances, and test the hypothesis that the group means are equal for the data in Exercise 3-1.

3-3. Repeat Exercise 3-2, but assume that the variances may be unequal.

3-4. Establish 95% confidence limits for all contrasts between two means for the data of Exercise 3-1. Assume that the group variances are equal.

3-5. The Xe—O bond lengths in the perxenate ion in one compound are estimated to be 1.92, 1.88, 1.82, and 1.87, with estimated standard deviations (based on many degrees of freedom) of 0.03. In another compound, they are estimated to be 1.85, 1.86, and 1.81, with estimated standard deviations of 0.02. Test the following hypotheses

H_1: The bond lengths in the first compound are equal.
H_2: The bond lengths in the second compound are equal.
H_3: The mean bond lengths in the two compounds are equal.

3-6. Define w_i, x_{ij}, $\bar{x}_i$, $\bar{x}$ as in Section 3-5, and show that

$$\sum_{i,j} (x_{ij} - \mu)^2 = (\mu - \bar{x})^2 \sum_i w_i + \sum_{i,j} w_i(x_{ij} - \bar{x}_i)^2 + \sum_i w_i n_i (\bar{x}_i - \bar{x})^2.$$

How many degrees of freedom does each of these terms have? Show that each is distributed as χ^2.

3-7. In the one-way analysis of variance with equal numbers of observations and equal variances, show that the following two expressions for the between-classes sum of squares are equivalent:

$$n \sum_j (\bar{x} - \bar{x}_j)^2 \equiv \sum_{i<j} (\bar{x}_i - \bar{x}_j)^2.$$

3-8. Show that all the conclusions of Section 3-5 reduce to those of Section 3-3 when the sample sizes and variances are equal.

3-9. Treat the data of Example 3-4-1 by the method of Section 3-5, assuming that the variances have *known* ratios which are given by the variance estimates for the samples. Compare the significance levels with those of Example 3-5-2.

4

Method of Least Squares and Theory of Linear Hypotheses

4-1. METHOD OF LEAST SQUARES

In our preceding discussions, the importance of minimum variance estimates has been emphasized, one unbiased estimate of a population parameter being preferable to another if the first estimate has a smaller variance than the second. The *method of least squares* is an application of this idea to a multivariate problem.

We will present in this section the general theory of least squares, mainly in matrix notation, and illustrated with simple numerical examples. Detailed examples of applications to specific scientific problems are deferred until Chapter 6.

We suppose that experimental observation has given rise to n different quantities

$$f_1, f_2, \ldots, f_n \tag{1}$$

and further that each of these n observations is known to depend *linearly* on a set of $m \leqslant n$ parameters

$$x_1, \ldots, x_m. \tag{2}$$

There is in addition a random error e_i associated with each observation f_i, so that the *observational equations* may be written

$$
\begin{aligned}
f_1 &= a_{11}x_1 + a_{12}x_2 + \cdots + a_{1m}x_m + e_1 \\
f_2 &= a_{21}x_1 + a_{22}x_2 + \cdots + a_{2m}x_m + e_2 \\
&\cdots\cdots\cdots\cdots\cdots\cdots\cdots\cdots\cdots\cdots \\
f_n &= a_{n1}x_1 + a_{n2}x_2 + \cdots + a_{nm}x_m + e_n
\end{aligned}
\tag{3}
$$

The set of linear equations (3) may be expressed in matrix notation as

$$\mathbf{F}_{n,1} = \mathbf{A}_{n,m}\mathbf{X}_{m,1} + \mathbf{E}_{n,1} \tag{3a}$$

The matrix **A** of rank m is assumed to be known and is frequently called the *design matrix*. We assume that the physical problem is such that it is the values of the parameters **X** which are of importance. Our problem then is to obtain estimates $\hat{\mathbf{X}}$ for these parameters.

If the number of observations is equal to the number of parameters and if Eqs. (3) are consistent, we can of course solve for the unique values **X** which satisfy (3); the error terms **E** will be zero in such a case. Because of the experimental error associated with each f_i, we generally choose to make more observations than there are parameters. Such a procedure will allow us to obtain better estimates $\hat{\mathbf{X}}$ of the parameters **X** and at the same time to obtain estimates of the variances of these estimates. The condition $n > m$ expresses the fact that the parameters are "overdetermined." Because of the errors **E**, there will not in general be a unique solution for **X** in terms of a particular observed set of functions **F**. (The equations (3) with both **X** and **E** unknown have an infinite number of solutions.) One could of course select any m of the equations and solve for the m parameters, but what we seek is some sort of a best average solution.

We will assume that the errors e_i have a joint distribution with zero means, i.e.,

$$\mathcal{E}\{\mathbf{F}\} \equiv \mathbf{F}^0 = \mathbf{AX}, \tag{4}$$

and a variance-covariance matrix $\mathbf{M}_f$ of rank n:

$$\mathbf{M}_f \equiv \begin{pmatrix} \sigma_1{}^2 & \sigma_1\sigma_2\rho_{12} & \cdots & \sigma_1\sigma_n\rho_{1n} \\ \sigma_1\sigma_2\rho_{12} & \sigma_2{}^2 & \cdots & \sigma_2\sigma_n\rho_{2n} \\ \cdot & & \cdots & \cdot \\ \sigma_1\sigma_n\rho_{1n} & \sigma_2\sigma_n\rho_{2n} & \cdots & \sigma_n{}^2 \end{pmatrix}, \tag{5}$$

where

$$\sigma_i{}^2 \equiv m_{ii} = \mathcal{E}\{e_i{}^2\} = \text{var } (f_i) \tag{6}$$

and

$$\sigma_i\sigma_j\rho_{ij} \equiv m_{ij} = \mathcal{E}\{e_ie_j\} = \text{cov } (f_i, f_j). \tag{7}$$

Thus we see that one of our basic assumptions is that the errors e_i in the observations f_i are drawn from populations with finite second moments. It may be noted at this point that this is the only requirement and that the theory of least squares does not depend on the assumption that the errors follow a normal distribution, although the latter assumption is commonly and mistakenly believed to be necessary. It may be shown (Section 4–8) that there exist estimators

$$\hat{\mathbf{X}} \equiv \{\hat{x}_j\} \tag{8}$$

such that for any linear function of **X**,

$$L = \mathbf{G}_{1,m}\mathbf{X}_{m,1}, \tag{9}$$

the estimator

$$\hat{L} = \mathbf{G}\hat{\mathbf{X}} \tag{10}$$

is a minimum-variance unbiased estimator of L. The estimators $\hat{\mathbf{X}}$ with this property are independent of $\mathbf{G}$.

Example 4–1–1

Suppose that there are two parameters x_1 and x_2. The linear function (9) may be written

$$L = g_1 x_1 + g_2 x_2,$$

with the estimator (10)

$$\hat{L} = g_1 \hat{x}_1 + g_2 \hat{x}_2.$$

Further, if the estimators are unbiased, we have

$$\mathcal{E}\{\hat{L}\} = g_1 \mathcal{E}\{\hat{x}_1\} + g_2 \mathcal{E}\{\hat{x}_2\} \equiv g_1 x_1 + g_2 x_2 = L$$

and

$$\sigma^2(\hat{L}) = g_1{}^2 \sigma^2(\hat{x}_1) + g_2{}^2 \sigma^2(\hat{x}_2) + 2 g_1 g_2 \operatorname{cov}(\hat{x}_1, \hat{x}_2).$$

It is a remarkable fact that the values x_1 and x_2 which give rise to the minimum $\sigma^2(\hat{L})$ are independent of g_1 and g_2.

In Section 4–8 we will show that these estimators are identical with those obtained by a simple formalism due to Gauss, who treated the special case

$$\mathbf{M}_f \equiv \mathbf{I}, \tag{11}$$

i.e., the case of uncorrelated errors e_i with equal variances. Gauss' method of least squares calls for the minimization of the sum of squares

$$S = \sum_i (f_i - \hat{f}_i)^2, \tag{12}$$

where

$$\hat{\mathbf{F}} \equiv \mathbf{A}\hat{\mathbf{X}}. \tag{13}$$

If we define a matrix of residuals

$$\mathbf{V}_{n,1} \equiv \mathbf{F} - \hat{\mathbf{F}} \equiv \mathbf{F} - \mathbf{A}\hat{\mathbf{X}}, \tag{14}$$

minimization of S defined by (12) is equivalent to minimization of the quadratic form

$$S = \mathbf{V}'\mathbf{V}. \tag{15}$$

This suggests that the appropriate minimization problem in the case of a non-identity moment matrix is the minimization of

$$S = \mathbf{V}'\mathbf{M}_f{}^{-1}\mathbf{V}. \tag{16}$$

Using this approach, we proceed as follows:

$$\begin{aligned}
\mathbf{V}'\mathbf{M}_f{}^{-1}\mathbf{V} &= (\mathbf{F} - \mathbf{A}\hat{\mathbf{X}})'\mathbf{M}_f{}^{-1}(\mathbf{F} - \mathbf{A}\hat{\mathbf{X}}) \\
&= \mathbf{F}'\mathbf{M}_f{}^{-1}\mathbf{F} + \hat{\mathbf{X}}\mathbf{A}'\mathbf{M}_f{}^{-1}\mathbf{A}\hat{\mathbf{X}} - \mathbf{F}'\mathbf{M}_f{}^{-1}\mathbf{A}\hat{\mathbf{X}} - \hat{\mathbf{X}}'\mathbf{A}\mathbf{M}_f{}^{-1}\mathbf{F}. \quad (17)
\end{aligned}$$

Introducing the differential operator δ, we have the following condition for a minimum:

$$\delta(\mathbf{V'M}_f^{-1}\mathbf{V}) = 2(\delta\hat{\mathbf{X}})'(\mathbf{A'M}_f^{-1}\mathbf{A}\hat{\mathbf{X}} - \mathbf{A'M}_f^{-1}\mathbf{F}) = 0, \qquad (18)$$

giving rise to the so-called normal equations

$$(\mathbf{A'M}_f^{-1}\mathbf{A})\hat{\mathbf{X}} = \mathbf{A'M}_f^{-1}\mathbf{F}$$

or

$$\mathbf{B}\hat{\mathbf{X}} = \mathbf{A'M}_f^{-1}\mathbf{F}, \qquad (19)$$

where $\mathbf{B} \equiv \mathbf{A'M}_f^{-1}\mathbf{A}$ is known as the matrix of the normal equations. Equation (19) can be solved to obtain the required estimates $\hat{\mathbf{X}}$:

$$\hat{\mathbf{X}} = \mathbf{B}^{-1}\mathbf{A'M}_f^{-1}\mathbf{F}. \qquad (20)$$

It is remarkable that the problem of minimizing the generalized sum of squares of residuals gives rise to the same best values of $\hat{\mathbf{X}}$ as does the problem of minimizing the variance of an arbitrary linear combination of $\hat{\mathbf{X}}$. The *least-squares estimate* of $\mathbf{X}$ is the estimate which minimizes the variance of the estimate of *any* linear function of the parameters, and it is partly for this reason that the least-squares estimates are so important.

It should be emphasized again that the results of the least-squares treatment are independent of any severe restrictions on the distribution of errors in $\mathbf{F}$; it is required only that the second moments be finite. It is often mistakenly stated that the principle of least squares depends on a normal distribution of errors. This erroneous statement is perhaps due to the fact that, *if* normal errors are assumed, it can be shown that the principle of maximum likelihood leads to the same solution for the $\hat{\mathbf{X}}$ as does the principle of least squares. Thus, for normally distributed errors, the least-squares estimate is identical with the maximum-likelihood estimate. A similar result was found in Example 1–7–6 for the estimation of the mean in a univariate population from several samples.

Suppose now that we know $\mathbf{M}_f$ only to within a scale factor:

$$\mathbf{M}_f = \sigma^2\mathbf{N} \qquad (21)$$

and

$$\mathbf{M}_f^{-1} = \frac{1}{\sigma^2}\,\mathbf{N}^{-1}, \qquad (22)$$

where $\mathbf{N}$ is known but σ^2 is unknown. That is, we know the relative values of all the components of the variance-covariance matrix but not the absolute values. (This is an extension of the type of information needed for the analysis-of-variance model in Section 3–5.) We have then for the normal equations

$$\frac{1}{\sigma^2}\,\mathbf{A'N}^{-1}\mathbf{A}\hat{\mathbf{X}} = \frac{1}{\sigma^2}\,\mathbf{A'N}^{-1}\mathbf{F}. \qquad (23)$$

The σ^2 may be eliminated from both sides of the equation, and the solution is thus seen to be independent of the scale of the moment matrix. The matrix

$$\mathbf{P} \equiv \mathbf{N}^{-1} \tag{24}$$

is known as the *weight matrix*, and σ^2 is the variance of an observation of unit weight. Suppose, for example, that

$$\mathbf{M}_f = \sigma^2 \mathbf{I}. \tag{25}$$

The weight matrix is

$$\mathbf{I}^{-1} = \mathbf{I}, \tag{26}$$

and the weights for all observations are unity, while the variances are all equal to σ^2.

We shall see below that σ^2 may be looked upon as a parameter to be estimated and that the estimate has many of the characteristics of a goodness-of-fit parameter.

To reiterate the result of the least-squares treatment, we have

$$\hat{\mathbf{X}} = (\mathbf{A'PA})^{-1}\mathbf{A'PF}. \tag{27}$$

In non-matrix notation, we solve the linear equations

$$\sum_{j=1}^{m} b_{ij}\hat{x}_j = c_i, \quad i = 1, \ldots, m \tag{28}$$

where

$$b_{ij} = \sum_{k=1}^{n} \sum_{r=1}^{n} a_{ki}a_{rj}p_{kr} \tag{29}$$

and

$$c_i = \sum_{k=1}^{n} \sum_{r=1}^{n} a_{ki}f_r p_{kr}. \tag{30}$$

In case the weight matrix is diagonal, i.e.,

$$p_{ij} = 0 \quad \text{for} \quad i \neq j, \tag{31}$$

weights

$$w_i = p_{ii} \tag{32}$$

may be assigned to the individual equations. The definitions (29) and (30) reduce to

$$b_{ij} = \sum_{k=1}^{n} a_{ki}a_{kj}w_k \tag{33}$$

and

$$c_i = \sum_{k=1}^{n} a_{ki}f_k w_k. \tag{34}$$

This is equivalent to multiplying each of the observational equations (1) by the *square root* of the appropriate weight and treating the system as unweighted, i.e.,

$$a^*_{pq} = w_p^{1/2} a_{pq} \tag{35}$$

$$f^*_p = w_p^{1/2} f_p \tag{36}$$

$$b_{ij} = \sum_{k=1}^{n} a^*_{ki} a^*_{kj} \tag{37}$$

$$c_i = \sum_{k=1}^{n} a^*_{ki} f^*_k. \tag{38}$$

Errors in the Parameter Estimates. Now that the best least-squares values have been obtained as a solution of the normal equations, it remains to be shown that the variance-covariance or moment matrix for the derived estimates is equal to the inverse $\mathbf{B}^{-1}$ of the matrix of the normal equations. We may write the desired matrix as follows:

$$\mathbf{M}_x = \mathcal{E}\{(\hat{\mathbf{X}} - \mathbf{X})(\hat{\mathbf{X}} - \mathbf{X})'\} \tag{39}$$

Thus

$$\begin{aligned}
\mathbf{M}_x &= \mathcal{E}\{\mathbf{B}^{-1}\mathbf{A}'\mathbf{M}_f^{-1}(\mathbf{F} - \mathbf{F}^0)(\mathbf{F} - \mathbf{F}^0)'\mathbf{M}_f^{-1}\mathbf{A}\mathbf{B}^{-1}\} \\
&= \mathbf{B}^{-1}\mathbf{A}'\mathbf{M}_f^{-1}\mathcal{E}\{(\mathbf{F} - \mathbf{F}^0)(\mathbf{F} - \mathbf{F}^0)'\}\mathbf{M}_f^{-1}\mathbf{A}\mathbf{B}^{-1}.
\end{aligned} \tag{40}$$

But since

$$\mathbf{M}_f \equiv \mathcal{E}\{(\mathbf{F} - \mathbf{F}^0)(\mathbf{F} - \mathbf{F}^0)'\}, \tag{41}$$

we have

$$\begin{aligned}
\mathbf{M}_x &= \mathbf{B}^{-1}\mathbf{A}'\mathbf{M}_f^{-1}\mathbf{M}_f\mathbf{M}_f^{-1}\mathbf{A}\mathbf{B}^{-1} \\
&= \mathbf{B}^{-1}
\end{aligned} \tag{42}$$

as stated above.

Now since

$$\begin{aligned}
\mathbf{B} &= \mathbf{A}'\mathbf{M}_f^{-1}\mathbf{A} \\
&= \frac{\mathbf{A}'\mathbf{P}\mathbf{A}}{\sigma^2},
\end{aligned} \tag{43}$$

it follows that

$$\mathbf{M}_x \equiv \mathbf{B}^{-1} = \sigma^2(\mathbf{A}'\mathbf{P}\mathbf{A})^{-1}. \tag{44}$$

To obtain the moment matrix for the parameter estimates, either we must know σ^2, the variance of an observation of unit weight, in which case $\mathbf{M}_x$ is completely determined, or we must have an unbiased estimate of σ^2, in which case we will have unbiased estimates of the elements of the moment matrix. We shall see below that an unbiased estimate of σ^2 is indeed available from the results of the least-squares treatment.

Let us now examine the quantity

$$\mathcal{E}\{\mathbf{V}'\mathbf{P}\mathbf{V}\} \equiv \sigma^2\mathcal{E}\{\mathbf{V}'\mathbf{M}_f^{-1}\mathbf{V}\} \tag{45}$$

which is the generalized weighted sum of the squared residuals. Now

$$\mathbf{V}'\mathbf{M}_f^{-1}\mathbf{V} = \mathbf{V}'\mathbf{M}_f^{-1}(\mathbf{F} - \mathbf{A}\hat{\mathbf{X}}) = \mathbf{V}'\mathbf{M}_f^{-1}\mathbf{F} \tag{46}$$

since the equation

$$\mathbf{V}'\mathbf{M}_f^{-1}\mathbf{A} = \mathbf{0} \tag{47}$$

is equivalent to the statement of the normal equations. Further,

$$
\begin{aligned}
\mathbf{V'M}_f^{-1}\mathbf{F} &= (\mathbf{F'} - \hat{\mathbf{X}}'\mathbf{A'})\mathbf{M}_f^{-1}\mathbf{F} \\
&= \mathbf{F'M}_f^{-1}\mathbf{F} - \hat{\mathbf{X}}'\mathbf{A'}\hat{\mathbf{M}}_f^{-1}\mathbf{F} \\
&= \mathbf{F'M}_f^{-1}\mathbf{F} - \hat{\mathbf{X}}'\mathbf{B}\hat{\mathbf{M}},
\end{aligned}
\tag{48}
$$

which, again by use of the normal equations, may be shown to be equal to

$$
(\mathbf{F} - \mathbf{F}^0)'\mathbf{M}_f^{-1}(\mathbf{F} - \mathbf{F}^0) - (\hat{\mathbf{X}} - \mathbf{X})'\mathbf{B}(\hat{\mathbf{X}} - \mathbf{X}). \tag{49}
$$

We have thus shown that

$$
\begin{aligned}
\mathcal{E}\{\mathbf{V'M}_f^{-1}\mathbf{V}\} \\
= \mathcal{E}\{(\mathbf{F} - \mathbf{F}^0)'\mathbf{M}_f^{-1}(\mathbf{F} - \mathbf{F}^0)\} - \mathcal{E}\{(\hat{\mathbf{X}} - \mathbf{X})'\mathbf{B}(\hat{\mathbf{X}} - \mathbf{X})\}. \tag{50}
\end{aligned}
$$

This may be shown to result in

$$
\mathcal{E}\{\mathbf{V'M}_f^{-1}\mathbf{V}\} = n - m \tag{51}
$$

where n and m are the ranks of $\mathbf{M}_f^{-1}$ and $\mathbf{B}$ respectively.*

Thus,

$$
\mathcal{E}\{\mathbf{V'PV}\} = (n - m)\sigma^2, \tag{52}
$$

and an unbiased estimate of σ^2 is given by

$$
\hat{\sigma}^2 = \frac{\mathbf{V'PV}}{n - m}. \tag{53}
$$

Consequently an unbiased estimate of $\mathbf{M}_x$ is

$$
\hat{\mathbf{M}}_x = \frac{\mathbf{V'PV}}{n - m}(\mathbf{A'PA})^{-1}, \tag{54}
$$

or simply the inverse of the normal-equations matrix multiplied by the unbiased estimate of σ^2.

It should be carefully noted that none of these developments depends upon the assumption of normality for the distribution of errors in the f_i. It is required only that the f_i be unbiased finite variance estimates of the population means. *The least-squares estimate $\hat{\mathbf{X}}$ is the unbiased minimum-variance estimate of $\mathbf{X}$ regardless of the form of the distribution*, and an unbiased estimate of the matrix $\mathbf{M}_x$ is given by (54). We will, however, for

---

* If x_i $(i = 1, \ldots, n)$ are random variables with zero means and finite variances, with variance-covariance matrix $\mathbf{M}$ of rank n, then we may show that

$$
\mathcal{E}\{\mathbf{X'M}^{-1}\mathbf{X}\} = n.
$$

Proof:

$$
\begin{aligned}
\mathcal{E}\{\mathbf{X'M}^{-1}\mathbf{X}\} &\equiv \mathcal{E}\{\text{Trace } (\mathbf{X'M}^{-1}\mathbf{X})\} \\
&= \mathcal{E}\{\text{Trace } (\mathbf{XX'M}^{-1})\} \\
&= \text{Trace } \mathcal{E}\{\mathbf{XX'M}^{-1}\} \\
&= \text{Trace } \mathbf{MM}^{-1} \\
&= \text{Trace } \mathbf{I} \\
&= n.
\end{aligned}
$$

The result (51) follows from the fact that $\mathbf{F} - \mathbf{F}^0$ and $\hat{\mathbf{X}} - \mathbf{X}$ are random variables with zero means and with variance-covariance matrices with ranks n and m respectively.

the purpose of hypothesis testing, assume a normal error distribution. Furthermore, the estimate of σ^2 (53), although unbiased, has certain optimum properties if a distribution of the normal type is assumed. We have already pointed out that for the normal distribution the maximum-likelihood estimate coincides with the least-squares estimate.

Example 4–1–2

Suppose that two parameters, x_1 and x_2, are to be determined from three observations, f_1, f_2, and f_3, which are known to have the forms

$$f_1 = 3x_1 + x_2$$
$$f_2 = 2x_1 + x_2$$
$$f_3 = 3x_1 + 2x_2.$$

The observations are all found to have the value 4.0. It is assumed that the variances of the three measurements are equal, to $2^2 = 4$ for example, and that there is a correlation coefficient of 0.50 between the first two observations. The unnormalized moment matrix for the observations is thus

$$\mathbf{N} = \begin{pmatrix} 4.0 & 2.0 & 0.0 \\ 2.0 & 4.0 & 0.0 \\ 0.0 & 0.0 & 4.0 \end{pmatrix}.$$

The weight matrix is

$$\mathbf{P} = \mathbf{N}^{-1} = \begin{pmatrix} 0.3333 & -0.1667 & 0.0000 \\ -0.1667 & 0.3333 & 0.0000 \\ 0.0000 & 0.0000 & 0.2500 \end{pmatrix}.$$

We have further

$$\mathbf{F} = \begin{pmatrix} 4.0 \\ 4.0 \\ 4.0 \end{pmatrix} \quad \text{and} \quad \mathbf{A} = \begin{pmatrix} 3.0 & 1.0 \\ 2.0 & 1.0 \\ 3.0 & 2.0 \end{pmatrix}.$$

Making the necessary computations, we find

$$\mathbf{A'PA} = \begin{pmatrix} 4.583 & 2.333 \\ 2.333 & 1.333 \end{pmatrix}$$

and

$$\hat{\mathbf{X}} = (\mathbf{A'PA})^{-1}\mathbf{A'PF} = \begin{pmatrix} 1.00 \\ 0.75 \end{pmatrix}.$$

The matrix of residuals is

$$\mathbf{V} = \mathbf{F} - \mathbf{A}\hat{\mathbf{X}} = \begin{pmatrix} 0.25 \\ 1.25 \\ -0.50 \end{pmatrix},$$

and

$$\mathbf{V'PV} = 0.5000.$$

Since the number of observations is 3 and the number of parameters is 2, an unbiased estimate of σ^2 is

$$\hat{\sigma}^2 = \frac{\mathbf{V'PV}}{3-2} = 0.5000.$$

The estimated moment matrix for the parameters is then

$$\hat{\mathbf{M}}_x = \frac{\mathbf{V'PV}}{3-2}(\mathbf{A'PA})^{-1}$$

$$= \begin{pmatrix} 1.000 & -1.750 \\ -1.750 & 3.437 \end{pmatrix}.$$

The marginal standard deviations are estimated to be

$$\hat{\sigma}(x_1) = (1.000)^{1/2} = 1.000$$
$$\hat{\sigma}(x_2) = (3.437)^{1/2} = 1.854,$$

so that we might quote the results of the least-squares analysis as

$$\hat{x}_1 = 1.00, \qquad \hat{\sigma}_1 = 1.00;$$
$$\hat{x}_2 = 0.75, \qquad \hat{\sigma}_2 = 1.85.$$

However, the correlation matrix

$$\{\rho_{ij}\} = \begin{pmatrix} 1.00 & -0.94 \\ -0.94 & 1.00 \end{pmatrix}$$

has such a large off-diagonal term that it would seem inappropriate to quote the estimates of the marginal standard deviations without mentioning the high correlation. A large positive error in $\hat{x}_1$ is probable only if it is associated with a large negative error in $\hat{x}_2$.

4–2. GEOMETRICAL INTERPRETATION OF THE ERROR MATRIX

A geometrical interpretation of the error matrix is very useful and instructive. The quadratic form

$$S_0 = (\hat{\mathbf{X}} - \mathbf{X})'\mathbf{M}_x^{-1}(\hat{\mathbf{X}} - \mathbf{X}) \equiv \mathbf{\Delta'M}_x^{-1}\mathbf{\Delta} \equiv \mathbf{\Delta'B\Delta} \tag{1}$$

is the equation of a hyperellipsoid centered at the point $\mathbf{\Delta} = \mathbf{0}$ * or $\mathbf{X} = \hat{\mathbf{X}}$ in the m-dimensional parameter space. In most applications, the probability distribution function for the errors in the parameters will be a function of S_0 alone, so that the ellipsoid described by the above equation is an ellipsoid of constant probability.

Let us consider the ellipsoid for the special case of $S_0 = 1$; we will call this the ellipsoid of standard deviation. If we denote the elements of $\mathbf{\Delta}$ by δ_{ij}, the *projection* of this ellipsoid on the (x_1, x_2) plane is an ellipse given by the equation

$$\frac{\delta_1{}^2}{\sigma_1{}^2} + \frac{\delta_2{}^2}{\sigma_2{}^2} - \frac{2\rho_{12}}{\sigma_1\sigma_2}\delta_1\delta_2 = 1 - \rho^2{}_{12} \tag{2}$$

* The null matrix is denoted by $\mathbf{0}$.

The half-lengths of the projections of this ellipse on the two coordinate axes are the *marginal standard deviations* σ_1 and σ_2. Similarly, the marginal standard deviation for each parameter is the half-length of the projection of the entire hyperellipsoid on the associated coordinate axis. If δ_1 is fixed, we have

$$\mathcal{E}\{\delta_2 \mid \delta_1\} = \rho_{12}\frac{\sigma_2}{\sigma_1}\delta_1 \equiv -\frac{b_{21}}{b_{22}}\delta_1 \qquad (3)$$

Thus the conditional expected value of δ_2 lies on the line with slope $\rho_{12}\sigma_2/\sigma_1$ denoted B in Figure 4–1. This line is called the *regression line* of δ_2 on δ_1.

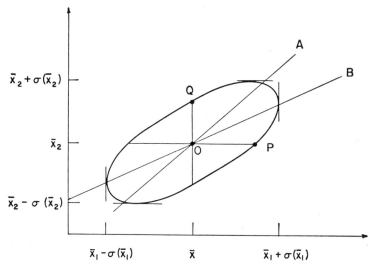

Fig. 4–1. Ellipse of standard deviation for two correlated parameters. The projections of the ellipse on the axes are the marginal standard deviations. The segments OQ and OP are the conditional standard deviations $\sigma(x_2 \mid x_1)$ and $\sigma(x_1 \mid x_2)$.

Similarly, the line with slope $(1/\rho_{12})\sigma_2/\sigma_1$, denoted A in the figure, is the regression line of δ_1 on δ_2. The *conditional standard deviation* of δ_2, $\sigma_{2|1}$ is equal to half the length of the line segment parallel to the δ_2 axis and terminated by the ellipse. This conditional standard deviation is independent of the value of δ_1.

In general, for the m-dimensional case, we may write

$$\mathcal{E}\{\delta_1 \mid \delta_2, \ldots, \delta_m\} \equiv \delta_{1|2 \ldots m}$$

$$= \sum_{j \neq 1} -\frac{b_{1j}}{b_{11}}x_j. \qquad (4)$$

The quantities $(-b_{ij}/b_{11})$ are known as the partial regression coefficients of x_1 on x_j. Similarly, the conditional variance is given by

$$\mathcal{E}\{\delta_1{}^2 \mid \delta_2, \ldots, \delta_m\} \equiv \sigma^2{}_{1|2\ldots m} = \frac{1}{b_{11}}. \tag{5}$$

The conditional variance is always less than the marginal variance unless the correlation of x_1 with x_j is zero for all values of j, in which case the marginal and conditional variances are equal.

A more detailed discussion of the probability distribution itself must await the introduction of a specific distribution function for the errors in the observations.

By finding the orthogonal transformation which diagonalizes the matrix $\mathbf{M}_x^{-1} \equiv \mathbf{B}$, one finds linear combinations $\mathbf{\Delta}_1$ of the parameter estimates $\mathbf{\Delta}_0$ which have mutual covariances equal to zero, a sufficient condition for statistical independence in the case of a multivariate normal distribution. The principal axes of the error ellipsoid will be parallel to the new parameter axes. If

$$\mathbf{TM}_x^{-1}\mathbf{T}' = \mathbf{D}, \tag{6}$$

where $\mathbf{D}$ is diagonal, then

$$\mathbf{\Delta}'_0\mathbf{M}_x^{-1}\mathbf{\Delta}_0 \equiv \mathbf{\Delta}'_1\mathbf{D}\mathbf{\Delta}_1 = \mathbf{\Delta}'_1\mathbf{TM}_x^{-1}\mathbf{T}'\mathbf{\Delta}_1 \tag{7}$$

and

$$\mathbf{\Delta}_1 = \mathbf{T}'^{-1}\mathbf{\Delta}_0 = \mathbf{T}\mathbf{\Delta}_0, \tag{8}$$

since $\mathbf{T}$ is assumed to be orthogonal.

Since this diagonalization is carried out on the matrix $\mathbf{B}$, it is unnecessary actually to carry out the least-squares solution to determine which linear combinations of parameter estimates are independent in this sense.

4–3. MULTIVARIATE NORMAL DISTRIBUTION AND DISTRIBUTION PROPERTIES OF QUADRATIC FORMS

Although the developments of Section 4–1 show that the best parameter values and estimated variances can be derived without specific assumptions regarding the error distribution function, it is clear that for the establishment of confidence limits and the testing of hypotheses such assumptions must be made. For reasons which have been made clear earlier, we will devote most of our attention to distributions related to the normal distribution function.

The m-dimensional multivariate normal density function with zero means can be written

$$\phi(\mathbf{X}) = C \exp\left(-\tfrac{1}{2}\mathbf{X}'\mathbf{M}^{-1}\mathbf{X}\right) \tag{1}$$

with

$$C = \frac{[\det(\mathbf{M}^{-1})]^{1/2}}{(2\pi)^{m/2}}. \tag{2}$$

It can be shown that the matrix $\mathbf{M}^{-1}$ in the exponential quadratic form is the inverse of the variance-covariance matrix simply by performing the appropriate integrals, e.g.,

$$\{\text{cov}\,(x_i,\,x_j)\} = C \int_{-\infty}^{+\infty} \cdots \int_{-\infty}^{+\infty} \mathbf{XX}' \exp\left(-\tfrac{1}{2}\mathbf{X}'\mathbf{M}^{-1}\mathbf{X}\right) dx_1 \cdots dx_m. \quad (3)$$

Let

$$\mathbf{X} = \mathbf{TY} \quad (4)$$

such that

$$\mathbf{X}'\mathbf{M}^{-1}\mathbf{X} \equiv \mathbf{Y}'\mathbf{Y}. \quad (5)$$

Then

$$\{\text{cov}\,(x_i,\,x_j)\} = \frac{1}{(2\pi)^{m/2}} \int_{-\infty}^{+\infty} \cdots \int_{-\infty}^{+\infty} \mathbf{TYY}'\mathbf{T}' e^{-\mathbf{Y}'\mathbf{Y}/2}\, dy_1 \cdots dy_m$$

$$= \mathbf{T}\left[\frac{1}{(2\pi)^{m/2}} \int_{-\infty}^{+\infty} \cdots \int_{-\infty}^{+\infty} \mathbf{YY}' e^{-\mathbf{Y}'\mathbf{Y}/2}\, dy_1 \cdots dy_m\right]\mathbf{T}'. \quad (6)$$

But the matrix enclosed in the brackets in (6) is the identity matrix, since the variables y_k are independent. Hence

$$\mathcal{E}\{\mathbf{XX}'\} = \{\text{cov}\,(x_i,\,x_j)\} = \mathbf{TIT}' = \mathbf{TT}'. \quad (7)$$

But

$$\mathbf{TT}' = \mathbf{M} \quad (8)$$

and thus

$$\{\text{cov}\,(x_i,\,x_j)\} = \mathbf{M}. \quad (9)$$

We will be interested in the probability distribution of the quadratic form

$$\mathbf{X}'\mathbf{M}^{-1}\mathbf{X}. \quad (10)$$

Making the linear transformation

$$\mathbf{Y} = \mathbf{TX}, \quad (11)$$

we have

$$\mathbf{X}'\mathbf{M}^{-1}\mathbf{X} = \mathbf{Y}'\mathbf{Y} = y_1^2 + y_2^2 + \cdots y_m^2. \quad (12)$$

The quadratic form of interest is the sum of m unit normal deviates and is thus distributed as χ^2 with m degrees of freedom.

If we consider the multivariate normal distribution with non-zero means,

$$\phi(\mathbf{X}) = \frac{(\det \mathbf{M}^{-1})^{1/2}}{(2\pi)^{m/2}} \exp\left[-\tfrac{1}{2}(\mathbf{X} - \mu)'\mathbf{M}^{-1}(\mathbf{X} - \mu)\right], \quad (13)$$

we can show in a similar manner that the quadratic form

$$\mathbf{X}'\mathbf{M}^{-1}\mathbf{X} \quad (14)$$

is distributed as non-central χ^2 with non-centrality parameter

$$\xi^2 = \mu'\mathbf{M}^{-1}\mu. \quad (15)$$

When μ is zero, the non-centrality parameter vanishes and the distribution reduces to that of ordinary χ^2 as derived in the preceding paragraph.

It is useful to note that a general quadratic form $\mathbf{X'RX}$ of rank q and order m follows the χ^2 distribution with q degrees of freedom if and only if the quadratic form

$$\mathbf{X'(M^{-1} - R)X} \tag{16}$$

is of rank $m - q$.

4–4. DISTRIBUTION OF QUADRATIC FORMS ARISING FROM THE LEAST-SQUARES PROBLEM

Given a quadratic form $\mathbf{X'BX}$ of rank m, let us further assume that the x_i are subject to p linearly independent linear restraints:

$$\mathbf{Q}_{p,m}\mathbf{X}_{m,1} = \mathbf{0}_{p,1}. \tag{1}$$

Under these circumstance, $\mathbf{X'BX}$ has the χ^2 distribution with $m - p$ degrees of freedom, since there are now only $m - p$ rather than m independent variables x_i.

Let us now consider the quadratic form

$$\mathbf{V'M}_f{}^{-1}\mathbf{V} \tag{2}$$

where $\mathbf{V}$ is the matrix of residuals from the least-squares fit. We have seen in Eq. (47) of Section 4–1 that

$$\mathbf{V'M}_f{}^{-1}\mathbf{A} = \mathbf{0}, \tag{3}$$

and, making the identification

$$\mathbf{Q'} = \mathbf{M}_f{}^{-1}\mathbf{A}, \tag{4}$$

we have

$$\mathbf{QV} = 0. \tag{5}$$

The matrix $\mathbf{Q}$ is of rank m; hence

$$\mathbf{V'M}_f{}^{-1}\mathbf{V} \tag{6}$$

is distributed as $\chi^2{}_{n-m}$. Since

$$\mathcal{E}\{\chi^2{}_n\} = n, \tag{7}$$

we are not surprised to see for the special case of the normal distribution what we have proved for the general case:

$$\mathcal{E}\{\mathbf{V'M}_f{}^{-1}\mathbf{V}\} = n - m. \tag{8}$$

Thus

$$\hat{\sigma}^2 = \frac{\mathbf{V'PV}}{n - m}, \tag{9}$$

our unbiased estimate of σ^2, is distributed as

$$\sigma^2 \frac{\chi^2{}_{n-m}}{n - m}. \tag{10}$$

We have seen above that

$$\mathbf{V'M}_f{}^{-1}\mathbf{V} = (\mathbf{F} - \mathbf{F}^0)'\mathbf{M}_f{}^{-1}(\mathbf{F} - \mathbf{F}^0) - (\hat{\mathbf{X}} - \mathbf{X})'\mathbf{B}(\hat{\mathbf{X}} - \mathbf{X}). \tag{11}$$

Since $(\mathbf{F} - \mathbf{F}^0)'\mathbf{M}_f^{-1}(\mathbf{F} - \mathbf{F}^0)$ is distributed as χ^2_n and $\mathbf{V}'\mathbf{M}_f^{-1}\mathbf{V}$ is distributed as χ^2_{n-m}, it follows that $(\hat{\mathbf{X}} - \mathbf{X})'\mathbf{B}(\hat{\mathbf{X}} - \mathbf{X})$ is distributed as χ^2_m, which follows also from the fact that $\mathbf{B}$ is of rank m if the least-squares problem possesses a solution. We could thus test deviations from the best least-squares values for the parameters by the use of a χ^2 test if σ^2, the absolute scale of the variance-covariance matrix, were known. More frequently, however, as we have indicated above, σ^2 is estimated by $\hat{\sigma}^2$, the goodness-of-fit parameter, and another course must be taken.

Denoting, as before, the estimated moment matrix for the parameters by

$$\hat{\mathbf{M}}_x \equiv \hat{\sigma}^2(\mathbf{A}'\mathbf{P}\mathbf{A})^{-1}, \tag{12}$$

we seek the distribution of

$$(\hat{\mathbf{X}} - \mathbf{X})'\hat{\mathbf{M}}_x^{-1}(\hat{\mathbf{X}} - \mathbf{X}). \tag{13}$$

We know that

$$\mathbf{P} = \sigma^2\mathbf{M}_f^{-1} \tag{14}$$

so that

$$(\hat{\mathbf{X}} - \mathbf{X})'\hat{\mathbf{M}}_x^{-1}(\hat{\mathbf{X}} - \mathbf{X}) = (\hat{\mathbf{X}} - \mathbf{X})'\mathbf{B}(\hat{\mathbf{X}} - \mathbf{X})\frac{\sigma^2}{\hat{\sigma}^2}. \tag{15}$$

Now since $\hat{\sigma}^2$ is distributed as $\sigma^2\chi^2_{n-m}/(n - m)$ independently of $(\hat{\mathbf{X}} - \mathbf{X})'\mathbf{B}(\hat{\mathbf{X}} - \mathbf{X})$, we find that

$$\frac{(\hat{\mathbf{X}} - \mathbf{X})'\hat{\mathbf{M}}_x^{-1}(\hat{\mathbf{X}} - \mathbf{X})}{m} \tag{16}$$

is distributed as

$$\frac{\chi^2_m/m}{\chi^2_{n-m}/(n - m)} \equiv F_{m,n-m}. \tag{17}$$

Thus in order to test the hypothesis

$$H_0\colon \mathbf{X} = \mathbf{X}_H \tag{18}$$

we compute the quantity

$$\frac{S_H}{m} = \frac{1}{m}(\hat{\mathbf{X}} - \mathbf{X}_H)'\hat{\mathbf{M}}_x^{-1}(\hat{\mathbf{X}} - \mathbf{X}_H) \tag{19}$$

and test as $F_{m,n-m}$. If S_H/m exceeds $F_{m,n-m,\alpha}$ we may reject the hypothesis H_0 at the α significance level. A generalization of this procedure will be presented in Section 4–6.

4–5. LINEAR LEAST SQUARES WITH CONSTRAINTS

Let us again solve the least-squares problem, but let us suppose that the x_i are not independent but are constrained to satisfy a set of linear equations,

$$\mathbf{Q}_{b,m}\mathbf{X}_{m,1} = \mathbf{Z}_{b,1}, \tag{1}$$

where the rank of $\mathbf{Q}$ is b. On introduction of Lagrange multipliers $\Lambda_{1,b}$, the variation function is

$$G = \mathbf{V}'\mathbf{M}_f^{-1}\mathbf{V} - 2\Lambda(\mathbf{QX} - \mathbf{Z}). \tag{2}$$

We have, letting $\bar{\bar{\mathbf{X}}}$ denote the least-squares estimates under the constraints,

$$\delta G = 2\mathbf{V}'\mathbf{M}_f^{-1}\delta\mathbf{V} - 2\Lambda\mathbf{Q}\,\delta\mathbf{X}$$
$$0 = 2[-\mathbf{F}'\mathbf{M}_f^{-1}\mathbf{A} + \bar{\bar{\mathbf{X}}}'\mathbf{B} - \Lambda\mathbf{Q}]\,\delta\mathbf{X} \tag{3}$$

and

$$\Lambda\mathbf{Q} = \bar{\bar{\mathbf{X}}}'\mathbf{B} - \mathbf{F}'\mathbf{M}_f^{-1}\mathbf{A}. \tag{4}$$

Here we note that

$$\mathbf{F}'\mathbf{M}_f^{-1}\mathbf{A} = \hat{\mathbf{X}}'\mathbf{B}, \tag{5}$$

where $\hat{\mathbf{X}}$ is the best least-squares solution without the constraints. Thus

$$\Lambda\mathbf{Q} = (\bar{\bar{\mathbf{X}}} - \hat{\mathbf{X}})'\mathbf{B}$$
$$\Lambda\mathbf{Q}\mathbf{B}^{-1}\mathbf{Q}' = (\bar{\bar{\mathbf{X}}} - \hat{\mathbf{X}})'\mathbf{Q}'$$
$$= \mathbf{Z}' - \hat{\mathbf{X}}'\mathbf{Q}'. \tag{6}$$

Thus

$$\Lambda = (\mathbf{Z}' - \hat{\mathbf{X}}'\mathbf{Q}')(\mathbf{Q}\mathbf{B}^{-1}\mathbf{Q}')^{-1}. \tag{7}$$

Eliminating Λ from (6) and (7), we obtain

$$(\bar{\bar{\mathbf{X}}} - \hat{\mathbf{X}})'\mathbf{B} = (\mathbf{Z}' - \hat{\mathbf{X}}'\mathbf{Q}')(\mathbf{Q}\mathbf{B}^{-1}\mathbf{Q}')^{-1}\mathbf{Q}$$

or

$$\bar{\bar{\mathbf{X}}}' = \hat{\mathbf{X}}' + (\mathbf{Z}' - \hat{\mathbf{X}}'\mathbf{Q}')(\mathbf{Q}\mathbf{B}^{-1}\mathbf{Q}')^{-1}\mathbf{Q}\mathbf{B}^{-1}. \tag{8}$$

We may again, of course, use the unscaled matrix $\mathbf{A}'\mathbf{PA}$ rather than $\mathbf{B}$ in the solution of the equations (8).

Since the variance-covariance matrix for $\hat{\mathbf{X}}$ is $\mathbf{B}^{-1}$, we find that the variance-covariance matrix for $\bar{\bar{\mathbf{X}}}$ is

$$\mathbf{M}_x = \mathbf{B}^{-1} - \mathbf{B}^{-1}\mathbf{Q}'(\mathbf{Q}\mathbf{B}^{-1}\mathbf{Q}')^{-1}\mathbf{Q}\mathbf{B}^{-1}. \tag{9}$$

The weighted sum of squares of residuals under the constraints is given by

$$R_Q = \mathbf{V}'\mathbf{PV} + (\bar{\bar{\mathbf{X}}} - \hat{\mathbf{X}})'(\mathbf{A}'\mathbf{PA})(\bar{\bar{\mathbf{X}}} - \hat{\mathbf{X}}), \tag{10}$$

where $\mathbf{V}$ is the matrix of residuals without the constraints, i.e., $\mathbf{V} = \mathbf{F} - \mathbf{A}\hat{\mathbf{X}}$. The expected value of R_Q is $(n - m + b)\sigma^2$. The second term on the right-hand side of (10) may be written

$$R_H = R_Q - R_0, \tag{11}$$

where

$$R_0 = \mathbf{V}'\mathbf{PV} \tag{12}$$

is the unconditional least sum of squares, and R_H is the additional sum of squares due to the constraints. A simple manipulation shows that

$$R_H = (\mathbf{Z} - \mathbf{Q}\hat{\mathbf{X}})'(\mathbf{Q}(\mathbf{A}'\mathbf{PA})^{-1}\mathbf{Q}')^{-1}(\mathbf{Z} - \mathbf{Q}\hat{\mathbf{X}}). \tag{13}$$

Examination of (13) indicates that it is not necessary actually to carry out the solution of (8) for $\overline{\overline{\mathbf{X}}}$ in order to calculate the value of R_H for any set of constraints (1).

4–6. MULTIVARIATE LINEAR HYPOTHESES

We are now in a position to use some of the results of the preceding section in the testing of hypotheses and the setting of confidence limits on the values of the least-squares parameters. Some of these we have already discussed. We have shown above that

$$\frac{1}{m}(\hat{\mathbf{X}} - \mathbf{X})'\hat{\mathbf{M}}_x^{-1}(\hat{\mathbf{X}} - \mathbf{X}) \tag{1}$$

is distributed as $F_{m,n-m}$. Thus a multivariate confidence region is given by the ellipsoid

$$(\hat{\mathbf{X}} - \mathbf{X})\hat{\mathbf{M}}_x^{-1}(\hat{\mathbf{X}} - \mathbf{X}) = mF_{m,n-m,\alpha}. \tag{2}$$

The probability that this region does not include the true value of $\mathbf{X}$ is α. A more general formulation for the discussion of various hypotheses follows.

Let us consider a general hypothesis which says something about the values of the parameters, either all of them or a subset of them. We will confine ourselves to the *linear hypothesis*, which may be written

$$\mathbf{Q}_{b,m}\mathbf{X}_{m,1} = \mathbf{Z}_{b,1}. \tag{3}$$

The *rank* of the hypothesis is the rank of $\mathbf{Q}$, which we assume to be $b \leq m$. The null hypothesis is that the true values of the $\mathbf{X}$ satisfy these equations. It seems reasonable to test the hypothesis by comparing the least sum of squares of residuals when H_0 is true to the least sum of squares when no restrictions are placed on the solution. Application of the results of the preceding sections show that when H_0 is true, the additional sum of squares due to the hypothesis,

$$R_H = R_Q - R_0, \tag{4}$$

is distributed as $\sigma^2\chi^2{}_b$, independently of R_0. R_0 is distributed as $\sigma^2\chi^2{}_{n-m}$. Hence the ratio of the two,

$$\frac{R_H}{R_0} = \frac{R_Q - R_0}{R_0} \tag{5}$$

is distributed as

$$\frac{b}{n-m}F_{b,n-m}.^* \tag{6}$$

As is the case with Student's t, the distribution of the ratio R_H/R_0 is independent of σ^2 and hence of the scale of the weight matrix.

We have seen above that

$$R_H = (\mathbf{Z} - \mathbf{Q}\hat{\mathbf{X}})'(\mathbf{Q}(\mathbf{A}'\mathbf{PA})^{-1}\mathbf{Q}')^{-1}(\mathbf{Z} - \mathbf{Q}\hat{\mathbf{X}}). \tag{7}$$

* It is important to note that R_Q/R_0 is *not* distributed as a variance ratio, since R_Q and R_0 are not *independently* distributed as χ^2 variates.

Furthermore,

$$R_0 = \mathbf{V'PV} = (n - m)\hat{\sigma}^2 \tag{8}$$

where $\hat{\sigma}^2$ is the unbiased estimate of σ^2 when there are no restraints. Thus

$$\frac{R_H}{R_0} = \frac{(\mathbf{Z} - \mathbf{Q\hat{X}})'(\mathbf{Q(A'PA)}^{-1}\mathbf{Q'})^{-1}(\mathbf{Z} - \mathbf{Q\hat{X}})}{(n - m)\hat{\sigma}^2} \tag{9}$$

But

$$\frac{\mathbf{A'PA}}{\hat{\sigma}^2} \equiv \hat{\mathbf{M}}_x^{-1} \tag{10}$$

so that

$$\frac{n - m}{b} \frac{R_H}{R_0} = \frac{(\mathbf{Z} - \mathbf{Q\hat{X}})'(\mathbf{Q\hat{M}}_x\mathbf{Q'})^{-1}(\mathbf{Z} - \mathbf{Q\hat{X}})}{b} \tag{11}$$

is distributed as $F_{b,n-m}$. We reject the hypothesis if the computed value of this quantity exceeds the tabulated value of $F_{b,n-m,\alpha}$.

One of the commonest tests to be made is that of the hypothesis that the entire set of parameters derived from the least-squares procedure is compatible with some theoretical model. Let the theoretical model have parameters $\mathbf{X}^T$. The null hypothesis is

$$H_0: \mathbf{X} = \mathbf{X}^T \tag{12}$$

i.e.,

$$\begin{aligned} x_1 &= x_1{}^T \\ x_2 &= x_2{}^T \\ &\cdots\cdots \\ x_m &= x_m{}^T. \end{aligned} \tag{13}$$

This corresponds to the identification of the matrices $\mathbf{Q}$ and $\mathbf{Z}$ as

$$\mathbf{Q}_{m,m} = \mathbf{I}_{m,m} \quad \text{and} \quad \mathbf{Z}_{m,1} = \mathbf{X}^T. \tag{14}$$

The hypothesis is m-dimensional, and the quantity to be tested as $F_{m,n-m}$ is

$$\frac{(\hat{\mathbf{X}} - \mathbf{X}^T)'\hat{\mathbf{M}}_x^{-1}(\hat{\mathbf{X}} - \mathbf{X}^T)}{m}. \tag{15}$$

This is a more general way of looking at the multivariate confidence region described in Section 4–6.

At the other extreme, we may wish to test a hypothesis about the value of a single parameter, regardless of what values the other parameters have. In this circumstance, taking x_1 as the parameter of interest, we have

$$\begin{aligned} \mathbf{Q} &= (1 \quad 0 \quad 0 \quad \cdots \quad 0) \\ \mathbf{Z} &= x_1{}^T. \end{aligned} \tag{16}$$

If the hypothesis

$$H_0: x_1 = x_1{}^T \tag{17}$$

is true, then

$$(n - m)\frac{R_H}{R_0} = \frac{(\hat{x}_1 - x_1{}^T)^2}{\hat{\sigma}_1{}^2}, \tag{18}$$

where $\hat{\sigma}_1^2$ is the estimated variance of x_1, is distributed as $F_{1,n-m}$. This is simply the square of the usual Student's t for $n - m$ degrees of freedom. Thus the confidence limits for a single parameter in the multivariate case are again given by Student's t, using the estimated *marginal variance* in the definition of t. The number of degrees of freedom is, as expected, the number of observations minus the number of adjusted parameters.

Many hypotheses of interest will of course have values of b lying between 1 and m.

Example 4–6–1

Let us consider some hypotheses concerning the parameters estimated in Example 4–1–2:

$$H_1: x_1 = 6.0$$
$$H_2: x_2 = 6.0$$
$$H_3: x_1 = 6.0, \quad x_2 = 6.0$$
$$H_4: x_1 = x_2$$

For hypotheses 1 and 2, we compute

$$\frac{(\hat{x}_i - x_i)^2}{\hat{\sigma}_i^2}$$

and test against $F_{1,1,\alpha}$. The calculated values are

$$\frac{5^2}{1} = 25 \quad \text{and} \quad \frac{5.25^2}{3.437} = 8.$$

$F_{1,1,0.05} = 161.45$, so that neither hypothesis can be rejected at the 5% significance level.

H_3 is a hypothesis of rank 2, and we thus test

$$\frac{(\hat{\mathbf{X}}^T - \hat{\mathbf{X}})'\hat{\mathbf{M}}_x^{-1}(\mathbf{X}^T - \hat{\mathbf{X}})}{2} = (5.00 \quad 5.25)\begin{pmatrix} 9.167 & 4.667 \\ 4.667 & 2.667 \end{pmatrix}\begin{pmatrix} 5.00 \\ 5.25 \end{pmatrix} \times \frac{1}{2}$$
$$= 253$$

against $F_{2,1,0.05} = 199.50$. The hypothesis may thus be rejected at the 5% significance level.

H_4 on the other hand merely specifies that the two parameters are equal, without specifying a common value. We have

$$\mathbf{Q} = (1 \quad -1)$$
$$\mathbf{Z} \equiv z = 0$$
$$\mathbf{Q}\hat{\mathbf{M}}_x\mathbf{Q}' = (1 \quad -1)\begin{pmatrix} 1.000 & -1.750 \\ -1.750 & 3.437 \end{pmatrix}\begin{pmatrix} 1 \\ -1 \end{pmatrix} = 7.937$$
$$\frac{R_H}{R_0} = \frac{(z - \hat{x}_1 + \hat{x}_2)^2}{7.937} = \frac{(0.25)^2}{7.937}$$
$$= 0.008.$$

The hypothesis can certainly not be rejected. We may set 95% confidence limits for the difference $x_1 - x_2 = z$ by setting

$$\frac{(z - 0.25)^2}{7.937} \leqslant 161.45,$$

or

$$|z - 0.25| < 35.8$$
$$-35.6 < x_1 - x_2 < 36.0.$$

It should be noted that the hypotheses not rejected were accepted on the basis of the large values of F characteristic of the one degree of freedom for the denominator. In other words, the estimate of σ^2 is extremely poor because the number of observations exceeded the number of parameters by only one. The confidence intervals for all the linear functions in the hypotheses would have been considerably shorter if there had been more degrees of freedom. For example, increasing the number of degrees of freedom from 1 to 2 results in an approximately 10-fold decrease in the value of F.

4–7. POWER OF THE VARIANCE-RATIO TEST FOR A MULTIDIMENSIONAL LINEAR HYPOTHESIS

To determine the power of the variance-ratio test which we have just been discussing, it is necessary to examine the distribution of

$$\frac{R_H/b}{R_0/(n - m)} \tag{1}$$

when the hypothesis is not true. The distribution of the denominator is that of a central χ^2 divided by the number of degrees of freedom whether or not the hypotheses is true. On the other hand, the denominator is distributed as central χ^2/b only if the hypothesis is true; otherwise it is distributed as non-central χ^2/b with the non-centrality parameter

$$\xi^2 = \theta'(\mathbf{QB^{-1}Q'})^{-1}\theta$$

$$= \frac{\theta'(\mathbf{Q(A'PA)^{-1}Q'})^{-1}\theta}{\sigma^2} \tag{2}$$

where

$$\theta = \mathbf{QX} - \mathbf{Z} \tag{3}$$

measures the departure from truth of the hypothesis. The statistic of interest is thus distributed as non-central F. One of the most important features of the distribution is that the power of the test for a given number of degrees of freedom always increases with the value of the non-centrality parameter ξ^2.

4–8. ALTERNATIVE DERIVATION OF THE LEAST-SQUARES NORMAL EQUATIONS

We present in this section a derivation of the least-squares normal equations from the point of view of minimizing the variance of an arbitrary linear function of the parameters. Although the material presented here is unnecessary for the use or understanding of the least-squares method, it does provide an interesting example of the application of the calculus of variations to a matrix equation.

We wish to minimize the variance of

$$\hat{L} = \mathbf{G}\hat{\mathbf{X}} \tag{1}$$

as an estimator of

$$L = \mathbf{GX}. \tag{2}$$

(See Section 4–1.) We proceed as follows: Let us define a matrix $\mathbf{H}$ such that

$$\mathbf{G}_{1,m} = \mathbf{H}_{1,n}\mathbf{A}_{n,m}. \tag{3}$$

This matrix is not unique. The problem of minimizing the variance of the linear function (1) is equivalent to that of minimizing the variance of

$$L = \mathbf{HF} \tag{4}$$

subject to the conditions (3). Given the matrix $\mathbf{G}$, we wish to determine $\mathbf{H}$ such that (3) is satisfied and $\mathbf{HF}$ has minimum variance as an estimator for L. We may write

$$
\begin{aligned}
\text{var } (\mathbf{HF}) &= \mathcal{E}\{(\mathbf{HF} - \mathbf{HF}^0)^2\}. \\
&= \mathcal{E}\{(\mathbf{H}(\mathbf{F} - \mathbf{F}^0))^2\} \\
&= \mathcal{E}\{\mathbf{H}(\mathbf{F} - \mathbf{F}^0)(\mathbf{F} - \mathbf{F}^0)'\mathbf{H}'\} \\
&= \mathbf{H}\mathcal{E}\{(\mathbf{F} - \mathbf{F}^0)(\mathbf{F} - \mathbf{F}^0)'\}\mathbf{H}' \\
&= \mathbf{H}\mathbf{M}_f\mathbf{H}'
\end{aligned} \tag{5}
$$

by definition.

Because of the restraint

$$\mathbf{HA} = \mathbf{G} \tag{6}$$

we introduce a matrix of Lagrange multipliers $\boldsymbol{\Lambda}_{1,m}$ and state the minimization problem as follows:

$$\delta[\mathbf{H}\mathbf{M}_f\mathbf{H}' - 2\boldsymbol{\Lambda}(\mathbf{A}'\mathbf{H}' - \mathbf{G}')] = 0. \tag{7}$$

The solution follows as

$$
\begin{aligned}
2\mathbf{H}\mathbf{M}_f \, \delta\mathbf{H}' - 2\boldsymbol{\Lambda}\mathbf{A}' \, \delta\mathbf{H}' &= 0 \\
\mathbf{H}\mathbf{M}_f &= \boldsymbol{\Lambda}\mathbf{A}' \\
\mathbf{H} &= \boldsymbol{\Lambda}\mathbf{A}'\mathbf{M}_f^{-1}.
\end{aligned} \tag{8}
$$

Multiplying on the right by $\mathbf{A}$, we obtain

$$\mathbf{HA} = \boldsymbol{\Lambda}\mathbf{A}'\mathbf{M}_f^{-1}\mathbf{A} \tag{9}$$

or
$$\Lambda = \mathbf{HA}(\mathbf{A}'\mathbf{M}_f^{-1}\mathbf{A})^{-1}, \tag{10}$$
and
$$\mathbf{H} = \mathbf{HA}(\mathbf{A}'\mathbf{M}_f^{-1}\mathbf{A})^{-1}\mathbf{A}'\mathbf{M}_f^{-1}$$
$$= \mathbf{G}(\mathbf{A}'\mathbf{M}_f^{-1}\mathbf{A})^{-1}\mathbf{A}'\mathbf{M}_f^{-1}. \tag{11}$$

If we multiply (11) on the right by $\mathbf{F}$, we obtain
$$\mathbf{HF} \equiv \mathbf{G}\hat{\mathbf{X}} = \mathbf{G}(\mathbf{A}'\mathbf{M}_f^{-1}\mathbf{A})^{-1}\mathbf{A}'\mathbf{M}_f^{-1}\mathbf{F} \tag{12}$$
where
$$\hat{\mathbf{X}} = (\mathbf{A}'\mathbf{M}_f^{-1}\mathbf{A})^{-1}\mathbf{A}'\mathbf{M}_f^{-1}\mathbf{F} \tag{13}$$

is obtained, as before, by a solution of the normal equations:
$$(\mathbf{A}'\mathbf{M}_f^{-1}\mathbf{A})\hat{\mathbf{X}} = \mathbf{A}'\mathbf{M}_f^{-1}\mathbf{F}. \tag{14}$$

REFERENCES

AITKEN, A. C. 1934. On least squares and linear combinations of observations. *Proc. Roy. Soc. Edinburgh* A55, 42–47.

DWYER, P. S. 1945. A matrix presentation of least squares and correlation theory with matrix justification of improved methods of solution. *Ann. Math. Statist.* 16, 278–286.

GAUSS, C. F. 1873. Theoria combinationis observationum erroribus minimis obnoxiae. *Werke* (Göttingen), vol. 4, p. 393.

HOTELLING, H. 1931. The generalization of Student's ratio. *Ann. Math. Statist.* 2, 360–378.

PLACKETT, R. L. 1949. A historical note on least squares. *Biometrika* 36, 458–460.

RAO, C. 1959. Some problems involving linear hypotheses in multivariate analysis. *Biometrika* 46, 49–58.

EXERCISES

4-1. The following normal-equations matrix was found in a three-parameter least-squares problem:
$$\begin{pmatrix} 3.00 & 3.00 & 1.00 \\ 3.00 & 7.00 & 2.00 \\ 1.00 & 2.00 & 2.00 \end{pmatrix}.$$

The estimate of σ^2, $\mathbf{V}'\mathbf{PV}/(n - m)$, was 1.70. What are the estimated conditional standard deviations and correlation coefficients? What are the estimated marginal standard deviations and correlation coefficients? What is the equation for the ellipsoid of standard error? Plot the sections of this ellipsoid perpendicular to the axis corresponding to parameter number three.

4-2. Suppose that there is complete linear dependence of one parameter on another and one attempts to determine the least-squares estimates for the values of the parameter set. Is this linear dependence always obvious from inspection of the matrix of normal equations? If not, at which point will it become obvious? Discuss in terms of the theory of linear equations. What approach might be used to obtain a solution in such a case?

4-3. We have formulated the solution of the general least-squares problem in a way which demands that the moment matrix for the observations possess an inverse. Show that it is necessary only that the rank of this matrix be at least equal to the number of parameters, and formulate the normal equations in an alternative way which does not require the inverse to be found.

4-4. Suppose that a set of data is fit to a model with six linear parameters, with a resulting $\hat{\sigma}^2 = 3.2$. Suppose that the fit to another model, again with six parameters (none of which are the same), results in $\hat{\sigma}^2 = 1.6$. Common sense would lead us to prefer the second model over the first. This situation does not correspond to any problems we have considered in the linear hypothesis tests of this chapter, which always assume that the model is correct. Discuss this problem, and suggest possible methods for handling it. How would your arguments be influenced if there were three parameters in common between the two models?

5

Miscellaneous Topics

5-1. CHOICE OF WEIGHTS FOR LEAST-SQUARES TREATMENTS

The least-squares method derived in Chapter 4 demands that the weight matrix $\mathbf{P}$ be known to within a scale factor in order for a solution to be found. This is equivalent to a knowledge of the relative values of the elements of the variance-covariance matrix for the observations. The scale factor, σ^2, is of course estimated from the goodness of fit of the data to the model. In many practical cases, the weight matrix will be diagonal, so the requirement is that we know the relative variances of the individual observations.

In practice, we will have only *estimates* of the variances of the indivdual observations, and in the absence of any further knowledge regarding the distribution of errors in the populations from which the observations are drawn, these estimates may be taken as providing the best weights for the least-squares analysis. If these estimates are not the true population variances, some bias will be introduced into the estimates of the variances of the parameters. On the other hand, the estimates of the parameters themselves will be unbiased, provided only that the observations are unbiased. This follows from the fact that, regardless of the value of $\mathbf{M}$,

$$\varepsilon\{\hat{\mathbf{X}}\} = \varepsilon\{\mathbf{B}^{-1}\mathbf{A}'\mathbf{M}^{-1}\mathbf{F}\} = \mathbf{B}^{-1}\mathbf{A}'\mathbf{M}^{-1}\varepsilon\{\mathbf{F}\} = \mathbf{B}^{-1}\mathbf{A}'\mathbf{M}^{-1}\mathbf{F}^0 = \mathbf{X}. \quad (1)$$

As is the case for some of the analysis-of-variance models discussed in Chapter 3, these estimates, although unbiased, may not be the minimum-variance estimates of the parameters if the weights are not known with certainty.

One of the commoner mistakes in weighting is that of neglecting correlations between errors in the observations. If we assume a diagonal weight matrix, when in fact there are large correlations, the least-squares

solution, particularly the estimates of the variances of the derived parameters, may be seriously affected. If there is any knowledge whatsoever
concerning the correlations, it would seem prudent to include this in the
form of a non-diagonal weight matrix. The estimation of such correlations
may in some cases be quite simple—as simple as the estimation of the
variance. Example 1–6–14 provides a good illustration.

Example 5–1–1

Suppose that the number of electrons scattered from a gas is
measured at intervals of 0.01° in the scattering angle θ. The observation consists in measuring an intensity $I(\theta)$ at each such angle. It
is possible to use these observations as input to a least-squares
analysis to determine interatomic distances in the molecules of the
scattering gas. Now suppose that the principal errors in the data
arise from noise which has a typical wavelength which is several
hundredths of a degree in θ; i.e., the typical error might be some
event (electronic or photographic) such as would cause a single
observation to be too high, the next to be too high but not by so
much, and such that the error would have less and less effect on an
observation as the angle increases from the point of the initial event.
There would thus be a high correlation between the errors in successive points, but this would slowly die away. A possible model for the
correlation matrix would be

$$\rho_{ij} = \rho_{12}{}^{|i-j|}.$$

We would have for $\rho_{12} = 0.5$, for example,

$$\{\rho_{ij}\} = \begin{pmatrix} 1 & 0.5 & 0.25 & 0.125 & \cdots \\ 0.5 & 1 & 0.5 & 0.25 & \cdots \\ 0.25 & 0.5 & 1 & 0.5 & \cdots \\ 0.125 & 0.25 & 0.5 & 1 & \cdots \\ \cdots & \cdots & \cdots & \cdots & \cdots \end{pmatrix}.$$

If the correlation matrix is assumed to have this particularly simple
form, there are methods of actually estimating the value of ρ_{12}.* In
fact, the correlations in an electron diffraction experiment are generally not so simple. The best approach is to examine the results of
many least-squares fits to get an experimental estimate of the nature
and magnitude of the correlations characteristic of a particular
experimental technique.

The last statement of the preceding example is pertinent not only to the
problem of estimating correlations but to that of estimating variances as

---

* For example, Plackett, Chapter 7 (see Bibliography).

well. It is often much wiser to use estimates of population variances obtained from long experience in the experimental technique than it is to use variance estimates obtained simply from the measurements at hand. This is particularly true when the measurements are being based on extremely small samples, for there is the danger here that some weights will be greatly overestimated in comparison with others. As in the analysis of variance, estimates of the variances made with large numbers of degrees of freedom are more stable than estimates based on a very few degrees of freedom.

Example 5-1-2

Assume that the measured intensity of an x-ray diffraction spot, $I(hkl)$, has been shown to be subject to an average estimated standard deviation of $0.10 \times I(hkl)$. On a particular set of films, a number of spots have been measured twice and in general bear out the expectations regarding the magnitudes of the errors. The two readings for $I(101)$ were 5020 and 5010. The estimated standard deviation from this sample is $\sqrt{50}$. It would, however, seem unreasonable to assign a weight of $1/50$ to this observation in a least-squares treatment. It would seem far safer to use the weight of $(1/501.5)^2$, which is drawn from the over-all experience with the experimental technique. Of course, if such small estimated variances were repeatedly encountered, one would be inclined to revise his estimate of a standard deviation of $0.10 \times I$ for the intensity readings. Alternatively, he might suspect that there is some systematic error in his intensity readings.

It is the population variance that is important in determining the weights, and not the sample variance. Hence, if we have what we regard as a better estimate of the population variance than that which the sample variance provides, we should by all means prefer it over the sample variance.

Suppose that the moment matrix for the observations, hence the weight matrix, has been a bad choice. We might ask whether we can predict the effect that this will have on the outcome of the least-squares analysis and the subsequent hypothesis tests. A treatment of a specialization of this problem has been given by Watson (1955) and Watson and Hannan (1956). These treatments show that the confidence limits for linear hypotheses can be related in a rather complex fashion to the eigenvalues of the true variance-covariance matrix. Although this method may be applied to more complicated cases, it may be just as desirable to get a feeling for the effect of improper weighting schemes in a particular case by carrying out the least-squares analysis and making the desired hypothesis tests using a variety of weight matrices, some perhaps with rather unrealistic estimates. If the results of the hypothesis tests appear to be rather sensitive to the weights chosen, it would be wise to test these hypotheses at a higher significance level than one would customarily use. On the other hand, one might find that the hypothesis tests are rather insensitive to the weights, in which case he would be happily surprised and proceed to test the hypotheses with great confidence in the results.

Example 5–1–3

Suppose that sample variances are not attainable for any of the observations. If no other information is available as to the population variances, all the observations might be given unit weight. It should be noted carefully that such a scheme may not lead to reliable error estimates. On the other hand, if a particular weighting scheme has been shown to be appropriate for similar experiments in the past, it should by all means be used.

5–2. PROPAGATION OF ERROR

Suppose that we have obtained estimates of a set of parameters and their associated errors from a least-squares analysis and wish to make statements regarding the errors in linear functions of the derived parameters. This problem has been alluded to in earlier sections of the book but will be restated here for the sake of completeness.

Suppose that a multivariate distribution is specified in terms of the deviations from the mean; i.e., we consider a density function

$$\phi(\mathbf{G}) \equiv \phi(g_1, \ldots, g_n) \tag{1}$$

where the random variables g_i have zero means. A matrix of second moments $\mathbf{M}_g$ of rank n is also specified. If a set of related quantities f_i $(i = 1, 2, \ldots, m)$ is a set of linear functions of the g_i,

$$\mathbf{F}_{m,1} = \mathbf{T}_{m,n}\mathbf{G}_{n,1} \tag{2}$$

then

$$\mathbf{M}_f \equiv \mathcal{E}\{\mathbf{F}\mathbf{F}'\} = \mathcal{E}\{\mathbf{T}\mathbf{G}\mathbf{G}'\mathbf{T}'\} = \mathbf{T}\mathcal{E}\{\mathbf{G}\mathbf{G}'\}\mathbf{T}' = \mathbf{T}\mathbf{M}_g\mathbf{T}'. \tag{3}$$

Note again that it is not necessary that the distribution be normal, but only that the second moments exist. $\mathbf{F}$ may have more or fewer components than $\mathbf{G}$, or the same number. In any case, the rank of $\mathbf{M}_f$ is no greater than the rank of $\mathbf{M}_g$. If m is greater than n, the components of $\mathbf{F}$ will not be linearly independent, $\mathbf{M}_f$ will be singular, and the corresponding m-dimensional ellipsoid of error will be degenerate, that is, some of the principal axes will be of zero length.

As can be shown from the result of Example 1–5–6, if $\mathbf{G}$ has the multivariate normal density function:

$$\phi(\mathbf{G}) = C \exp \left(-\tfrac{1}{2}\mathbf{G}'\mathbf{M}_g^{-1}\mathbf{G}\right), \tag{4}$$

then $\mathbf{F}$ has the density function

$$\phi(\mathbf{F}) = C' \exp \left(-\tfrac{1}{2}\mathbf{F}'\mathbf{M}_f^{-1}\mathbf{F}\right), \tag{5}$$

provided that $\mathbf{M}_f$ is non-singular. These relations are useful when one wishes to calculate the errors of quantities of physical interest which are not those obtained directly from the least-squares analysis.

5–3. NON-LINEAR LEAST SQUARES

The treatment of least-squares and linear-hypothesis tests presented in Chapter 4, although elegant, does not usually fulfill the requirements of scientific problems, many of which are distinguished by their non-linearity. The set of functions f_i which we measure are usually non-linear functions of the parameters x_i which we are trying to estimate. In this section, we will show how such problems may be attacked and how the conclusions of some of the preceding sections may be changed.

Linearization of Non-linear Problems. In general we will have a set of n observable functions f_i of m parameters x_j:

$$f_i = f_i(x_1, \ldots, x_m), \quad i = 1, \ldots, n. \tag{1}$$

We can expand the function in a Taylor series about the point $(x_1^0, \ldots, x_m^0)$, the terms to first order being

$$f_i \approx f_i(x_1^0, \ldots, x_m^0) + \frac{\partial f_i}{\partial x_1}(x_1 - x_1^0) + \cdots + \frac{\partial f_i}{\partial x_m}(x_m - x_m^0) \tag{2}$$

or

$$f_i - f_i^0 \approx \sum_{j=1}^{m} \frac{\partial f_i}{\partial x_j}(x_j - x_j^0) \tag{3}$$

or

$$\Delta f_i = \sum_{j=1}^{m} \frac{\partial f_i}{\partial x_j} \Delta x_j. \tag{4}$$

If the expansion is valid, the problem has thus been reduced to one of linear form, where the design matrix $\mathbf{A}$ is now identified with the matrix of first partial derivatives of the functions with respect to the parameters, and the vector of observables $\mathbf{F}$ is identified with the deviations of the actual observed functions from the values of the functions at the expansion point. Thus,

$$\mathbf{A} \equiv \{a_{ij}\} \equiv \left\{\frac{\partial f_i}{\partial x_j}\right\} \tag{5}$$

$$\mathbf{F} \equiv \{\Delta f_i\} \tag{6}$$

$$\mathbf{X} \equiv \{\Delta x_j\}. \tag{7}$$

The procedure is then as follows: We first choose, as best we can, approximate values for the parameters x_j. These approximate values are the $x_j{}^0$. The values of the functions calculated for these approximate parameters are the $f_i{}^0$. The differences between the observed values of the functions and the calculated values

$$\Delta f_i \equiv f_i - f_i{}^0 \equiv f_i{}^{\text{obs}} - f_i{}^{\text{calc}} \tag{8}$$

play the role of the linear functions used in the least-squares treatments of Chapter 4. The least-squares equations are solved in the usual way to determine the Δx_j. Improved values of x_j are thus obtained as

$$x_j = x_j{}^0 + \Delta x_j. \tag{9}$$

Using these new x_j as approximate values in calculating new values for the f_i should result in better agreement than was the case previously. The agreement may not be as good as we wish, however, and the procedure is then repeated. If the problem being treated by least-squares is truly linear, the solution to the first set of normal equations gives the desired answer. In the non-linear problem, however, an iterative procedure must be used, for after the new parameter values are found, the derivatives, and hence the design matrix, will have changed. This iterative procedure is continued until the changes in the parameters are very small or zero. At this point the iterative least-squares procedure is said to have *converged*. This successive approximation to the best solution is sometimes known as a *refinement* of the parameters.

Each iteration in such a refinement is carried out exactly as for the linear case. As usual, the weights are chosen inversely proportional to the variances of the observations. The general procedure followed at the completion of the refinement is to assume that the errors in the parameters are again given by the inverse of the matrix of the normal equations, and linear hypotheses concerning the parameters or functions of the parameters are made and tested in the usual way. This is a procedure which must be carried out with some care, and the effects of non-linearity must be closely scrutinized. We will return to this point later in the section.

Let us now examine some of the steps in the non-linear least-squares procedure in somewhat greater detail.

Validity of the Taylor Expansion. The application of the least-squares method to non-linear problems is valid only insofar as the Taylor expansion is valid for the region of parameter values over which the refinement takes place. Two of the difficulties which can arise will now be described. Consider the function f_i, shown in Figure 5–1 plotted as a function of x_j. Suppose that the best fit to the data is given by a parameter set which includes the value a for x_j. The corresponding value of f_i is $f_i{}^{(a)}$, which for the sake of simplicity we will assume to be the observed value of f_i as well. Now if at some stage of the refinement the parameter has the value b

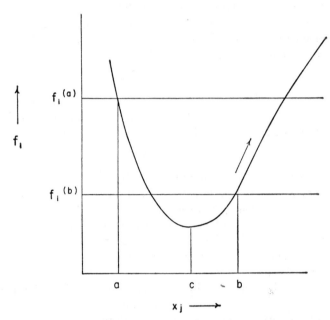

Fig. 5–1. A function f_i which depends non-linearly on a parameter x_j. If the correct value of x_j is a, and if at some iteration in the non-linear least-squares procedure x_j has the value b, then the inclusion of this function in the least-squares procedure will tend to make x_j move in the wrong direction, as indicated by the arrows.

with a corresponding value $f_i^{(b)}$ for the function, the Taylor expansion will tell us that the agreement will be improved by increasing x_j rather than by going toward a. It is true that the agreement for this function will be improved, but it is possible that the agreement for other functions may be worse. Thus in the refinement, this particular function will be working against the others. If it had a high weight, or if there were too many functions of a similar nature, it is possible, even probable, that the iterative least-squares procedure would never converge to a minimum-variance solution. It is likely that the procedure will converge to an incorrect solution which may well be a local minimum of the sum of squares of residuals.

Such a tendency for the refinement to converge to a false minimum for the sum of squares can sometimes be discovered by taking different initial values for the parameters. In fact, if there are few enough parameters, one can effectively eliminate this danger by starting with parameters chosen over the entire range of reasonable values (if this is indeed known) and testing to see whether the refinement always converges to the same point. The likelihood of convergence to the correct value depends in each case on

the detailed nature of the multiparametric error surface in the neighborhood of the initial point, but a general statement can be made that
convergence to the correct value is unlikely if there are changes in the
signs of the derivatives for too many of the observations. On the other
hand, if there are no changes of sign, convergence is almost always
assured.

These points are illustrated again in Figure 5–2, where another danger

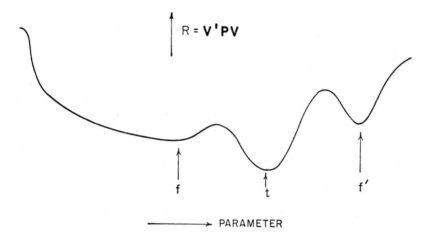

$$R = \mathbf{V'PV}$$

PARAMETER

Fig. 5–2. Schematic representation of the agreement factor as a function of a parameter set. The point t is the absolute minimum of the agreement factor, and it is pre-
sumably this parameter set which we seek in a problem in non-linear estimation. The
points f and f' however are local minima of the agreement factor, and if parameter sets
in the neighborhood of these points are chosen as the starting points for refinements, it
is likely that the true set will never be reached. In fact, using the Hartley modification
of the Gauss-Newton method, convergence to the "false minima" f and f' is assured.

is indicated. It may be that two greatly different sets of parameter values
will have the same, or close to the same, value of the sum of squares of
residuals. In the mathematical sense, either of these is an acceptable
solution, and one may reach one or the other depending on the choice of
an initial trial set. If such a situation is detected, the decision between
the two must come from areas outside those of statistics. In most cases,
one is forced to ask the question as to which is physically the more reasonable and be honest enough to admit that the experiment gave an ambiguous
answer.

Another difficulty arises if the initial value is at an extremum of the
function with respect to a parameter, e.g., the point c in Figure 5–1. The
first derivative vanishes at this point, and the Taylor expansion taken to
the first term only indicates (incorrectly) that the agreement can be

neither improved nor worsened by changes in this parameter. If this situation holds for only a few of the total number of functions, no particular difficulty in the refinement is expected. On the other hand, if all the functions exhibit extrema for this particular parameter value, and if the least-squares procedure is carried out blindly, as it often is, unfortunately, on large problems, the resulting matrix of normal equations is singular, and no solution exists.

One possible solution of the problem is as follows: The functions f_i may now be expressed as

$$f_i = f_i{}^0 + \sum_{k \neq j} \frac{\partial f_i}{\partial x_k} \Delta x_k + \frac{1}{2} \frac{\partial^2 f_i}{\partial x_j{}^2} (\Delta x_j)^2. \tag{10}$$

If all the functions are of this form, we may treat $(\Delta x_j)^2$ as the parameter to be estimated and proceed as usual, using the second derivatives with respect to x_j in the design matrix. When attempting such a solution, one can obtain the embarrassing result that the estimated $(\Delta x_j)^2$ is negative; this may mean that the true minimum for the sum of squares is at or very near the initial point, i.e., that Δx_j is really zero. If this is the case, the least-squares approach is not really applicable to this part of the problem, since the least-squares approach demands an extremum that lies within the region of possible parameter values. If parameter values are restricted to some region defined by inequalities, the methods of *linear programing* might be used to obtain a solution.

If only a few of the functions are of this particular type, but it is still desired to include them in the refinement, we may write

$$(f_i - f_i{}^0)^{1/2} = \pm \left(\frac{1}{2} \frac{\partial^2 f_i}{\partial x_j{}^2} \right)^{1/2} \Delta x_j + \cdots. \tag{11}$$

Unfortunately, we do not know whether the sign in the above equation should be positive or negative, so that in the initial stages of a refinement procedure these terms are best omitted. In the final stages of refinement, however, where the effort is usually directed toward estimation of the errors in the parameters, such terms may very well have a large effect. In some circumstances, small departures of the parameters from these special positions may cause large disagreements, and we should like this fact to be included in the error estimates. At this point in the refinement, the agreement will generally be fairly good, so that the $f_i - f_i{}^0$ will be small. The term may thus be included in the usual least-squares treatment in the form suggested by the above equation, and although the changes in the parameter values resulting from the inclusion of these terms should be small, our confidence in the parameter estimates should be increased because of the information which has been added.

Choice of Initial Parameter Values. It is clear from the above discussion that difficulties with the Taylor expansion are less likely to occur if the initial values of the parameters are as close as possible to the final or true values. We may thus inquire into the strategy to be used in fixing the initial values. In some cases, e.g., the classical refinement of the fundamental physical constants by DuMond and Cohen (1953), the choice of the initial values is obviously simplified. The previous best values were taken for the starting point, and the least-squares treatment was truly a refinement of quantities already well known. The same situation may well apply in many other experimental situations, where new data have been collected in order to obtain better values for parameters whose values are already known to a good approximation.

In most other cases, graphical, analytic, or intuitive methods will be used to obtain the initial values. If these values are known or suspected to be far from the correct values, a sensible strategy would seem to be as follows: In the initial refinement cycles, use only the functions which vary rather slowly with the parameter values if there are enough such functions for the analysis to be carried out. Omit at this stage the functions which vary rapidly with parameter value, as these are much more likely to give rise to the problem discussed above—that of being on the wrong side of a maximum or minimum in the function. As the refinement proceeds, these functions might be added, perhaps at first with small weight, then later with full weight. Since they are very sensitive to the exact parameter values, they are invaluable in a precise estimation of these values. On the other hand, assigning them too much weight early in the refinement could result in the attainment of a false minimum.

Convergence of Non-linear Least Squares. It cannot be shown that the non-linear least-squares procedure will always converge to even a local minimum of $\mathbf{V'PV}$, the weighted sum of squared residuals. Hartley (1961) has shown, however, that under certain rather general conditions convergence will always take place provided the following modification of the Gauss-Newton procedure described above is used: The least-squares normal equations are solved in the usual way to obtain corrections $\Delta\mathbf{X}$ to the parameter estimates. Now consider a scalar multiplier

$$0 \leqslant q \leqslant 1 \tag{12}$$

and let the corrected values of the parameter estimates be

$$\mathbf{X}_{\text{new}} = \mathbf{X}_{\text{old}} + q\,\Delta\mathbf{X}. \tag{13}$$

The value of the quadratic form $\mathbf{V'PV}$ will be a function of q. The starting set of parameters for the next iteration is that set (13) for which $\mathbf{V'PV}$ is a minimum as a function of q. Thus the usual solution gives the direction in parameter space of the correction, while a numerical minimization of $\mathbf{V'PV}$ gives the magnitude. In practice, a convenient way of determining the best value of q may be to calculate $\mathbf{V'PV}$ for $q = 0$, $\frac{1}{2}$, and 1 and fit a parabola to the results.

Even if a minimum is reached, it may or may not be the absolute minimum. The physical reasonableness of the parameters and a knowledge of the nature of the observed functions, e.g., their departures from linearity, their curvature, etc., will in many cases either convince one that the true minimum has been achieved or that there is, on the other hand, a strong possibility of difficulty.

As a practical point, difficulties in convergence may be experienced because of the limited accuracy of any digital computer. If the solution is far from any minimum, or if some correlation coefficients for the corrected parameters are very large, i.e., if the matrix of the normal equations is almost singular, the round-off errors even in a machine of rather large word-length may well be severe enough to cause the problem to become indeterminate.

Hypothesis Tests in the Non-linear Case. It has been pointed out in the preceding paragraphs that the non-linear least-squares procedure does often converge to the appropriate set of parameter values which minimizes the mean square error. The situation with regard to estimates of errors in the parameters and linear hypotheses concerning the parameters is not quite so straightforward.

If the estimated errors are small enough that the functions are truly linear over the range of several standard deviations in each parameter, the methods of testing linear hypotheses discussed in Chapter 4 can be applied in the same way. A normal distribution of errors in the observations will result in a normal distribution in the parameter estimates, and the variance-ratio (F) tests can be applied to the appropriate quadratic forms. If there are departures from linearity in this range, the tests will no longer be exact, and no general statement can be made about the effect on the hypothesis tests without knowing the exact nature of the functions.

We will frequently be interested in testing non-linear hypotheses of the form

$$Q_k(x_1, x_2, \ldots, x_m) = Z_k, \quad k = 1, 2, \ldots, b. \tag{14}$$

No satisfactory procedure for testing such a general hypothesis can be formulated in any meaningful way, so we again resort to a linearization of the problem. Let us expand Q_k in a Taylor series about the point $(x_1{}^0, \ldots, x_m{}^0)$:

$$Q_k - Q_k{}^0 = \sum_{i=1}^{m} \frac{\partial Q_k}{\partial x_i} (x_i - x_i{}^0) + \cdots. \tag{15}$$

Considering only the first term, the hypothesis has been reduced to a linear hypothesis, which we then test in the usual way, making the assumption that the variance-covariance matrix for the Δx_i is that derived from the least-squares treatment. It should be carefully noted that this linearization is in addition to the one for the expansion of the original observed functions in the Taylor series, and care must again be taken to ensure that the linearization is valid over the range of parameters likely to be involved in the hypothesis test. Such a range would probably be a few times the standard deviation for each parameter, or say within a concentric ellipsoid of error which has about three or four times the extent of the ellipsoid of standard deviation. Non-linear hypotheses about parameters obtained from a linear least-squares procedure are of course subject to the same restrictions.

If the hypothesis to be made is the especially simple one that assigns fixed values to all the parameters, we are making a linear hypothesis about parameters which have been determined from a non-linear observational situation. The validity of the linear hypothesis then depends only upon the validity of using the quadratic form $\mathbf{V'PV}/(n - m)$ as an estimate of σ^2 and on the invariance of the matrix $\mathbf{B} = \mathbf{A'PA}$ over the range of parameters considered in the hypothesis. In the non-linear case, it is certainly better actually to calculate $\mathbf{F}$, and hence $\mathbf{V}$, for the hypothesized parameters than to use the equation, valid for the linear case, that states

$$\mathbf{V'PV} = \mathbf{F'PF} - \hat{\mathbf{X}}'\mathbf{B}\hat{\mathbf{X}}. \tag{16}$$

In fact, the agreement between the values for $\mathbf{V'PV}$ obtained in the two ways may be used as a criterion of linearity over the parameter range of interest. It would perhaps be wisest to compute both and to use whichever one would cause us to err on the conservative side when testing the hypothesis. As is usual with the case of inexact tests, one may wish to make the test at a greater significance level than would be used if the problem were strictly suitable for the application of the methods used.

More accurate tests have been proposed for testing non-linear hypotheses, but these are often too complex to be used in practice, and of course they depend on the particular departures from non-linearity. In many physical problems, it is a satisfactory approach to use the tests for the linear case, but to use them with care, scrutinizing them especially for the effects of any non-linearity.

Beale (1960) has proposed a parameter for estimating a sort of average non-linearity. The value of this parameter may be used to assess the importance of non-linearity and to modify the usual confidence regions appropriately if the non-linearity is severe. A procedure such as Beale's has much to recommend it, but it does not appear to have been applied widely by physical scientists.

5–4. SIGNIFICANCE TESTS ON THE VALUE OF R

We consider here a statistic not commonly used in the statistical literature but one of considerable prominence among crystallographers. This is an agreement factor, or "R factor," defined in the following way: Given a set of observed functions

$$f_1^{\text{obs}}, \ldots, f_n^{\text{obs}} \tag{1}$$

and a set of calculated values for these functions

$$f_1^{\text{calc}}, \ldots, f_n^{\text{calc}} \tag{2}$$

based on some parameter set, the quantity

$$R' = \frac{\sum |f_i^{\text{obs}} - f_i^{\text{calc}}|}{\sum f_i^{\text{obs}}} \tag{3}$$

is a sort of average relative discrepancy between the observed and calculated values which is called the conventional R factor. More closely related to the statistical quantities of greatest utility is the generalized weighted R factor:

$$R = \left[\frac{\sum_i \sum_j (f_i^{\text{obs}} - f_i^{\text{calc}}) w_{ij} (f_j^{\text{obs}} - f_j^{\text{calc}})}{\sum_{i,j} f_i^{\text{obs}} w_{ij} f_j^{\text{obs}}} \right]^{1/2} \tag{4}$$

where w_{ij} is an element in the appropriate weight matrix. In the case of a diagonal weight matrix, this reduces to simply

$$R = \left[\frac{\sum_i (f_i^{\text{obs}} - f_i^{\text{calc}})^2 w_{ii}}{\sum_i (f_i^{\text{obs}})^2 w_{ii}} \right]^{1/2}. \tag{5}$$

In matrix notation, the generalized R factor defined by (4) is

$$R = \left[\frac{(\mathbf{F}^{\text{obs}} - \mathbf{F}^{\text{calc}})' \mathbf{P} (\mathbf{F}^{\text{obs}} - \mathbf{F}^{\text{calc}})}{(\mathbf{F}^{\text{obs}})' \mathbf{P} (\mathbf{F}^{\text{calc}})} \right]^{1/2}. \tag{6}$$

Suppose that a least-squares refinement of p parameters $\mathbf{X}$ has resulted in a best (in the least-squares sense) set of parameters $\hat{\mathbf{X}}$ with corresponding calculated function values $\hat{\mathbf{F}}^{\text{calc}}$. We wish to test the hypothesis

$$H_0 : \mathbf{X} = \mathbf{X}_1. \tag{7}$$

Let the function values calculated for the parameter set $\mathbf{X}_1$ be denoted by $\mathbf{F}_1^{\text{calc}}$, and define the residuals,

$$\begin{aligned} \mathbf{V}_0 &\equiv \mathbf{F}^{\text{obs}} - \hat{\mathbf{F}}^{\text{calc}} \\ \mathbf{V}_1 &\equiv \mathbf{F}^{\text{obs}} - \mathbf{F}_1^{\text{calc}}. * \end{aligned} \tag{8}$$

We have seen in Section 4–6 that

$$\frac{\mathbf{V}'_1 \mathbf{P} \mathbf{V}_1 - \mathbf{V}'_0 \mathbf{P} \mathbf{V}_0}{\mathbf{V}'_0 \mathbf{P} \mathbf{V}_0} \tag{9}$$

* For the linear model, $\mathbf{V}_0 = \mathbf{F} - \mathbf{A}\hat{\mathbf{X}}$ and $\mathbf{V}_1 = \mathbf{F} - \mathbf{A}\mathbf{X}_1$, where $\mathbf{F} \equiv \mathbf{F}^{\text{obs}}$.

is distributed as

$$\frac{p}{n - p} F_{p,n-p}. \tag{10}$$

It is clear that the ratio (9) is simply related to the generalized R factor. In fact,

$$\mathbf{V'PV} = R^2 \mathbf{F}^{obs'} \mathbf{PF}^{obs}. \tag{11}$$

Hence

$$\frac{\mathbf{V'_1 PV_1} - \mathbf{V'_0 PV_0}}{\mathbf{V'_0 PV_0}} = \frac{R_1{}^2 - R_0{}^2}{R_0{}^2} \tag{12}$$

where R_1 is the generalized R factor for the parameters $\mathbf{X}_1$, and R_0 is the generalized R factor for the best parameter set. Thus,

$$\frac{R_1{}^2 - R_0{}^2}{R_0{}^2} \tag{13}$$

is also distributed as $\dfrac{p}{n - p} F_{p,n-p}$. A simple manipulation shows that the hypothesis

$$H_0: \mathbf{X} = \mathbf{X}_1 \tag{14}$$

can be tested at the $100\alpha\%$ significance level by comparing the R factor ratio

$$\Re = \frac{R_1}{R_0} \tag{15}$$

with

$$\Re_{p,n-p,\alpha} \equiv \left[\frac{p}{n - p} F_{p,n-p,\alpha} + 1 \right]^{1/2}. \tag{16}$$

If the computed $\Re$ satisfies

$$\Re > \Re_{p,n-p,\alpha}, \tag{17}$$

we can reject the hypothesis at the $100\alpha\%$ significance level.

If $n - p$ is large, a frequent situation in crystallography, then

$$F_{p,n-p} \approx \frac{\chi^2{}_p}{p}, \tag{18}$$

so that we may test $\Re$ against

$$\Re_{p,n-p,\alpha} \approx \left[\frac{\chi^2{}_{n-p}}{n - p} + 1 \right]^{1/2}. \tag{19}$$

Suppose that instead of testing a complete set of p alternative parameters, we wish merely to restrict a subset of b of these p parameters to have certain fixed values. We can carry out a least-squares refinement holding these b parameters fixed, and, from the above analysis and the section on the testing of linear hypotheses, we can conclude that the R-factor ratio

$$\mathfrak{R} = \frac{R \text{ (}b \text{ fixed parameters, } p - b \text{ varied)}}{R \text{ (all } p \text{ parameters varied)}} \tag{20}$$

may be tested against values of

$$\mathfrak{R}_{b,n-p,\alpha} \equiv \left[\frac{b}{n-p} F_{b,n-p,\alpha} + 1 \right]^{1/2}. \tag{21}$$

In general, the ratio of the R factor with b restraints on the parameters to the R factor with no restraints on the parameters is to be tested as $\mathfrak{R}_{b,n-p,\alpha}$.

A Practical Note. In a non-linear problem, such as is common in crystallography and other branches of chemical physics, the test should be made on R factors actually computed from the difference between the observed values of the functions and the values calculated from the non-linear relation

$$\mathbf{F} = \mathbf{F(X)}, \tag{22}$$

rather than from the linear approximation

$$\mathbf{F} = \mathbf{AX}. \tag{23}$$

Although in a non-linear problem, the test is not exact in any case, this recommended procedure will give results much closer to the truth than a procedure based on the linear approximation. The properly computed value of $\mathbf{V'PV}$ is assumed to be distributed as χ^2, and it is only the uncertainty in the estimation of the effective number of degrees of freedom for the hypothesis[*]—depending on the nature of the non-linearity—which causes the test to be inexact. The difference between the agreement factor calculated and that predicted from the linear relation can serve as a measure of the non-linearity. See Beale (1960).

Example 5-4-1

Suppose that $n - p = 1000$ and $p = 100$, not untypical values for x-ray crystallographic investigations. What would be a significant value of the R-factor ratio $\mathfrak{R}$? For $n - p = 1000$, $F_{p,n-p}$ is approximated closely by $\chi^2{}_p/p$. For $p = 100$, $\chi^2{}_{p,0.05} = 124.34$. A significant value of $\mathfrak{R}$ is given approximately by

$$\mathfrak{R}_{100,1000,0.05} \approx \left[\frac{124.34}{1000} + 1 \right]^{1/2} = 1.061.$$

Hence if the best least-squares adjustment resulted in an R factor of 0.100, a structure with an R factor of 0.107 could be rejected at the 5% level. For lesser degrees of freedom, significant values of the ratio become larger. A table of significant values of $\mathfrak{R}$ (Table V) is included in the Appendix for a number of significance levels and a spectrum of degrees of freedom.

---

[*] The concept of degrees of freedom depends on linear relations.

Example 5–4–2

In a crystal structure determination from 22 neutron diffraction intensities from a powder pattern, two parameters, x and K, were refined for each of several other values of a parameter y. The problem was extremely non-linear in y; in fact the matrix is singular for $y = 0$. The refinement consequently could not be carried out by the usual methods. These refinements gave the following results:

$|y|$	R
0.00	0.050
0.01	0.055
0.02	0.070
0.03	0.100

The best agreement is for $|y| = 0.00$. We, therefore, take $R = 0.050$ as the best value of the R factor. The ratio for the four cases thus becomes

y	$\Re$
0.00	1.00
0.01	1.10
0.02	1.40
0.03	2.00

The number of degrees of freedom for the best refinement, $n - m$, is 20. The dimension of the hypothesis

$$H_0\colon y = y_0$$

is 1. Significant values of

$$\Re_{1,20,\alpha} = \left[\frac{1}{20} F_{1,20,\alpha} + 1\right]^{1/2}$$

are

α	$\Re_{1,20,\alpha}$
0.05	1.104
0.01	1.185
0.005	1.225

Thus $|y| = 0.01$ is a barely acceptable hypothesis at the 5% significance level, while $|y| = 0.02$ must be rejected at even the 0.5% level.

In applying these tests, the user must remember that it is the generalized weighted R factor rather than the conventional R' which must be used. Experience has shown, however, that the two are often approximately equal when refinement is complete, provided that there are no really large or small weights. The ratios $\Re = R_1/R_0$ and $\Re' = R'_1/R'_0$ are even more likely to be equal. Therefore, the tests may be made with ratios of conventional R factors, provided that it is remembered that the tests are not exact. The uncertainty involved in so doing is probably no worse in most cases than the uncertainty introduced because of non-linearity in the least-squares and in the hypotheses, if they are non-linear as well. Tests with the generalized R factor are to be preferred when these values are available.

5–5. PROBLEM IN EXPERIMENTAL DESIGN

If the observational equations are written

$$\mathbf{F} = \mathbf{AX} + \mathbf{E} \tag{1}$$

the matrix **A** is often called the *design matrix*, as it is an abstraction of the actual experiment which was performed. The matrix **A** tells us which particular functions of the parameters we have measured. The very broad field of experimental design has as one of its important problems the specification of the matrix **A**, that is, the design of the experiment. Which functions should be measured in order to obtain specified information about the parameters in the minimum amount of time? How should **A** be chosen in order that the matrix of the normal equations will be approximately diagonal, i.e., so that the estimated correlations between parameters will be as small as possible? What accuracy in the measurements of the functions is required to test a given hypothesis H_0 against an alternative hypothesis H_1 at significance level α and with power β? These are all problems in experimental design. It is hoped that readers of this book will have attained enough familiarity with the problems and methods of least-squares adjustments and hypothesis-testing to be able to formulate and solve many of these problems for themselves. We will present here a partial solution of one aspect of the first problem above.

Given a set of observational equations

$$\mathbf{F} = \mathbf{AX} + \mathbf{E}, \tag{2}$$

we assume a variance-covariance matrix for **F** of

$$\mathbf{M}_f \equiv \sigma^2 \mathbf{P}^{-1}. \tag{3}$$

We presume however that it is possible to change the weights of the individual observations by some changes in the experiment, perhaps merely by spending more time with each observation. The general solution to the least-squares problem is, as we have seen,

$$(\mathbf{A'PA})\hat{\mathbf{X}} = \mathbf{A'PF}. \tag{4}$$

If **P** is a diagonal matrix,

$$\mathbf{P} = \begin{pmatrix} p_1 & 0 & 0 & \ldots & 0 \\ 0 & p_2 & 0 & \ldots & 0 \\ \cdot & \cdot & \cdot & \cdot & \cdot & \cdot \\ 0 & 0 & 0 & \ldots & p_n \end{pmatrix} \tag{5}$$

(or any matrix for which the square root $P^{1/2}$ is defined), then, as we have noted before, the normal equations are obtained in identical form if we multiply the observational equations through by the matrix $P^{1/2}$ to obtain

$$P^{1/2}F = P^{1/2}AX + P^{1/2}E \tag{6}$$

and treat the problem as one with observed functions

$$G = P^{1/2}F \tag{7}$$

and design matrix $P^{1/2}A$. G then has the variance-covariance matrix $\sigma^2 I$, so that the form is that of an unweighted least squares. In this section, we will make some comments on this aspect of experimental design, that is, on the choice of the weights (when we have such freedom) in a linear-regression situation. We shall restrict ourselves to the case of the diagonal weight matrix.

A reasonable approach would seem to be that of deciding before the experiment is carried out what its aims are. In general, we should be able at the beginning to set out the linear hypotheses which we wish to test. Suppose that we have decided that the purpose of the experiment is the test of the linear hypothesis

$$QX = Z. \tag{8}$$

We ask whether it is possible to optimize the weights for testing this hypothesis, and, if so, how. For this purpose, we will choose to maximize the power of the linear-hypothesis test, that is, we will minimize the probability that the hypothesis is accepted as true when it is actually false. Now we have previously noted that the power of the variance-ratio test increases monotonically with the non-centrality parameter ξ^2. Hence our problem reduces to that of maximizing ξ^2 under whatever additional criteria we may wish to impose.

Now ξ^2 is given by the expression

$$\xi^2 = \frac{\theta'(Q(A'PA)^{-1}Q')^{-1}\theta}{\sigma^2}. \tag{9}$$

If we assume the weight matrix to be normalized by σ^2 so that

$$P \equiv M_f^{-1},$$

then

$$\xi^2 = \theta'(Q(A'PA)^{-1}Q')^{-1}\theta. \tag{10}$$

Now suppose that we wish to maximize ξ^2 under the condition that some linear function of the weights

$$\sum_i r_i p_i \tag{11}$$

is a constant. (The reason for this will become apparent in a moment.) A variation function for the solution of the problem would be

$$\mathcal{F} = \xi^2 + \lambda \sum_i r_i p_i, \tag{12}$$

and, if an extremum exists, it is given by the solution of the non-linear equations

$$\frac{\partial \xi^2}{\partial p_i} = -\lambda r_i, \quad i = 1, \ldots, n, \tag{13}$$

that is,

$$\frac{1}{r_i} \frac{\partial \xi^2}{\partial p_i} = \frac{1}{r_j} \frac{\partial \xi^2}{\partial p_j}, \quad i, j = 1, \ldots, n. \tag{14}$$

These equations could possibly be solved by an iterative procedure to obtain a solution for the p_i. There is, however, one severe difficulty, and that is that the p_i are restricted to positive values. The solution for the maximum ξ^2 will frequently be on the boundary of the region defined by

$$p_i \geqslant 0, \quad i = 1, \ldots, n. \tag{15}$$

That is, some of the weights will be zero. Were it not for the fact that the power of the test also increases with the number of degrees of freedom, only m of the weights would have a finite value. Since an extremum is not necessarily reached, the calculus of variations approach above is not adequate, and the problem must be attacked by some other means. Specifically, the method of *non-linear programing* is adapted to the solution of extremum problems where the best values of the parameters may lie at the boundaries of regions defined by inequalities. Present programing methodology would appear to be inadequate for the solution of the present problem in a general way.

Now suppose that the experimental quantities are the results of a counting experiment in which each observation has a Poisson distribution. (We further assume that the number of counts is high enough for the error distribution to be approximately normal, so that the variance-ratio tests on the hypotheses are applicable.) Suppose that n different counting rates, with expectation values f_i^0 counts per minute, are to be measured. We have a total time T at our disposal to make the measurements. Let the time spent on the measurement of f_i be T_i minutes. If N_i is the number of counts received, we have

$$f_i = \frac{N_i}{T_i}$$

and

$$f_i^0 = \frac{N_i^0}{T_i}. \tag{16}$$

Since

$$\sigma^2(N_i^0) = N_i^0, \tag{17}$$

the variance of the measurement f_i is

$$\sigma^2(f_i) = \frac{N_i^0}{T_i^2} = \frac{f_i^0}{T_i}. \tag{18}$$

The corresponding weight for the ith observation is then

$$p_i = \frac{T_i}{f_i^0}. \tag{19}$$

We wish now to maximize ξ^2 under the condition that

$$T = \sum_i T_i = \sum_i f_i^0 p_i \tag{20}$$

is constant. As noted above, for problems of any great complexity, the techniques for carrying out this maximization are not readily available. Some simple examples, however, will illustrate the possible usefulness of this approach.

Example 5–5–1

Suppose that we have two observables and two parameters connected by the very simple relation

$$f_1^0 = x_1$$
$$f_2^0 = x_2$$

with weights p_1 and p_2. Then

$$\mathbf{A} = \begin{pmatrix} 1 & 0 \\ 0 & 1 \end{pmatrix}, \quad (\mathbf{A'PA})^{-1} = \begin{pmatrix} 1/p_1 & 0 \\ 0 & 1/p_2 \end{pmatrix}.$$

Consider the hypothesis

$$ax_1 + bx_2 = z$$

that is,

$$\mathbf{Q} = (a \quad b).$$

Then

$$\mathbf{Q(A'PA)^{-1}Q'} = \frac{a^2}{p_1} + \frac{b^2}{p_2}$$

and ξ^2 is given by

$$\xi^2 = \theta^2 \frac{p_1 p_2}{a^2 p_2 + b^2 p_1}.$$

We wish to maximize ξ^2 under the condition that

$$T_1 + T_2 = f_1^0 p_1 + f_2^0 p_2 = 1.$$

(We have normalized the total time to unity.) Let

$$\mathcal{F} = \xi^2 + \lambda(f_1^0 p_1 + f_2^0 p_2).$$

Then

$$\frac{\partial \mathcal{F}}{\partial p_1} = \frac{a^2 p_2^2}{(a^2 p_2 + b^2 p_1)^2} + \lambda f_i^0 = 0$$

$$\frac{\partial \mathcal{F}}{\partial p_2} = \frac{b^2 p_1^2}{(a^2 p_2 + b^2 p_1)^2} + \lambda f_2^0 = 0$$

or, equating equivalent expressions for λ, we have

$$\frac{a^2 p_2^2}{b^2 p_1^2} = \frac{f_1^0}{f_2^0}$$

or

$$\frac{p_2}{p_1} = \left|\frac{b}{a}\right| \left(\frac{f_1^0}{f_2^0}\right)^{1/2}$$

and

$$\frac{T_2}{T_1} = \left|\frac{b}{a}\right| \left(\frac{f_2^0}{f_1^0}\right)^{1/2}.$$

Suppose that the hypothesis takes the form

$$\mathbf{QX = Z}$$

with

$$\mathbf{Q} = (1 \quad 1)$$

that is,

$$x_1 + x_2 = z.$$

Then $b/a = 1$. Suppose further that $f_2^0/f_1^0 = 4$. Then

$$T_2 = 2T_1;$$

we spend twice as long on the observation of larger magnitude. Since

$$\sigma^2(\hat{x}_1 + \hat{x}_2) = \sigma^2(\hat{x}_1) + \sigma^2(\hat{x}_2)$$

$$= \frac{1}{p_1} + \frac{1}{p_2}$$

$$= \frac{f_1^0}{T_1} + \frac{f_2^0}{T_2},$$

for the optimum solution we have just found,

$$T_1 = \tfrac{1}{3}, \; T_2 = \tfrac{2}{3} \quad \text{and} \quad f_1 = \tfrac{1}{4}, f_2 = 1.$$

Thus

$$\sigma^2(\hat{x}_1 + \hat{x}_2) = 9.$$

Suppose that instead we had made the expected relative errors in both observations equal. This results in

$$f_1^0 T_1 = f_2^0 T_2$$

or, for the present example,

$$T_1 = \tfrac{4}{5}$$
$$T_2 = \tfrac{1}{5},$$

and

$$\sigma^2(\hat{x}_1 + \hat{x}_2) = 21.25.$$

In maximizing ξ^2, we have minimized $\sigma^2(x_1 + x_2)$, a result that always holds for a one-dimensional hypothesis. Note the obvious fact that for $a = 1$ and $b = 0$, we should spend all the time on observation f_1.

The preceding example makes clear the fact that in order to determine the best weights or counting times we must know the counting rates for the individual observations beforehand. If the procedure suggested in this section were to be applied to an actual experiment, rough values for the individual observations should be obtained by rapid counting. The method of this section would then be applied to obtain the optimum apportionment of experimental time for the testing of particular hypotheses.

Example 5–5–2

Suppose that a crystal structure is known approximately. Then the values of the x-ray diffraction intensities will also be approximately known. A new experiment is planned in which counting techniques will be used for the collection of the diffraction intensities. The purpose of the experiment is to test the equality of certain bond lengths. The formalism developed here could tell us which reflections should be concentrated on in the available time. The approximate structure is necessary not only so that the relative $\mathbf{F}$ values will be known but also so that the linear approximation $\mathbf{F}^0 = \mathbf{AX}$ with a known design matrix $\mathbf{A}$ will be valid. Although we give here no examples for multidimensional problems, the following example shows how some general results of a qualitative nature can be derived.

Example 5–5–3

Suppose that we have a series of observations of the form

$$f_i^0 = q_i \exp\left(-B\rho_i\right)$$

where B is a parameter to be determined. If we wish to test the hypothesis $B = B_0$, we may show, using the linear approximation (valid in the neighborhood of B_0)

$$df_i^0 = -\rho_i q_i \exp\left(-B\rho_i\right) dB$$
$$= -\rho_i f_i^0 \, dB,$$

that

$$\xi^2 = (B - B_0)^2 \sum_i \rho_i^2 (f_i^0)^2 p_i$$

$$= (B - B_0)^2 \sum_i \rho_i^2 f_i^0 t_i$$

if the previous assumptions made about counting times are still valid. The non-centrality parameter is greatest when all the time is spent on the observation which has the greatest product,

$$\rho_i^2 f_i^0.$$

This is no surprise to crystallographers, who know that the "temperature factor" B is most sensitive to high-intensity reflections at high values of $\rho_i = (\sin \theta_i/\lambda)^2$, where θ_i is the scattering angle for the ith observation. This example shows the exact form of the dependence under certain simplifying assumptions, neglecting possible correlation with other parameters.

As we have already suggested, the above discussion and examples have neglected one important factor in proceeding on the assumption that the power of the hypothesis test increases with ξ^2. This is true only if the number of degrees of freedom for the estimation of σ^2 remains the same, and for most problems, an attempt to maximize ξ^2 will tell us that no time at all should be spent on $n - m$ of the observations. Practically speaking, however, we know that the number of observations should not be equal to the number of parameters, even if σ^2 is presumed to be known from the variances of the observations derived from the Poisson distribution. We should have an independent estimate of σ^2, for we shall wish to detect unknown sources of experimental error or inadequacies in the theoretical model. Thus, we wish to keep the number of degrees of freedom high. Rather than using the conditions $T_i \geqslant 0$ in the necessary non-linear programing techniques, we shall probably wish to demand that $T_i \geqslant T_0$, where T_0 is a minimum amount of time to be spent on each observation.

A general treatment of the interaction between ξ^2 and the number of degrees of freedom in the determination of the power of the test would be rather difficult to apply systematically.

A simpler way to design the least-squares experiment is to choose the weights such that

$$\det (\mathbf{A'PA})^{-1}$$

is a minimum. This does not emphasize any particular hypothesis but minimizes the volume of the hyperellipsoid of standard deviation, which seems a reasonable thing to do. This procedure is related to that of maximizing the power of the hypothesis test where $\mathbf{Q}$ is given by the unit matrix. The reader is referred to a recent paper (Box and Lucas, 1959) for the details of some applications to non-linear problems.

5–6. EMPIRICAL FITTING OF POLYNOMIALS TO EXPERIMENTAL DATA

We shall occasionally be interested in determining a polynomial approximation to a function of a variable θ. The function, which may be theoretical or empirical, is assumed to be tabulated at a finite number of values of θ, which we denote by

$$\theta_1, \theta_2, \ldots, \theta_n. \tag{1}$$

In general we seek the polynomial fit not because of any presumed theoretical validity for such an expression for explaining the data but rather as a convenient method of representing the data and for evaluation of the function at other than the tabulated points. We will use the method of least squares to determine the best values c_i in the expression

$$f(\theta) = c_0 + c_1\theta + c_2\theta^2 + \cdots + c_{p-1}\theta^{p-1} + e(\theta), \tag{2}$$

where $e(\theta)$ is the lack of fit. We not only shall want to determine the coefficients c_i for a given value of p, but we also shall be interested in determining the value of p which gives a sufficiently good fit to the data: when does it gain us very little to add more terms to the expansion?

We proceed as before, and write

$$\mathbf{F} = \mathbf{AC} + \mathbf{E} \tag{3}$$

where the design matrix is now given by

$$\mathbf{A} = \begin{pmatrix} 1 & \theta_1 & \theta_1{}^2 & \cdots & \theta_1{}^{p-1} \\ 1 & \theta_2 & \theta_2{}^2 & \cdots & \theta_2{}^{p-1} \\ \cdot & \cdot & \cdot & \cdots & \cdot \\ 1 & \theta_n & \theta_n{}^2 & \cdots & \theta_n{}^{p-1} \end{pmatrix}. \tag{4}$$

It is usually assumed that the weight matrix is I/σ^2, that is, that all the values $f(\theta_i) = f_i$ are equally well known and that there are no correlations between adjacent values of f_i; this assumption is of course not necessary for the treatment of the problem. The least-squares normal equations are obtained in the usual way, and we have

$$\hat{\mathbf{C}} = (\mathbf{A'PA})^{-1}\mathbf{A'PF}, \tag{5}$$

or if $\mathbf{P} = \mathbf{I}/\sigma^2$,

$$\hat{\mathbf{C}} = (\mathbf{A'A})^{-1}\mathbf{A'F}. \tag{6}$$

If the deviations of the f_i from the resulting polynomial are assumed to be approximately normally distributed, we can test the hypothesis

$$H_0: c_{p-1} = 0 \tag{7}$$

by computing the variance ratio

$$(n - p)\frac{R_{p-1} - R_p}{R_p}, \tag{8}$$

where

$$R_p = \mathbf{V'PV} \tag{9}$$

for the p-parameter fit, and comparing with $F_{1,n-p,\alpha}$. If this ratio is not significant, we may drop the pth term c_{p-1} and test for the significance of the next lower power. We can continue in this way and retain terms only to the power where a significant improvement in the sum of squares is obtained. Of course, adding more terms will always improve the agreement, and we must therefore weigh the utility of the formula (we prefer a simpler one) against the increased accuracy obtained with a larger number of terms by a proper choice of the significance level α.

Once obtained, the polynomial function

$$\hat{f}(\theta) = \hat{c}_0 + \hat{c}_1\theta + \cdots + \hat{c}_{p-1}\theta^{p-1} \tag{10}$$

may be used to predict values $f(\theta)$ where θ is not one of the tabulated values. By the principle of the propagation of error, we have for the variance of this estimate of $f(\theta)$

$$\text{var}\,(\hat{f}(\theta)) = (1 \quad \theta \quad \cdots \quad \theta^{p-1})\mathbf{M}_c \begin{pmatrix} 1 \\ \theta \\ \cdot \\ \cdot \\ \cdot \\ \theta^{p-1} \end{pmatrix}. \tag{11}$$

$\mathbf{M}_c$ is of course estimated by $(\mathbf{A'PA})^{-1}\hat{\sigma}^2$, so that an estimate of var $(\hat{f}(\theta))$ is given by

$$\widehat{\text{var}}\,(\hat{f}(\theta)) = (1 \quad \theta \quad \cdots \quad \theta^{p-1})(\mathbf{A'PA})^{-1} \begin{pmatrix} 1 \\ \theta \\ \cdot \\ \cdot \\ \cdot \\ \theta^{p-1} \end{pmatrix} \hat{\sigma}^2 \tag{12}$$

where

$$\hat{\sigma}^2 = \frac{\mathbf{V'PV}}{n - p} \tag{13}$$

as usual. This result may also be written

$$\widehat{\text{var}}\,(\hat{f}(\theta)) = \sum_{i=0}^{p-1} \sum_{j=0}^{p-1} \hat{\sigma}(c_i)\hat{\sigma}(c_j)\hat{\rho}_{ij}\theta^{i+j} \tag{14}$$

where the $\hat{\sigma}(c_i)$ and $\hat{\rho}_{ij}$ are the estimated standard deviations and correlation coefficients.

Since simple powers of x are quite non-orthogonal functions, the treatment above is susceptible to numerical solution only when the value of p is small. It will be difficult to obtain sufficient accuracy in the solution if p is greater than about 6. It is far preferable to use orthogonal polynomials in the fit, for increased accuracy, fewer terms, and uniformity of error over the range fitted. Polynomials of the Chebychev type are highly recommended, and reference should be made to books on numerical procedures for the definitions and discussion of their properties.*

The procedure for carrying out the analysis is the same. If we wish to expand the function $f(\theta)$ in terms of other functions (which may or may not be polynomials):

$$g_1(\theta),\, g_2(\theta),\, \ldots,\, g_p(\theta) \tag{15}$$

in the form

$$f(\theta) = c_1 g_1(\theta) + \cdots + c_p g_p(\theta) + e(\theta), \tag{16}$$

our design matrix becomes

* For example, the book by Lanczos (see Bibliography).

$$\mathbf{A} = \begin{pmatrix} g_1(\theta_1) & g_2(\theta_1) & \cdots & g_p(\theta_1) \\ g_1(\theta_2) & g_2(\theta_2) & \cdots & g_p(\theta_2) \\ & & \cdots & \\ g_1(\theta_n) & g_2(\theta_n) & \cdots & g_p(\theta_n) \end{pmatrix}, \tag{17}$$

and the general term of the normal equations matrix becomes

$$b_{ij} = (\mathbf{A'A})_{ij} = \sum_{k=1}^{n} g_i(\theta_k)g_j(\theta_k), \tag{18}$$

but this is zero for $i \neq j$ if the functions g_i and g_j are properly orthogonalized over the interval of the fit. The matrix of the normal equations thus becomes diagonal and susceptible to rapid and accurate inversion. In such a case, we have

$$\hat{c}_i = \frac{\displaystyle\sum_{k=1}^{n} g_i(\theta_k)f_k}{\displaystyle\sum_{k=1}^{n} g_i^2(\theta_k)}. \tag{19}$$

A good discussion of function fitting using Chebychev polynomials is given in Plackett's book (see Bibliography).

Example 5–6–1

The following table presents power series fits to the x-ray scattering factor curve for scandium as a function of $x = 0.40\pi(\sin\theta/\lambda)$:

x	f_{obs}	$p = 1$	$p = 2$	$p = 3$	$p = 4$	$p = 5$	$p = 6$
				f_{calc}			
0.0	21.00	11.43	18.52	20.78	20.99	20.93	20.96
0.1	17.83	11.43	17.10	18.01	17.96	18.02	17.97
0.2	15.56	11.43	15.68	15.53	15.37	15.44	15.43
0.3	13.27	11.43	14.26	13.36	13.19	13.20	13.24
0.4	11.33	11.43	12.85	11.49	11.39	11.35	11.38
0.5	9.81	11.43	11.43	9.92	9.92	9.86	9.85
0.6	8.67	11.43	10.01	8.65	8.75	8.71	8.66
0.7	7.88	11.43	8.59	7.69	7.85	7.86	7.81
0.8	7.28	11.43	7.17	7.02	7.18	7.24	7.23
0.9	6.76	11.43	5.76	6.66	6.71	6.77	6.80
1.0	6.32	11.43	4.34	6.60	6.39	6.33	6.26
R_p		2409810	198621	3168	980	678	555

The error matrix for the observations was assumed to be diagonal, with a constant variance of $(0.0004)^2$. Suppose that we choose to test the significance of the extra terms in the expansion at the $\alpha = 0.05$ level; e.g., we will reject the hypothesis $c_5 = 0$, when it is true, 5% of the time. We form the variance ratios

$$F^{(6)} = (11 - 6)\frac{678 - 555}{555} = 1.108$$

$$F^{(5)} = (11 - 5)\frac{980 - 678}{678} = 2.67$$

$$F^{(4)} = (11 - 4)\frac{3168 - 980}{980} = 15.65$$

$$F^{(3)} = (11 - 3)\frac{198621 - 3168}{3168} = 493.$$

These are to be compared respectively with the tabulated values of

$$F_{1,5,0.05} = 6.61$$
$$F_{1,6,0.05} = 5.99$$
$$F_{1,7,0.05} = 5.59$$
$$F_{1,8,0.05} = 5.32.$$

We conclude by this criterion that four parameters must be included to obtain a satisfactory fit, but that we cannot reject the hypotheses $c_5 = 0$ and $c_4 = 0$. The actual expansions are as follows:

$p = 1: f = 11.428$
$p = 2: f = 18.517 - 14.178x$
$p = 3: f = 20.781 - 29.271x + 15.093x^2$
$p = 4: f = 20.995 - 32.672x + 24.012x^2 - 5.946x^3$
$p = 5: f = 20.933 - 30.524x + 13.270x^2 + 11.244x^3 - 8.595x^4$
$p = 6: f = 20.963 - 32.826x + 32.262x^2 - 42.359x^3 + 52.797x^4$
$$- 24.578x^5.$$

The variance-ratio comparisons have told us that the $p = 4$ case represents a satisfactory fit to the data in the sense that the hypotheses

H_0: the four-term fit is as satisfactory as the five-term fit;
H_0': the five-term fit is as satisfactory as the six-term fit

cannot be rejected.

The correlation matrix for the best coefficients for the $p = 6$ case is

$$\begin{pmatrix} 1.000 & -0.612 & 0.419 & -0.329 & 0.276 & -0.242 \\ -0.612 & 1.000 & -0.953 & 0.889 & -0.833 & 0.786 \\ 0.419 & -0.953 & 1.000 & -0.984 & 0.954 & -0.922 \\ -0.329 & 0.889 & -0.984 & 1.000 & -0.992 & 0.975 \\ 0.276 & -0.833 & 0.954 & -0.992 & 1.000 & -0.995 \\ -0.242 & 0.786 & -0.922 & 0.975 & -0.995 & 1.000 \end{pmatrix}.$$

Two facets of the non-orthogonality of the expansion functions are apparent in the latter two tables. First of all, the high values of many of the correlation coefficients suggest that the normal-equations matrix is almost singular and that it would thus be difficult to invert accurately, even with a large-scale digital computer, if the number of coefficients were increased much further. Secondly, the five-term expansion is not obtained simply by dropping off the sixth term of the six-term expansion. All the coefficients must be readjusted when a single term is dropped. This would not be the case if functions orthogonal over the observed set x had been used.

5–7. EFFECTS OF NON-NORMALITY ON HYPOTHESIS TESTS

Most of the specific hypothesis tests which we have discussed depend upon normal distributions of the random variables involved. Although many experimentally measured quantities are so distributed, either because of the central limit theorem or because many common distributions have the normal distribution as a limiting form, we are still interested in knowing whether any unknown departures from normality can strongly affect the hypothesis tests we have made.* Fortunately, hypotheses concerning the mean are not usually seriously affected by moderate departures from normality. In particular, Student's t and the variance ratio (F) can be used with some confidence, even if the distributions concerned are quite non-normal. As mentioned in Section 2–3, departures from normality are frequently measured by the *skewness*

$$\lambda_3 = \frac{k_3}{k_2^{3/2}} \tag{1}$$

and the *kurtosis*

$$\lambda_4 = \frac{k_4}{k_2^2} \tag{2}$$

where the k_i are the ith cumulants of the distribution. These quantities are both zero for the normal distribution, since all cumulants higher than the second vanish for the normal distribution.

The distribution of Student's t is not seriously affected by moderate kurtosis, although skewness does affect the distribution more seriously; on the other hand, skewness has little effect on the distribution of the absolute value of t, $\phi(|t|)$. Similarly, the distribution of F is rather insensitive to moderate values of the skewness and kurtosis. By moderate values of the skewness and kurtosis, we imply values approximately in the range -1 to $+1$. Many distributions met with in practice will fulfill this requirement. To take an extreme example, the uniform distribution has skewness 0 and kurtosis -1.2. All the cumulants of the Poisson distribution are equal to the parameter λ; hence the skewness is given by $\lambda^{-1/2}$ and the kurtosis by λ^{-1}. Even for the small value 1 for λ, these values of the skewness and kurtosis are compatible with confident use of the t or F tests, so that for all practical purposes we may regard the Poisson distribution as fulfilling

* A test is said to be *robust* if its significance levels are not severely affected by departures from the assumed conditions (such as normality).

the requirements for all the hypothesis tests we have developed concerning the mean.

Although hypotheses concerning the mean can be tested even when there are considerable departures from normality, it is clear that hypotheses concerning the higher moments of the distribution will be affected by non-normality, since it is the higher moments that determine the shape of the distribution. In particular, hypotheses concerning the variance will be radically affected by departures from normality, particularly in the kurtosis. Similarly, hypotheses concerning the skewness and kurtosis themselves are difficult to test except for large samples, so that any supposed departures from normality cannot be detected with a high degree of probability for small samples. Tables for detecting these departures are available. (See, for example, Bennett and Franklin, page 95.) The use of χ^2 in a goodness-of-fit test is also of value in this connection (see Section 2–11).

5–8. LEAST-SQUARES PLANE THROUGH A SET OF POINTS

A common crystallographic application of least-squares techniques, an application which recurs in other problems as well, is that of fitting a plane to a set of points, the coordinates of which may be subject to random errors. In two dimensions, this involves determining the best line through the points (x, y) where both x and y are subject to error; in three dimensions, it involves finding an actual plane; and in more than three dimensions, a hyperplane is sought. It will be seen below that, when correctly formulated, this leads to an eigenvalue problem rather than to the simple linear normal equations of our previous least-squares treatment.

We assume that we are dealing with an n-dimensional space with a basis set composed of the linearly independent set of vectors

$$\mathbf{a}_1, \mathbf{a}_2, \ldots, \mathbf{a}_n.* \tag{1}$$

The metric for this space is

$$\mathbf{G}_{n,n}^{-1} \equiv \{\mathbf{a}_i \cdot \mathbf{a}_j\} \; \dagger \tag{2}$$

such that the distance between two points $\mathbf{X}^1{}_{n,1}$ and $\mathbf{X}^2{}_{n,1}$ is given by

$$(\mathbf{x}^1 - \mathbf{x}^2)'\mathbf{G}^{-1}(\mathbf{x}^1 - \mathbf{x}^2). \tag{3}$$

A vector of coefficients $\mathbf{m}_{1,n}$ and a distance d define a plane

$$\mathbf{mx} - d = 0. \tag{4}$$

The distance D^i of the point $\mathbf{x}^i$ to the plane described by $\mathbf{m}$ and d is

$$D^i = \frac{(\mathbf{mx}^i - d)}{(\mathbf{mGm'})^{1/2}}, \tag{5}$$

---

* The $\mathbf{a}_i$ are not vectors in the sense of the row or column matrices used in this section and elsewhere in this book. We are introducing geometrical concepts here on top of the usual matrix algebra.

† $\mathbf{a}_i \cdot \mathbf{a}_j$ is the scalar product of the two vectors $\mathbf{a}_i$ and $\mathbf{a}_j$ in the usual geometrical sense.

and we define a vector

$$\mathbf{D}_{1,p} \equiv (D^1 \quad D^2 \quad \cdots \quad D^p) \tag{6}$$

as a set of p such distances for the set of p points

$$\mathbf{X}_{n,p} \equiv (\mathbf{x}^1 \quad \mathbf{x}^2 \quad \cdots \quad \mathbf{x}^p). \tag{7}$$

It is convenient for the analysis to define the following augmented matrices:

$$\mathbf{y}^i_{n+1,1} \equiv \begin{pmatrix} \mathbf{x}^i \\ -1 \end{pmatrix}$$

$$\mathbf{Y}_{n+1,p} \equiv (\mathbf{y}^1 \quad \mathbf{y}^2 \quad \cdots \quad \mathbf{y}^p)$$

$$\mathbf{n}_{1,n+1} \equiv (\mathbf{m} \quad d) \tag{8}$$

$$\mathbf{H}_{n+1,n+1} \equiv \begin{pmatrix} \mathbf{G}_{n,n} & \mathbf{0}_{n,1} \\ \mathbf{0}_{1,n} & 0 \end{pmatrix}.$$

where $\mathbf{0}$ is the matrix all of whose elements are zero. With these definitions, Eq. (4) becomes

$$\mathbf{ny} = 0, \tag{9}$$

and the point-to-plane distance (5) becomes

$$D^i = \frac{\mathbf{ny}^i}{(\mathbf{nHn}')^{1/2}}. \tag{10}$$

Let us now introduce a weight matrix $\mathbf{W}_{p,p}$ whose meaning will be discussed below. Keeping in mind the normalization condition

$$\mathbf{nHn}' \equiv \mathbf{mGm}' = 1, \tag{11}$$

the function to be minimized may be written

$$\mathfrak{F} \equiv \mathbf{DWD}' - \lambda(\mathbf{nHn}' - 1). \tag{12}$$

Applying the usual variation procedure, we find that the solution to our problem of determining the best plane is given by the solution to the following eigenvalue equation:

$$(\mathbf{YWY}' - \lambda\mathbf{H})\mathbf{n}' \equiv (\mathbf{C} - \lambda\mathbf{H})\mathbf{n}' = 0. \tag{13}$$

The required $\mathbf{n}'$ is the eigenvector corresponding to the minimum eigenvalue λ of Eq. (13). This will correspond to the largest eigenvalue of $\mathbf{C}^\dagger\mathbf{H}$, where $\mathbf{C}^\dagger$ is the adjoint of $\mathbf{C}$. This eigenvalue may be obtained by standard numerical procedures. Less computation is required, however, if we first reduce the secular equation to one of the nth degree by solving the $(n+1)$st equation of (13) to obtain (for $n = 3$, for example)

$$n_4 \equiv d = -\frac{1}{c_{44}}(c_{41}m_1 + c_{42}m_2 + c_{43}m_3)$$

$$\equiv -\frac{\Gamma\mathbf{m}'}{\gamma} \tag{14}$$

and substitute this value of d in Eq. (13). If we partition the matrix $\mathbf{C}$ in the following way:

$$\mathbf{C} \equiv \begin{pmatrix} (\mathbf{XWX'})_{n,n} & \boldsymbol{\Gamma'}_{n,1} \\ \boldsymbol{\Gamma}_{1,n} & \gamma_{1,1} \end{pmatrix}, \tag{15}$$

the substitution (14) reduces Eq. (13) to

$$\left[\left(\mathbf{XWX'} - \frac{\boldsymbol{\Gamma'}\boldsymbol{\Gamma}}{\gamma} \right) - \lambda \mathbf{G} \right] \mathbf{m'} \equiv (\mathbf{A} - \lambda \mathbf{G})\mathbf{m'} = 0. \tag{16}$$

Nature of the Weight Matrix. Now from the theory of least squares presented in Chapter 4, we know that the weight matrix $\mathbf{W}$ is properly defined by

$$\mathbf{W} \equiv \mathbf{M}_d^{-1} \tag{17}$$

where $\mathbf{M}_d$ is the moment matrix for the perpendicular distances of the points from the plane. $\mathbf{M}_d$ may be obtained in a straightforward way from $\mathbf{M}_x$, the moment matrix for the coordinates $\mathbf{X}$. For $n = 3$, for example, using the definition of $\mathbf{D}$ in Eq. (6), we may write

$$\mathbf{D'}_{p,1} = \begin{pmatrix} \mathbf{m}_{1,3} & \mathbf{0}_{1,3} & \cdots & \mathbf{0}_{1,3} \\ \mathbf{0}_{1,3} & \mathbf{m}_{1,3} & \cdots & \mathbf{0}_{1,3} \\ \cdot & \cdot & \cdots & \cdot \\ \mathbf{0}_{1,3} & \mathbf{0}_{1,3} & \cdots & \mathbf{m}_{1,3} \end{pmatrix} \begin{pmatrix} \mathbf{x}^1 \\ \mathbf{x}^2 \\ \cdot \\ \mathbf{x}^p \end{pmatrix} - d \begin{pmatrix} 1 \\ 1 \\ \cdot \\ 1 \end{pmatrix}$$

$$\equiv \mathcal{M}_{p,3p} \mathcal{X}_{3p,1} - \mathcal{D}_{p,1} \tag{18}$$

where the matrices $\mathcal{M}$, $\mathcal{X}$, and $\mathcal{D}$ are defined by (18). By the usual formula for the propagation of error (Section 5–2), we obtain

$$\mathbf{M}_d = \mathcal{M}\mathbf{M}_x\mathcal{M}'$$
$$\equiv \{\mathbf{m}(\mathbf{M}_x^{ij})\mathbf{m'}\}, \tag{19}$$

where $(\mathbf{M}_x^{ij})$ is the 3×3 block of $\mathbf{M}_x$ corresponding to interactions between the points $\mathbf{x}^i$ and $\mathbf{x}^j$. In order to make the notation here completely clear, we show the following complete expression for the calculation of a single element of $\mathbf{M}_d$, namely the term in $\mathbf{M}_d$ for the interaction between points $\mathbf{x}^1$ and $\mathbf{x}^2$:

$$(\mathbf{M}_d)_{12} = (m_1\ m_2\ m_3) \begin{pmatrix} \mu(x_1, x_2) & \mu(x_1, y_2) & \mu(x_1, z_2) \\ \mu(y_1, x_2) & \mu(y_1, y_2) & \mu(y_1, z_2) \\ \mu(z_1, x_2) & \mu(z_1, y_2) & \mu(z_1, z_2) \end{pmatrix} \begin{pmatrix} m_1 \\ m_2 \\ m_3 \end{pmatrix} \tag{20}$$

where $\mu(x_1, x_2)$, for example, denotes the estimated element of $\mathbf{M}_x$:

$$\sigma(x_1)\sigma(y_2)\rho(x_1, y_2).$$

An attempt to introduce the weight matrix in this form into the initial variation problem leads to non-linear equations in $\mathbf{m}$ rather than to the simple eigenvalue expression. The best procedure would thus seem to be an iterative one, in which one assumes a vector $\mathbf{m}$, calculates the weights (which depend on $\mathbf{m}$) from Eqs. (17), (18), and (19), derives a new $\mathbf{m}$ by solution of the eigenvalue problem, and then recycles. In most cases of interest in two or three dimensions, **m** will be approximately known by inspection, so that the process will converge in probably no more than two iterations.

Because the weights depend on the equation of the line, and an iterative procedure is used, it is important to note that the minimum eigenvalue of Eq. (15) does not necessarily correspond to the best solution. When the solutions to the eigenvalue equation have been found, the quantity **DWD'** should be computed for each of the eigenvalues, using the (in general) different weight matrix for each eigenvalue. If the ellipsoids of error for the individual points are very eccentric, it frequently happens that the minimum **DWD'** does not correspond to the minimum eigenvalue. This, of course, is particularly likely to happen if the initial choice of least-squares plane for the iteration is far from the correct one.

Example 5–8–1

As an example of the latter difficulty, let us consider fitting a line to the following four points in a two-dimensional space:

$$\mathbf{X} = \begin{pmatrix} 1 & 1 & -1 & -1 \\ 2 & -2 & 2 & -2 \end{pmatrix}.$$

If the errors in the individual points were isotropic, it is clear that the best line would be that described by the equation

$$x_1 = 0.$$

Suppose however that the moment matrix for the coordinates has the following form:

$$\mathbf{M}_x = \begin{pmatrix} \frac{1}{4} & 0 & 0 & 0 & 0 & 0 \\ 0 & 4 & 0 & 0 & 0 & 0 \\ 0 & 0 & \frac{1}{4} & 0 & 0 & 0 \\ 0 & 0 & 0 & 4 & 0 & 0 \\ 0 & 0 & 0 & 0 & \frac{1}{4} & 0 \\ 0 & 0 & 0 & 0 & 0 & 4 \end{pmatrix}.$$

The moment matrix for the distances becomes

$$\mathbf{M}_d = (\tfrac{1}{4}m_1 + 4m_2)\mathbf{I}_{4,4},$$

with a corresponding weight matrix

$$\mathbf{W} = \frac{1}{\tfrac{1}{4}m_1 + 4m_2}\mathbf{I}_{4,4}.$$

The matrix $\mathbf{A} = \mathbf{XWX'}$ has eigenvalues

$$\lambda_1 = \frac{4}{\tfrac{1}{4}m_1 + 4m_2}$$

$$\lambda_2 = \frac{16}{\tfrac{1}{4}m_1 + 4m_2},$$

with eigenvectors corresponding to the lines
$$x_1 = 0$$
and
$$x_2 = 0.$$
(We have assumed a unit metric.) This result would lead one to regard the line $x_1 = 0$ as the appropriate solution as for the unweighted case. If, however, we use the appropriate values of **m** to calculate the weights and the quantities **DWD**$'$ for the two cases, we find that **DWD**$' = 16$ for the line $x_1 = 0$ and **DWD**$' = 4$ for the line $x_2 = 0$. Thus the line $x_2 = 0$ is the best weighted least-squares line, despite the fact that it always corresponds to the larger of the two eigenvalues. A careful look at the situation indicates that this is expected, since the errors perpendicular to this line are much greater than those perpendicular to the other.

Statistical Significance of the Derived Quantities. Having derived the vector **n**, we would like to be able to estimate the errors of its components. For this purpose, we require the matrix **M**$_n$. Since
$$\mathbf{Y'n'} = \mathbf{D'},$$
we have
$$\mathbf{YWY'n'} = \mathbf{YWD'} \equiv \mathbf{Cn'}$$
$$\mathbf{n'} = \mathbf{C^{-1}YWD'} \tag{21}$$
and hence
$$\mathbf{M}_n = \mathbf{C^{-1}YWM}_d\mathbf{WY'C^{-1}}$$
$$= \mathbf{C^{-1}}. \tag{22}$$
Thus, as we expect, the moment matrix for the derived quantities is the inverse of the matrix which corresponds to the normal-equations matrix in the usual least-squares method.

Now suppose that we have determined the best vector **n**. We may wish to ask whether another vector **n**$_0$ is also an acceptable solution. If the errors in the distances are assumed to have a normal distribution, the quantity
$$T^2 = (\mathbf{n}_0 - \mathbf{n})\mathbf{C}(\mathbf{n}_0 - \mathbf{n})' \tag{23}$$
has a distribution of the form
$$T^2 = nF_{n,N} \tag{24}$$
where F is the usual variance-ratio distribution. In Eq. (24), n is the number of derived parameters (strictly, the rank of **C**), and N is the number of degrees of freedom which entered into the estimation of **W**. (N may, for example, be the number of reflections by which a crystal structure is "over-determined.") If the value of T^2 calculated by Eq. (23) is less than the tabular value for a specified significance level, we cannot reject the

hypothesis that the plane is characterized by the vector $\mathbf{n}_0$. Speaking more loosely, we say that the difference between $\mathbf{n}$ and $\mathbf{n}_0$ is not statistically significant. Since N will often be fairly large, and since

$$\lim_{N \to \infty} nF_{n,N} = \chi^2(n), \tag{25}$$

it may be more convenient to use a table of χ^2 rather than of F for making the test.

The hypothesis

$$H_0: \text{the points are coplanar}$$

may be tested by examination of the quantity

$$\lambda \equiv \mathbf{DWD}',$$

which has the distribution of

$$T^2 = (p - n)F_{p-n,N}$$

if the hypothesis is true. Here again, we may often test against $\chi^2(p - n)$. The hypothesis is accepted if T^2 is less than the tabulated value of $\chi^2(p - n)$ for a particular significance level.

All these conclusions regarding errors and hypothesis tests depend upon the use of appropriate weights in the fit of the least-squares plane, and it is primarily for this reason that a correct derivation of the weights is important.

Least-Squares Plane with Conditions. An interesting extension of the problem discussed in this section is that of finding the best plane to fit p points, further requiring that the plane pass exactly through another $q < n$ points. Let the coordinates of these points be given by $\mathbf{Z}_{n+1,q}$ (corresponding to the $\mathbf{Y}_{n+1,p}$ for the non-fixed points). The condition may then be expressed

$$\mathbf{nZ} = \mathbf{0}_{1,q}. \tag{26}$$

The solution of the variation problem (which will not be reproduced here) leads to a result corresponding to Eq. (13):

$$\{\mathbf{C} - \lambda[\mathbf{I} - \mathbf{Z}(\mathbf{Z}'\mathbf{C}^\dagger\mathbf{Z})^{-1}\mathbf{Z}'\mathbf{C}^\dagger]\mathbf{H}\}\mathbf{n}' = 0. \tag{27}$$

Again, the most convenient method of solution is to multiply Eq. (27) by $\mathbf{C}^\dagger$ and find the eigenvector corresponding to the largest eigenvalue of the resulting matrix. (And again, there is danger that in some cases the best plane will not correspond to this eigenvalue.) Perhaps the most common example in three dimensions is the problem of finding the best plane to fit a given set of points with the restriction that the plane pass through the origin. Substituting

$$\mathbf{Z}' = (0 \quad 0 \quad 0 \quad -1)$$

in Eq. (27), one finds after some manipulation that the equation reduces to

$$(\mathbf{XWX}' - \lambda\mathbf{G})\mathbf{m}' = 0, \tag{28}$$

a result that is of course obvious since $d = 0$. If there is only one fixed point, the computation is minimized if one makes a change of origin to this point and then uses Eq. (28). The more general form, Eq. (27), is likely to be of greatest use for handling multiple fixed points in spaces of higher dimension.

This problem is closely related to that of a q-dimensional linear hypothesis, and a brief consideration will convince the reader that in this case

$$\lambda = \mathbf{DWD}'$$

will have approximately the χ^2 distribution with $p - n + q$ degrees of freedom.

Example 5–8–2

Let us fit a line to the following four points in a two-dimensional space: $(0.10, 0.48)$, $(0.73, 0.52)$, $(1.00, 0.70)$, and $(1.30, 0.70)$. Let us assume further that the axes $\mathbf{a}_1$ and $\mathbf{a}_2$ are orthogonal, with unit length, so that

$$\mathbf{H} = \begin{pmatrix} 1 & 0 & 0 \\ 0 & 1 & 0 \\ 0 & 0 & 0 \end{pmatrix}.$$

Further assume that we have been given a moment matrix for the coordinates as follows:

$$\mathbf{M}_x = \begin{pmatrix} 0.0100 & 0 & 0 & 0 & 0 & 0 & 0 & 0 \\ 0 & 0.0004 & 0 & 0 & 0 & 0 & 0 & 0 \\ 0 & 0 & 0.0009 & 0 & 0 & 0 & 0 & 0 \\ 0 & 0 & 0 & 0.0064 & 0 & 0.0056 & 0 & 0 \\ 0 & 0 & 0 & 0 & 0.0025 & 0 & 0 & 0 \\ 0 & 0 & 0 & 0.0056 & 0 & 0.0100 & 0 & 0 \\ 0 & 0 & 0 & 0 & 0 & 0 & 0.0100 & 0.0060 \\ 0 & 0 & 0 & 0 & 0 & 0 & 0.0060 & 0.0100 \end{pmatrix}.$$

Thus there is a non-zero correlation between the two coordinates of point four, and there is a non-zero correlation between the x_2 coordinates of points two and three. The computations are carried out as follows:

$$\mathbf{Y} = \begin{pmatrix} 0.10 & 0.73 & 1.00 & 1.30 \\ 0.48 & 0.52 & 0.70 & 0.70 \\ -1.00 & -1.00 & -1.00 & -1.00 \end{pmatrix}.$$

Assume as a first approximation that

$$\mathbf{m} = (0.1961 \quad -0.9806).$$

Then

$$\mathbf{M}_d = \begin{pmatrix} 769 & 0 & 0 & 0 \\ 0 & 6189 & 5385 & 0 \\ 0 & 5385 & 9712 & 0 \\ 0 & 0 & 0 & 9708 \end{pmatrix} \times 10^6$$

$$\mathbf{W} \equiv \mathbf{M}_d^{-1} = \begin{pmatrix} 1300 & 0 & 0 & 0 \\ 0 & 312 & -173 & 0 \\ 0 & -173 & 199 & 0 \\ 0 & 0 & 0 & 103 \end{pmatrix}$$

$$\mathbf{YWY}' \equiv \mathbf{C} = \begin{pmatrix} 299.7548 & 235.5022 & -391.3700 \\ 235.5022 & 405.9208 & -786.5800 \\ -391.3700 & -786.5800 & 1568.0000 \end{pmatrix}$$

$$\mathbf{C}^\dagger = \begin{pmatrix} 17775.72 & -61423.64 & -26376.10 \\ -61423.64 & 316845.05 & 143612.63 \\ -26376.10 & 143612.63 & 66215.42 \end{pmatrix}$$

$$\det \mathbf{C} = 11858 \times 10^2$$

$$\mathbf{C}^\dagger \mathbf{H} = \begin{pmatrix} 17775.72 & -61423.64 & 0 \\ -61423.64 & 316845.05 & 0 \\ -26376.10 & 143612.63 & 0 \end{pmatrix}.$$

Choose as a first approximation to the unnormalized $\mathbf{n}$,

$$^1\mathbf{n} = (1 \quad -5 \quad \cdots),$$

we have

$$\mathbf{C}^\dagger \mathbf{H} \; ^1\mathbf{n}' = 324894(1 \quad -5.065 \quad -2.291)' \equiv 324894 \; ^2\mathbf{n}'$$
$$\mathbf{C}^\dagger \mathbf{H} \; ^2\mathbf{n}' = 328886(1 \quad -5.066 \quad -2.292)' \equiv 328886 \; ^3\mathbf{n}'$$
$$\mathbf{C}^\dagger \mathbf{H} \; ^3\mathbf{n}' = 328948(1 \quad -5.066 \quad -2.292)'$$
$$\mathbf{n} = (0.1937 \quad -0.9811 \quad -0.4439),$$

and the equation of the line is

$$0.1937x - 0.9811y + 0.4439 = 0.$$

The values of the coefficients are nearly the same as those used in calculating the weights, so a recycling is not necessary.

$$\lambda = \frac{1185800}{328948} = 3.60.$$

The value of χ^2 for $p - n = 2$ and $\alpha = 0.05$ is 5.99, so that any departures from linearity are not significant at this level.

In the alternative method of solution indicated in Eq. (16), we proceed as follows:

$$\mathbf{\Gamma} = (-391.3700 \quad -786.5800)$$
$$\gamma = 1568.0000$$
$$\frac{\mathbf{\Gamma'\Gamma}}{\gamma} = \begin{pmatrix} 97.6853 & 196.3290 \\ 196.3290 & 394.5842 \end{pmatrix}$$
$$\mathbf{A} = \begin{pmatrix} 202.0695 & 39.1732 \\ 39.1732 & 11.3366 \end{pmatrix}$$
$$\mathbf{A^\dagger} = \begin{pmatrix} 11.3366 & -39.1732 \\ -39.1732 & 202.0695 \end{pmatrix}$$
$$\det \mathbf{A} = 756.24$$
$$\mathbf{A^\dagger m'} = 209.8\mathbf{m'} \text{ for } \mathbf{m} = (0.1937 \quad -0.9811)$$
$$\lambda = \frac{756.24}{209.8} = 3.60$$

which of course agrees with the previous results.

Let us determine the limits of acceptability for lines parallel to the best least-squares line, further assuming that $N = 2$, i.e., that our knowledge of the weights is rather poor:

$$\mathbf{n} - \mathbf{n}_0 = (0 \quad 0 \quad \Delta d)$$
$$T^2 = 1568.0(\Delta d)^2$$
$$= 2F.$$

Since $F_{2,2,0.05} = 19.0$, we can reject at this level of significance any line for which T^2 exceeds $2 \times 19.0 = 38.0$; the confidence region is given by

$$1568(\Delta d)^2 \leqslant 38$$
$$d \leqslant 0.16.$$

As a final example, let us determine the best line through the same four points, assuming further that the line must pass exactly through the point $(\frac{1}{2}, \frac{1}{2})$:

$$\mathbf{Z'} = (\tfrac{1}{2} \quad \tfrac{1}{2} \quad -1)$$
$$\mathbf{Z'CZ} = 1922.27$$
$$\frac{\mathbf{ZZ'C^\dagger}}{\mathbf{Z'C^\dagger Z}} = \begin{pmatrix} 1.18405 & -4.13623 & -1.97609 \\ 1.18405 & -4.13623 & -1.97609 \\ -2.63810 & 8.27246 & 3.95218 \end{pmatrix}$$
$$\left[\mathbf{I} - \frac{\mathbf{ZZ'C^\dagger}}{\mathbf{Z'C^\dagger Z}} \right] \mathbf{H} = \begin{pmatrix} -0.18405 & 4.13623 & 0 \\ -1.18405 & 5.13623 & 0 \\ 2.36810 & -8.27246 & 0 \end{pmatrix}$$
$$\mathbf{C^\dagger} \left[\mathbf{I} - \frac{\mathbf{ZZ'C^\dagger}}{\mathbf{Z'C^\dagger Z}} \right] \mathbf{H} = \begin{pmatrix} 6996 & -23766 & 0 \\ -23766 & 185298 & 0 \\ -8385 & 80766 & 0 \end{pmatrix}$$

and, by a procedure identical with that used for the unrestrained solution, we find

$$\mathbf{n} = (0.1299 \quad -0.9915 \quad -0.4308)$$
$$\lambda = 6.3.$$

Because of the single restraint, λ is now distributed approximately as χ^2_3. Since $\chi^2_{3,0.05} = 7.81$, we cannot reject the hypothesis that the points lie on a line passing through the point $(\frac{1}{2}, \frac{1}{2})$.

5–9. SOME FURTHER RESULTS ON CORRELATION COEFFICIENTS

Given a multivariate density function $\phi(x_1, x_2, \ldots, x_p)$, we have seen that the correlation coefficient is defined by

$$\rho_{ij} = \frac{\text{cov} (x_i, x_j)}{[\text{var} (x_i) \text{ var} (x_j)]^{1/2}}. \tag{1}$$

The corresponding quantity for the sample* is the product-moment correlation coefficient:

$$r_{ij} = \frac{\sum_{k=1}^{n} (x_{ik} - \bar{x}_i)(x_{jk} - \bar{x}_j)}{\left[\sum_k (x_{ik} - \bar{x}_i)^2 \sum_k (x_{jk} - \bar{x}_j)^2\right]^{1/2}}; \tag{2}$$

r_{ij} is a consistent but not an unbiased estimator of ρ_{ij} (unless $\rho_{ij} = 0$), as

$$\mathcal{E}\{r_{ij}\} = \rho_{ij}\left[1 - \frac{1 - \rho^2_{ij}}{2n} + \text{terms of order } \frac{1}{n^2}\right]. \tag{3}$$

The distribution of r_{ij} is rather complex, but for the special case of $\rho_{ij} = 0$ the null hypothesis

$$H_0: \rho_{ij} = 0 \tag{4}$$

can be tested by computing the quantity

$$t = \left[\frac{(n - 2)r^2_{ij}}{1 - r^2_{ij}}\right]^{1/2} \tag{5}$$

and using Student's t with $n - 2$ degrees of freedom. (This test is valid only if ϕ is multivariate normal.) If $\rho_{ij} \neq 0$, the test cannot be related exactly to one of the simple distributions.† However, if n is large (greater than about 50), the quantity $(z - \varsigma)$ where

$$z = \frac{1}{2} \log \frac{1 + r}{1 - r} \tag{6}$$

* The kth sample point is a p-dimensional vector $\mathbf{X}_k \equiv (x_{1k}, x_{2k}, \ldots, x_{pk})$.

† See F. N. David, *Tables of the Correlation Coefficient* (Cambridge University Press, Cambridge, 1938).

and

$$\zeta = \frac{1}{2} \log \frac{1 + \rho}{1 - \rho} \tag{7}$$

is approximately normally distributed with mean zero and variance $1/(n - 3)$.

Partial Correlation Coefficients. The product-moment correlation coefficients discussed above do not, in the multivariate case, give an obvious picture of the linear dependence of x_i and x_j on one another. The quantity ρ_{ij} includes not only the direct dependence of x_i on x_j but also indirect dependence arising out of the fact that both x_i and x_j are correlated with the other $p - 2$ variables. A more useful quantity for this purpose is the partial correlation coefficient denoted, for example, by $\rho_{12|3\ldots p}$, which is the correlation coefficient between the variables x_1 and x_2 when the other $p - 2$ variables remain fixed. This is known as a $(p - 2)$-order correlation coefficient; it is a measure of the direct linear dependence of variables x_1 and x_2. Correlation coefficients of intermediate order can be defined as well, but we will not discuss the matter further here. If **B** is the inverse of the variance-covariance matrix $\{\sigma_i\sigma_j\rho_{ij}\}$, we may show that $\rho_{12|3\ldots p}$ is given by the expression

$$\rho_{12|3\ldots p} = \frac{-b_{12}}{(b_{11}b_{22})^{1/2}}, \tag{8}$$

much as the conditional variance of the variable x_1 is given by

$$\sigma^2{}_{1|2\ldots p} = \frac{1}{b_{11}}. \tag{9}$$

The estimates $r_{12|3\ldots p}$ are defined in a similar way, and tests of significance are made as for the zero-order coefficient, except that the number of degrees of freedom is reduced by $p - 2$. Thus, to test the hypothesis

$$\rho_{12|3\ldots p} = 0, \tag{10}$$

we compute

$$t = \left\{ \frac{(n - p)r^2{}_{12|3\ldots p}}{1 - r^2{}_{12|3\ldots p}} \right\}^{1/2} \tag{11}$$

and test as Student's t with $n - p$ degrees of freedom.

Multiple Correlation. The multiple correlation coefficient R_1 defined by

$$1 - R_1{}^2 = \frac{\sigma^2{}_{1|2\ldots p}}{\sigma_1{}^2} \tag{12}$$

is a measure of the *total* linear dependence of the variable x_1 on all the other variables. It is the correlation coefficient between x_1 and the best linear approximation to x_1 by the other variables. It may be estimated by $\hat{R}_1$ defined by

$$1 - \hat{R}_1^2 = \frac{1}{b_{11}s_1^2}. \tag{13}$$

Here we may test the hypothesis

$$H_0: R_1 = 0 \tag{14}$$

by computing

$$F = \frac{\hat{R}_1^2/(p-1)}{(1 - \hat{R}_1^2)/(n-p)} \tag{15}$$

and testing as a variance ratio with $p-1$ and $n-p$ degrees of freedom. For $R_1 \neq 0$, the distribution of $\hat{R}_1^2$ is even more complex than that for the product-moment correlation coefficient, although for large values of n the distribution of $\hat{R}_1^2$ is approximately normal.

Example 5–9–1

The following sets of data were obtained for compounds containing O—H—O hydrogen bonds:

x_1 = O—H distance	x_2 = O—O distance	x_3 = O—H—O angle
1.06	2.52	175
0.97	2.86	156
0.95	2.84	167
1.00	2.56	166
1.01	2.64	171
0.99	2.65	161
1.02	2.72	164
0.94	2.74	171
0.99	2.82	180
0.95	2.90	151
0.96	2.69	168
1.06	2.55	173
0.99	2.80	168

The sample variance-covariance matrix is computed to be

$$\mathbf{M}_x = \frac{1}{12} \begin{pmatrix} 0.018176 & -0.043876 & 1.5910 \\ -0.043876 & 0.189537 & -5.3492 \\ 1.5910 & -5.3492 & 726. \end{pmatrix}.$$

This leads to estimated marginal standard deviations,

$$\hat{\sigma}_1 \equiv s_1 = 0.0389$$
$$\hat{\sigma}_2 \equiv s_2 = 0.1257$$
$$\hat{\sigma}_3 \equiv s_3 = 7.778,$$

and the following correlation matrix:

$$\{r_{ij}\} = \begin{pmatrix} 1.000 & -0.748 & 0.438 \\ -0.748 & 1.000 & -0.456 \\ 0.438 & -0.456 & 1.000 \end{pmatrix}.$$

The inverse matrix is

$$\mathbf{B} = \mathbf{M}_x^{-1} = \begin{pmatrix} 1540.44 & 330.27 & -0.9435 \\ 3302.27 & 150.65 & 0.3869 \\ -0.9435 & 0.3869 & 0.02145 \end{pmatrix}.$$

Estimates of the conditional standard deviations are given by $(1/b_{ii})^{1/2}$:

$$\dot{\sigma}_{1|23} \equiv s_{1|23} = 0.0255$$
$$\dot{\sigma}_{2|13} \equiv s_{2|13} = 0.0815$$
$$\dot{\sigma}_{3|12} \equiv s_{3|12} = 6.828.$$

(These estimates of the conditional standard deviations are biased. Unbiased estimates may be obtained by noting that

$$\mathcal{E}\{s^2_{1|2\ldots p}\} = \frac{n - p + 1}{n} \sigma^2_{1|2\ldots p}.$$

The partial correlation coefficients are found to be

$$r_{12|3} = -0.686$$
$$r_{13|2} = 0.164$$
$$r_{23|1} = -0.215.$$

It is even clearer that there is a marked correlation between variables x_1 and x_2 but not between either of these and the bond angle x_3. Let us make this statement more precise by carrying out the actual hypothesis tests: The tests of the hypotheses on the zero-order coefficients

$$H_0: \rho_{ij} = 0$$

are carried out by computing

$$t(i, j) = \left(\frac{(13 - 2)r^2_{ij}}{1 - r^2_{ij}} \right)^{1/2},$$

$$t(1, 2) = 3.74$$
$$t(1, 3) = 1.62$$
$$t(2, 3) = 1.70.$$

Since $t_{11,0.05} = 2.20$, we conclude that the hypothesis

$$\rho_{12} = 0$$

can be rejected at the 5% level but the other two hypotheses cannot.*
Similarly, we test the partial coefficients by computing

$$t(i, j) = \left(\frac{(13 - 3)r^2_{ij}}{1 - r^2_{ij}} \right)^{1/2}$$

$$t(1, 2) = 2.98$$
$$t(1, 3) = 0.53$$
$$t(2, 3) = 0.70.$$

---

* But watch out for making improper multiple tests. We have not here tested all hypotheses simultaneously.

Since $t_{10,0.05} = 2.23$, we can reject the hypothesis $\rho_{12|3} = 0$ at the 5% significance level. The correlation between the two bond lengths is significant, but that between the bond lengths and the bond angle is small and possibly not significant. We may reach the same conclusions by examining the multiple correlation coefficients

$$\hat{R}_i^2 = 1 - \frac{1}{b_{ii}s_i^2}$$

$$\hat{R}_1^2 = 0.5703$$
$$\hat{R}_2^2 = 0.5796$$
$$\hat{R}_3^2 = 0.2293.$$

The significance of these coefficients may be tested by computing

$$F(i) = \frac{10\hat{R}_i^2}{2(1 - \hat{R}_i^2)}$$

$$F(1) = 6.63$$
$$F(2) = 6.89$$
$$F(3) = 1.49.$$

These are tested against $F_{2,10,0.05} = 4.10$, and only the first two values are significantly different from zero, i.e., the linear approximations of x_1 and x_2 in terms of the other two parameters may be meaningful; the linear approximation of x_3 in terms of x_1 and x_2 is not.

Tests of significance of the correlation coefficients obtained in the usual linear least-squares procedure, e.g., in the refinement of crystal structures, have little meaning, as the correlation coefficients are simply reflections of the structure of the design matrix. It is of some interest, however, to examine their values to gain some insight into the nature of the dependence of the parameters on the observations. The following example gives some indication of this.

Example 5–9–2

In a least-squares fit to a three-component exponential decay curve (see Example 6–1–1), the following correlation matrix was found for the parameters

$$\{r_{ij}\} = \begin{pmatrix} 1.00 & -0.88 & 0.74 \\ -0.88 & 1.00 & -0.90 \\ 0.74 & -0.90 & 1.00 \end{pmatrix}.$$

The large positive correlation between x_1 and x_3 is at first sight somewhat startling, since one would expect any two exponential functions to be negatively correlated. One has only to remember that these correlation coefficients are the zero-order coefficients, and that it is the partial coefficients which give more information about the pair-wise correlations. These one obtains from the matrix inverse to $\{r_{ij}\}$ (or from the original matrix of the normal equations), and in this case they are found to be

$$r_{12|3} = -0.73$$
$$r_{13|2} = -0.25$$
$$r_{23|1} = -0.78.$$

The signs of all are negative as expected, and the magnitude of the correlation between x_1 and x_3 is not great. The large value of the zero-order coefficient arises because x_1 and x_3 are both highly correlated with x_2.

REFERENCES

BARTLETT, M. S. 1935. The effect of non-normality on the t-distribution. *Proc. Cambridge Phil. Soc.* 31, 223–231.

BEALE, E. M. L. 1960. Confidence regions in non-linear estimation. *J. Roy. Statist. Soc.* 22B, 41–88.

Box, G. E. P. 1953. Non-normality and tests on variances. *Biometrika* 40, 318–335.

Box, G. E. P., and H. L. LUCAS. 1959. Design of experiments in non-linear situations. *Biometrika* 46, 77–90.

Box, G. E. P., and G. S. WATSON. 1962. Robustness to non-normality of regression tests. *Biometrika* 49, 93–106.

Box, G. E. P., and K. B. WILSON. 1951. On the experimental attainment of optimum conditions. *J. Roy. Statist. Soc.* 13B, 1–45.

DuMOND, J. W. M., and E. R. COHEN. 1953. Least squares adjustment of the atomic constants, 1952. *Rev. Mod. Phys.* 25, 691–708.

ELFVING, G. 1952. Optimum allocation in regression theory. *Ann. Math. Statist.* 23, 255–262.

HAMILTON, W. C. 1961. On the least-squares plane through a set of points. *Acta Cryst.* 14, 185–189.

HARTLEY, H. O. 1961. The modified Gauss-Newton method for the fitting of non-linear regression functions by least squares. *Technometrics* 3, 269–280.

KIEFER, J. 1959. Optimum experimental designs. *J. Roy. Statist. Soc.* 22B, 271–319.

KIEFER, J., and J. WOLFOWITZ. 1959. Optimum designs in regression problems. *Ann. Math. Statist.* 30, 271–294.

PEARSON, K. 1901. On lines and planes of closest fit to systems of points in space. *Phil. Mag.* 2, 559–572.

RADNER, R. 1958. Minimax estimation for linear regressions. *Ann. Math. Statist.* 29, 1244–1250.

STRAND, T. G., D. A. KOHL, and R. A. BONHAM. 1963. Modification to the Newton. Raphson Method for the fitting of non-linear functions by least squares. *J. Chem. Phys.* 39, 1306–1310.

WATSON, G. S. 1955. Serial correlation in regression analysis. I. *Biometrika* 42, 327–341.

WATSON, G. S. and E. J. Hannan. 1956. Serial correlation in regression analysis. II. *Biometrika* 43, 436–438.

EXERCISES

5–1. Suppose that a set of parameters P is to be determined from a set of observations $f_i(t_i, P)$ of a physical quantity made at times t_i. The functional dependence on the parameters is different at the different times. Further assume that the variance-covariance matrix for the observations is the unit matrix. Let another set of functions $g_j(x_j, P)$ be defined by

$$g_i(x_j, P) = \sum_{i=1}^{n} f_i(t_i, P) \sin (x_j t_i).$$

For some reason, we prefer to estimate the parameters P by a least-squares fit to the functions g_j. Indicate a method for deriving an appropriate weight matrix for the quantities g_j. Is there an optimum choice of the points x_j which would lead to a simple form for the weight matrix? This problem has applications in a number of fields of physics, where the quantities of real interest are often the Fourier transforms of the observations.

5–2. Suppose that least-squares estimates and the variance-covariance matrix are known for the coordinates (x_1, y_1), (x_2, y_2), (x_3, y_3) of three points in the plane. Derive an approximate form for the variance-covariance matrix for the six-parameter set which describes the triangle defined by the three points: the three angles and the three sides. What is the rank of this matrix in the general case? Consider some special cases of your own choice.

5–3. Suppose that a variance-covariance matrix for ten quantities of physical interest is derived from the least-squares variance-covariance matrix for a five-parameter problem. What is the rank of this matrix? Describe a surface of constant probability.

5–4. A least-squares refinement has resulted in values for the parameters

$$x_1, x_2, x_3, x_4, x_5.$$

The quantities of physical interest are r_1 and r_2, where

$$r_1^2 = x_1^2 + x_2^2 + x_3^2$$
$$r_2^2 = x_1^2 + x_4^2 + x_5^2.$$

We desire in one case to test the one-dimensional hypothesis

$$H_0: r_1 = r_2$$

and in a second case to test the two-dimensional hypothesis

$$H_0: r_1 = r_1^0 \quad \text{and} \quad r_2 = r_2^0.$$

How may these hypotheses be linearized in terms of the parameters x_i? Give explicitly the matrices $\mathbf{Q}$ and $\mathbf{Z}$ of Section 4–

5–5. A method formerly much used in the non-linear least-squares refinement of crystal structures is that which ignores the off-diagonal terms in the matrix of the normal equations when these equations are solved, i.e., if $\mathbf{C} = \mathbf{A'PF}$ and $\mathbf{B} = \mathbf{A'PA}$, the approximation sets

$$\Delta x_i = \frac{c_i}{b_{ii}}.$$

If this process converges to a solution, under what circumstances will it converge to the same solution as the "full-matrix" treatment? Can one say anything with regard to the error estimates obtained?

5–6. Compute the product-moment correlation coefficient for the paired data (x, y) that follow, and test the hypothesis that $\rho_{xy} = 0$.

(15, 33), (14, 29), (22, 52), (22, 51), (38, 100), (20, 44),
(22, 46), (16, 27), (35, 68), (49, 133), (17, 34).

5-7. In the refinement of a crystal structure, the generalized R factor (see Section 5-4) was 0.097 for model C including all important parameters. The value of R for model B, with ten linear restraints on the parameters, was 0.100; for model A, with five additional restraints (fifteen in total), it was 0.114. There were 250 data. Test the significance of the improvement in fit in going from model A to model B to model C.

5-8. Derive a method for fitting a circle to points in the plane, assuming that the points have isotropic errors. Use the minimization of the sum of squares of circle-to-point distances along radius vectors as the criterion. Assume that the deviations of the points from the circle are small compared with the radius of the circle. The solution can be expressed in terms of an eigenvalue problem.

5-9. Determine the best least-squares line through the following fifteen points (t, x), assuming that there are no errors in the measurement of t and that the errors in the measurement of x are constant with $\sigma(x) = 0.3$:

$$(1, 2.3), (2, 3.5), (3, 3.5), (4, 4.2), (5, 4.3),$$
$$(6, 5.0), (7, 6.4), (8, 6.6), (9, 6.9), (10, 7.6),$$
$$(11, 9.2), (12, 9.0), (13, 10.4), (14, 10.0), (15, 11.4).$$

5-10. Determine the best least-squares line through the points of Exercise 5-9 if there are also errors in the measurement of t, with $\sigma(t) = 0.10t$.

5-11. Determine the best least-squares line through the points of Exercise 5-9, assuming errors in both x and t and further requiring that the line pass through the point $(0, 0)$. Can we reject the hypothesis that the line passes through the origin?

5-12. Does a quadratic fit of the form $x = a + bt + ct^2$ to the points of Exercise 5-9 (assuming no errors in t) give a significantly better fit than does the straight line? Formulate your answer in terms of a specific hypothesis test.

5-13. Show that when

$$f_1 = a_{11}x_1 + a_{12}x_2$$
$$f_2 = a_{21}x_1 + a_{22}x_2,$$

and f_1 and f_2 are to be estimated by counting Poisson-distributed events, and weights are assigned as $w_i = T_i/f_i$, the experimental design criterion of minimizing $\det (\mathbf{A'PA})^{-1}$ leads to the result that equal times should be spent on the two observations, regardless of the values of f_i and a_{ij}. Does this result hold for the general case when $\mathbf{A}$ is an nth-order square matrix? Show by a counterexample that it is not true for an $n \times m$ matrix $\mathbf{A}$ with $n > m$.

5-14. Discuss the relationship between a large correlation coefficient and a causal relationship.

6

Miscellaneous Applications

6–1. ANALYSIS OF RADIOACTIVE DECAY CURVES

The expected counting rate to be observed in the decay of a single radioactive component is

$$R(t) = xe^{-\lambda t} \tag{1}$$

where x is the counting rate at time $t = 0$ and λ is the decay constant, related to the half-life $t_{1/2}$ by the expression

$$\lambda t_{1/2} = \log_e 2. \tag{2}$$

Frequently the experimentalist is presented with a set of data which is the superposition of several such decay curves, each with a different half-life. The determination of the initial amounts x_i of the individual components is a typical example of a linear least-squares problem. The data to be fit may be expressed in the form

$$R(t_i) = \sum_{j=1}^{m} x_j e^{-\lambda_j t_i} + \epsilon(t_i) \tag{3}$$

The $R(t_i)$ correspond to the f_i of Chapter 4, the x_j are again the parameters to be determined, and the design matrix $\mathbf{A}$ is given by

$$a_{ij} = \exp\left(-\lambda_j t_i\right). \tag{4}$$

It is presumed that the λ_j are known. The problem is linear in the x_j, and no iteration is necessary. Although the errors $\epsilon(t_i)$ in the observed $R(t_i)$ should in general follow a Poisson distribution, we have previously shown that for the purpose of hypothesis tests we need not be especially worried about the departures from normality.

Example 6–1–1

The following data represent the results of a counting experiment in which it is assumed that there are three decaying components with half-lives 9.46 minutes, 20.40 minutes, and 110.00 minutes:

t_i	$R(t_i)$	$\hat{\sigma}(R)$
0.00	22458.	149.75
2.00	19784.	140.57
44.00	1499.2	27.468
47.00	1347.7	26.053
80.60	451.02	12.410
83.70	434.52	14.908

The least-squares analysis carried out in the usual way results in

$$\hat{x}_1 = 20669. \qquad \hat{\sigma}(\hat{x}_1) = 246.3$$
$$\hat{x}_2 = 1392.1 \qquad \hat{\sigma}(\hat{x}_2) = 222.7$$
$$\hat{x}_3 = 513.52 \qquad \hat{\sigma}(\hat{x}_3) = 34.0$$

where the estimated standard deviations $\hat{\sigma}(\hat{x}_i)$ are derived by multiplying the square root of the appropriate element of the matrix $\mathbf{B}^{-1}$ by the goodness-of-fit parameter $(\mathbf{V'PV}/(n - m))^{1/2} = 1.046$, which is satisfyingly close to unity, indicating that the weights have been properly chosen and that the theoretical model of three components is satisfactory.* The correlation matrix is

$$\begin{pmatrix} 1.00 & -0.88 & 0.74 \\ -0.88 & 1.00 & -0.90 \\ 0.74 & -0.90 & 1.00 \end{pmatrix},$$

thus illustrating the extreme non-orthogonality of exponential functions, even when the half-lives are (see Example 5–9–2) well separated.

In this particular case, it is of interest to test the hypothesis

$$H_0: x_2 = 0.$$

We compute

$$t = \frac{1392.1 - 0.0}{222.7}$$

$$= 6.251$$

and test as Student's t with $6 - 3 = 3$ degrees of freedom.

$$t_{3,0.01} = 5.84$$
$$t_{3,0.005} = 7.453.$$

The hypothesis can be rejected at the 1% significance level. The

---

* The two estimates of $\hat{\sigma}^2$, that from the fit of the model to the data and that from the knowledge that the observations are Poisson-distributed, are in good agreement.

least-squares fit can also be carried out, omitting the second component completely. The resulting parameter values are

$$\hat{x}_1 = 22025 \qquad \hat{\sigma}(\hat{x}_1) = 379$$
$$\hat{x}_3 = 705.6 \qquad \hat{\sigma}(\hat{x}_3) = 47.0.$$

The goodness-of-fit parameter, $(\mathbf{V'PV}/(n - m))^{1/2}$, is 3.392 for this case, suggesting that the omission of component two was not wise, as we have already seen from the hypothesis test above. The hypothesis may also be tested in the following way: Compute the increase in the weighted sum of squares due to the hypothesis, divide by the minimum weighted sum of squares, and test as $F_{1,n-m}/(n - m)$. We have

$$\frac{(\mathbf{V'PV})_1 - (\mathbf{V'PV})_0}{(\mathbf{V'PV})_0/(n - m)} = \frac{46.024 - 3.282}{3.282/3} = 39.07.$$

This, of course, is merely the square of the t computed above for the same hypothesis, and the hypothesis can again be rejected at the 1% level, since

$$F_{1,3,0.01} = t^2{}_{1,3,0.01} = 34.12.$$

In a non-linear least-squares situation, the two tests would probably not give the same result, and the latter test, which actually compares the sums of squares, would be preferred.

In many cases, it will be of interest to estimate not only values for the initial activities x_j but also the decay constants λ_j. The problem then is no longer linear. Although it may be linearized by the usual Taylor expansion, a more convenient approach,* which gives the identical results, is as follows: We assume that an approximate value for λ_j is available and that we are to determine corrections $\Delta\lambda_j$. We have

$$R(t_i) = \sum_j x_j \exp\left[-(\lambda_j t_i + \Delta\lambda_j t_i)\right] + \epsilon(t_i)$$
$$= \sum_j x_j \exp\left(-\lambda_j t_i\right) \exp\left(-\Delta\lambda_j t_i\right) + \epsilon(t_i) \tag{5}$$

We assume that the $\Delta\lambda_j$ are small enough so that we may express the exponential as the sum of its first two terms:

$$R(t_i) = \sum_j x_j \exp\left(-\lambda_j t_i\right)(1 - \Delta\lambda_j t_i) + \epsilon(t_i)$$
$$= \sum_j x_j \exp\left(-\lambda_j t_i\right) - x_j \Delta\lambda_j t_i \exp\left(-\lambda_j t_i\right) + \epsilon(t_i) \tag{6}$$

These equations are linear in the x_j and $\Delta\lambda_j x_j$, and these quantities are estimated by solving the normal equations in the usual way. The elements

* This method was brought to the author's attention by Dr. James Cumming.

of the design matrix are of the form $\exp(-\lambda_j t_i)$ and $-t_i \exp(-\lambda_j t_i)$. The procedure must be iterated until the $\Delta\lambda_j$ are zero.

The resulting error matrix for the parameters will of course refer to the quantities x_j and to $x_j \Delta\lambda_j$ rather than to the quantities of interest x_j and $\Delta\lambda_j$. It is satisfactory in most instances to set

$$\hat{\sigma}^2(\Delta\lambda_j) = \frac{\hat{\sigma}^2(x_j\Delta\lambda_j)}{\hat{x}_j{}^2}. \tag{7}$$

That this is likely to be a good approximation may be seen as follows: We have shown (Eq. (30) of Section 1–6) that, if x_j and $\Delta\lambda_j$ are statistically independent (not likely to be true here), we may write

$$\sigma^2(x_j\Delta\lambda_j) = \sigma^2(x_j)\sigma^2(\Delta\lambda_j) + x_j{}^2\sigma^2(\Delta\lambda_j) + \Delta\lambda_j{}^2\sigma^2(x_j). \tag{8}$$

The third term in this expression will, at convergence, be zero, and, if the relative error in $\hat{x}_j$ is small, the first term will be negligible compared with the second. Setting all quantities in Eq. (8) equal to their expected values, and dividing through by $\hat{x}_j{}^2$, we obtain the required result. It will usually be of interest to quote the error in the half-life rather than in the decay constant, and it is generally assumed that the relative errors are the same in the two quantities:

$$\frac{\hat{\sigma}(\hat{t}_{1/2})}{\hat{t}_{1/2}} = \frac{\hat{\sigma}(\hat{\lambda})}{\hat{\lambda}}. \tag{9}$$

This again is a good approximation provided the relative errors are small.

In performing hypothesis tests on the parameters or functions involving them, the effects of the non-linearities should of course be carefully examined. It should further be noted that it will in general not be possible to vary both the initial activities and the decay constants for many components, on account of the extreme non-orthogonality of the problem. No hard and fast rules can be given for such refinements, but it is clear that one should gain some experience in least-squares fits in this type of problem before quoting results with great confidence.

Example 6–1–2

A five-component decay curve with half-lives of 112 minutes, 10 minutes, 20.4 minutes, 15 hours, and 1 year was analyzed by the least-squares technique. The data points were taken at 10-minute to 30-minute intervals for the first day, and then less frequently to the last point at approximately $4\frac{1}{2}$ days. The last four half-lives were considered to be well known, and the first was refined, along with all the initial activities, by the method described above. Two iterations were required to produce convergence, the sequence of decay constants being

$$0.0061888 \rightarrow 0.0063039 \rightarrow 0.0063044.$$

The parameters obtained on the final iteration, together with their estimated standard deviations, were as follows:

$$\hat{x}_1 = 70355; \qquad \hat{\sigma}_1 = 420$$
$$\hat{x}_2 = 10680; \qquad \hat{\sigma}_2 = 2149$$
$$\hat{x}_3 = 95741; \qquad \hat{\sigma}_3 = 1960$$
$$\hat{x}_4 = 11616; \qquad \hat{\sigma}_4 = 276$$
$$\hat{x}_5 = 35; \qquad \hat{\sigma}_5 = 5$$

$$\widehat{x_1 \Delta \lambda_1} = 3.38 \times 10^{-2}; \qquad \hat{\sigma} = 1.87$$

The correlation matrix was

$$\begin{pmatrix} 1.00 & 0.58 & -0.78 & 0.04 & -0.03 & 0.88 \\ 0.58 & 1.00 & -0.92 & 0.02 & -0.02 & 0.47 \\ -0.78 & -0.92 & 1.00 & -0.03 & 0.03 & -0.66 \\ 0.04 & 0.02 & -0.03 & 1.00 & -0.04 & 0.07 \\ -0.03 & -0.02 & 0.03 & -0.04 & 1.00 & -0.11 \\ 0.88 & 0.47 & -0.66 & 0.07 & -0.11 & 1.00 \end{pmatrix}.$$

The value of $\Delta \lambda_1$ was estimated as

$$\widehat{\Delta \lambda_1} = \frac{3.3813 \times 10^{-2}}{70355}$$

$$= 4.8 \times 10^{-7}$$

corresponding to the value 0.0063044 for $\hat{\lambda}_1$ quoted above. The standard deviation of $\hat{\lambda}_1$ was estimated by dividing the estimated standard deviation in $\widehat{x_1 \Delta \lambda_1}$ by x_i:

$$\hat{\sigma}(\hat{\lambda}_1) = \frac{1.87}{70355} = 0.0000266.$$

The half-life of component number one was estimated to be

$$\hat{t}_{1/2}(1) = 109.946 \text{ minutes}$$

with an estimated standard deviation of

$$\hat{\sigma}(\hat{t}_{1/2}) = \hat{t}_{1/2} \frac{\hat{\sigma}(\hat{\lambda})}{\hat{\lambda}}$$

$$= \frac{109.946 \times 2.66 \times 10^{-5}}{6.3044 \times 10^{-3}}$$

$$= 0.464 \text{ minutes.}$$

This procedure for estimating the error in the half-life from the error in $\widehat{x_1 \Delta \lambda_1}$, although not rigorous, is a satisfactory approximation provided that the relative errors in $\hat{x}_1$ and in $\widehat{x_1 \Delta \lambda_1}$ are small, i.e., that

$$\hat{\sigma}(\hat{x}_1) \ll \hat{x}_1$$

and

$$\hat{\sigma}\widehat{(x_1 \Delta \lambda_1)} \ll \widehat{x_1 \Delta \lambda_1}.$$

Example 6-1-3

Consider the case of a two-component decay curve:

$$R_i = x_1 e^{-\lambda_1 t_i} + x_2 e^{-\lambda_2 t_i}.$$

We wish to estimate only the values of x_1 and x_2. Assuming unit weights, the matrix of the normal equations becomes

$$\mathbf{B} = \begin{pmatrix} \sum_i e^{-2\lambda_1 t_i} & \sum_i e^{-(\lambda_1 + \lambda_2) t_i} \\ \sum_i e^{-(\lambda_1 + \lambda_2) t_i} & \sum_i e^{-2\lambda_2 t_i} \end{pmatrix}.$$

If we assume that the points are closely spaced, we may replace each sum by an integral from $t = 0$ to $t = t_f$ where t_f is the final time. The matrix thus becomes

$$\mathbf{B} = \begin{pmatrix} \dfrac{1}{2\lambda_1}(1 - e^{-2\lambda_1 t_f}) & \dfrac{1}{\lambda_1 + \lambda_2}(1 - e^{-(\lambda_1 + \lambda_2) t_f}) \\ \dfrac{1}{\lambda_1 + \lambda_2}(1 - e^{-(\lambda_1 + \lambda_2) t_f}) & \dfrac{1}{2\lambda_2}(1 - e^{-2\lambda_2 t_f}) \end{pmatrix}.$$

The correlation coefficient ρ between $\hat{x}_1$ and $\hat{x}_2$ is given by

$$\rho = -\frac{b_{12}}{(b_{11} b_{22})^{1/2}}.$$

The value of the correlation coefficient is thus -1 if $\lambda_1 = \lambda_2$ or if t_f is small compared with the half-lives, as we might expect. The resolution of the two components should become better as the time of the experiment increases, and indeed it does. Note, however, that as the counting time t_f becomes infinite, the correlation coefficient approaches the limiting value of

$$\rho_{\lim} = -2\frac{(\lambda_1 \lambda_2)^{1/2}}{\lambda_1 + \lambda_2} = -\frac{2R^{1/2}}{1 + R}$$

where R is the ratio of the decay constants. If

$$R \ll 1 \quad \text{or} \quad R \gg 1,$$

the correlation coefficient is small. Even for a value of $R = 10$, though, the correlation coefficient is still as large as -0.57. This example gives some indication of why it may be difficult to refine a large number of components at the same time, particularly if the decay constants do not differ greatly. This is but another manifestation of the non-orthogonality of exponential functions.

Example 6–1–4

Counting data were collected for a mixture containing approximately equal quantities of a component with a 12.4-hour half-life and one with a 15.0-hour half-life. The count was carried out to about 70 hours, at which point the counting rate of the 12.4-hour half-life component should be about half that for the 15.0 hour component. The initial amounts of the two components were estimated by least squares. The data for the seventy points will not be reproduced here. The results were

$$\hat{x}_1 = 43142 \qquad \hat{\sigma}_1 = 323$$
$$\hat{x}_2 = 36898 \qquad \hat{\sigma}_2 = 236.$$

The matrix of the normal equations was

$$\mathbf{B} = \begin{pmatrix} 2.9502 \times 10^{-4} & 3.9692 \times 10^{-4} \\ 3.9692 \times 10^{-4} & 5.5190 \times 10^{-4} \end{pmatrix},$$

and its inverse was

$$\mathbf{B}^{-1} = \begin{pmatrix} 10.460 \times 10^4 & -7.5230 \times 10^4 \\ -7.523 \times 10^4 & 5.5916 \times 10^4 \end{pmatrix},$$

leading to the estimated standard deviations quoted above and a correlation coefficient of -0.984. It is interesting that the large correlation coefficient did not prevent a solution with reasonably small error estimates. Clearly, however, there is some linear dependence between the two parameters, as one would expect. To find the parameter estimates which are independent of one another in the fit, we diagonalize the matrix $\mathbf{B}$ and find for the eigenvectors $\mathbf{T}$ and eigenvalues ϵ

$$\mathbf{T}_1 = (\ \ 0.5880 \quad 0.8083); \qquad \epsilon_1 = 8.406 \times 10^{-4}$$
$$\mathbf{T}_2 = (-0.8083 \quad 0.5880); \qquad \epsilon_2 = 0.063 \times 10^{-4}.$$

Since $\epsilon_i = 1/\hat{\sigma}_i{}^2$, we have for the independent parameters

$$\hat{y}_1 = \ \ \ 0.5880\hat{x}_1 + 0.8083\hat{x}_2 = \ \ \ 55191, \quad \hat{\sigma}(\hat{y}_1) = \ \ 34$$
$$\hat{y}_2 = -0.8083\hat{x}_1 + 0.5880\hat{x}_2 = -13176, \quad \hat{\sigma}(\hat{y}_2) = 400.$$

It is of some interest to look at the simpler linear functions:

$$z_1 = x_1 + x_2$$
$$z_2 = x_1 - x_2.$$

The moment matrix for $\mathbf{Z}$ is

$$\mathbf{M}_z = \begin{pmatrix} 1 & 1 \\ 1 & -1 \end{pmatrix} \mathbf{M}_x \begin{pmatrix} 1 & 1 \\ 1 & -1 \end{pmatrix} = \begin{pmatrix} 10056 & 48684 \\ 48684 & 310976 \end{pmatrix}.$$

Thus

$$\hat{z}_1 = 80040, \quad \hat{\sigma}(\hat{z}_1) = 100$$
$$\hat{z}_2 = 6244, \quad \hat{\sigma}(\hat{z}_2) = 558.$$

The correlation coefficient is still large, namely

$$\rho_{12} = 0.87.$$

An attempt to refine the decay constants simultaneously led to a matrix so nearly singular that no solution could be obtained. This appears to be a general phenomenon, namely that while the initial amounts of two components with nearly equal half-lives can be determined, the degeneracy prohibits the refinements of the half-lives themselves.

6–2. REFINEMENT OF FORCE CONSTANTS FROM INFRARED SPECTRA

The molecular vibrational problem may be analyzed in terms of a vector of *normal coordinates* **Q** such that the kinetic energy T and the potential energy V for the harmonic motion are given by

$$2T = \dot{\mathbf{Q}}'\dot{\mathbf{Q}} \tag{1}$$
$$2V = \mathbf{Q}'\boldsymbol{\Lambda}\mathbf{Q} \tag{2}$$

where $\boldsymbol{\Lambda}$ is a diagonal matrix with elements λ_j related to the normal frequencies of vibration ν_j by

$$\lambda_j = 4\pi^2 c^2 \nu_j^2.* \tag{3}$$

The λ_j are referred to as the *force constants* of the normal vibrations.

The structural chemist is usually more interested in the vibrations in terms of internal coordinates **R**, which may be bond lengths, bond angles, etc. These will be related to the normal coordinates by a linear transformation **L** such that

$$\mathbf{R} = \mathbf{L}\mathbf{Q}. \tag{4}$$

In terms of these coordinates, the kinetic energy and potential energy are given by

$$2T = \dot{\mathbf{R}}'\mathbf{G}^{-1}\dot{\mathbf{R}} \tag{5}$$
$$2V = \mathbf{R}'\mathbf{F}\mathbf{R}. \tag{6}$$

In Eq. (5), **G** is a matrix which can be derived from the geometry of the molecule, i.e., the relationship between **R** and the Cartesian displacement coordinates of the molecule. The matrix **F** is a matrix of force constants for the internal coordinates.

The problem of finding the normal coordinates and normal frequencies, given the matrices **F** and **G**, is the problem of finding a transformation matrix **L** such that

$$\mathbf{L}'\mathbf{F}\mathbf{L} = \boldsymbol{\Lambda} \quad \text{and} \quad \mathbf{L}'\mathbf{G}^{-1}\mathbf{L} = \mathbf{I}, \tag{7}$$

* Here c is the velocity of light.

where $\mathbf{I}$ is the unit matrix. The solution of this problem is the familiar one of finding the eigenvalues λ_j of the matrix $\mathbf{F}$ in a space with metric $\mathbf{G}$:

$$(\mathbf{F} - \lambda_j \mathbf{G}^{-1})\mathbf{L}_j = 0 \tag{8}$$

where $\mathbf{L}_j$ is the jth column of the matrix $\mathbf{L}$, i.e., the eigenvector corresponding to the eigenvalue λ_j. In complete matrix form, we may write

$$\mathbf{GFL} = \mathbf{L}\Lambda. \tag{9}$$

Thus, knowing the force constants $\mathbf{F}$, we can determine Λ and hence the normal frequencies. More often, however, the problem is to determine the force constants from the observed frequencies.

In the general case of the N-atomic, non-linear, non-symmetric molecule, there will be $3N - 6$ values λ_j and $(3N - 6)(3N - 5)/2$ force constants corresponding to the terms of the symmetric matrix $\mathbf{F}$. Thus there are many more unknowns than there are observations. In order to solve the problem, it is necessary to assume that the force constants are not independent but may be expressed in terms of an independent set which contains fewer non-zero force constants than the number of observed frequencies. Such a set might be, for example, one which assumes only central forces between the atoms, i.e., assumes that there would be a non-zero force constant corresponding to each pair of atoms but that others would be zero. Even when such a set of force constants is chosen, there still may not be enough observations to permit a solution of the problem. Usually then it is assumed that the same set of force constants may be valid for a group of similar molecules. This is certainly a good assumption for isotopically substituted molecules and may hold for a homologous series of molecules.

Suppose that a set of independent force constants has been chosen, and that there are more observed frequencies than force constants. For each molecule, the expression

$$\mathbf{L'FL} = \Lambda \tag{10}$$

may be written

$$\lambda_i = \sum_{k,l} L'_{ik} F_{kl} L_{li} \tag{11}$$

$$= \sum_{k,l} L_{ki} L_{li} F_{kl}. \tag{12}$$

We assume that each of the force constants F_{kl} may be expressed in terms of the independent set ϕ_j $(j = 1, \ldots, p)$ by

$$F_{kl} = \sum_{j} C_{kl,j} \phi_j \tag{13}$$

where the $C_{kl,j}$ may be derived from the molecular geometry and the assumptions about the force constants. We may then write

$$\lambda_i = \sum_{k,l,j} L_{ki}L_{li}C_{kl,j}\phi_j. \tag{14}$$

Defining a design matrix

$$\mathbf{A} \equiv \{a_{ij}\} \tag{15}$$

with

$$a_{ij} = \sum_{k,l} L_{ki}L_{li}C_{kl,j}, \tag{16}$$

we have

$$\lambda_i = \sum_j a_{ij}\phi_j, \tag{17}$$

or

$$\Delta\lambda_i = \sum_j a_{ij}\Delta\phi_j, \tag{18}$$

which may be cast in our usual least-squares notation

$$\mathbf{F} = \mathbf{A}\mathbf{X} \tag{19}$$

by defining

$$\mathbf{F} = \begin{pmatrix} \Delta\lambda_1 \\ \Delta\lambda_2 \\ \cdot \\ \cdot \\ \cdot \\ \Delta\lambda_n \end{pmatrix} \quad \text{and} \quad \mathbf{X} = \begin{pmatrix} \Delta\phi_1 \\ \Delta\phi_2 \\ \cdot \\ \cdot \\ \cdot \\ \Delta\phi_p \end{pmatrix}. \tag{20}$$

As a practical procedure, the force constants are estimated and the eigenvalue equation is solved to obtain the matrix $\mathbf{L}$ and the eigenvalues λ_i^{calc}. The design matrix $\mathbf{A}$ may be computed from the values of $\mathbf{L}$ so obtained together with the known coefficients $C_{kl,j}$. Setting

$$\Delta\lambda_i = \lambda_i^{\text{obs}} - \lambda_i^{\text{calc}}, \tag{21}$$

we set up the least-squares equations and solve in the usual way for the corrections to the force constants $\Delta\phi_j$. Using the corrected force constants, the process is repeated until convergence is obtained. The weight matrix $\mathbf{P}$ is usually taken to be proportional to Λ^{-1}, which means that the variance of λ_i is assumed to be proportional to λ_i or, equivalently, that the standard deviation of the frequency ν_i is independent of ν. Clearly, this assumption should be modified if actual estimates of error for the individual frequencies are available.

Since any practical computation will assume some simplification of the force field for the reduction of the number of force constants refined, it must be emphasized that any solution for the values of the force constants has only as much meaning as the physical reasonableness of the model allows. The answers must be looked at in the light of the following statement: If the force model used is correct, then these $\hat{\phi}_j$ and $\hat{\sigma}(\hat{\phi}_j)$ are the best values for the force constants and their associated errors. Because of the extreme non-linear character of the eigenvalue problem, it is quite possible that two different non-equivalent force-field models may give equally good fits to the data. For the same reasons of non-linearity, some care should be taken in making hypothesis tests on the force constants, even when the model is assumed to be adequate. It is, however, still quite possible to ask whether addition of an additional force constant will significantly improve the agreement. One may, as usual, examine the increase in the sum of squares when this constant is omitted, and test as a variance ratio.

An excellent example of the least-squares technique as applied to this problem has been given by Schachtschneider and Snyder (1963) who have obtained good fits for 190 fundamental frequencies in 14 normal paraffins by assuming a valence force field with 33 independent force constants.

6–3. APPLICATION OF THE LEAST-SQUARES METHOD TO CRYSTALLOGRAPHY

A very common use of least-squares refinement in recent years has been in the field of crystallography. Although numerous examples from crystallography have been spread through the book, it is perhaps useful to state the general problem for the education of those unfamiliar with the field. In general, the intensity of an x-ray or neutron reflection from a crystal can be written

$$I(\mathbf{h}) = g(\theta)K\left|\sum_j f_j \exp\left(-\mathbf{h}'\mathbf{B}_j\mathbf{h}\right)\exp\left(-2\pi i\mathbf{h}'\mathbf{x}_j\right)\right|^2 \qquad (1)$$

where $\mathbf{h}$ is a vector giving the Miller indices of the reflection, $\mathbf{x}_j$ is a vector giving the position of the jth atom, f_j is a scattering factor for the jth atom (which may be dependent on θ, the scattering angle), $\mathbf{B}_j$ is a "temperature factor" matrix, $g(\theta)$ is a structure independent angle factor, K is a scale factor which may not be the same for all reflections but is constant over groups of reflections, and the summation is over all atoms j in the unit cell.

Once a satisfactory trial crystal structure is obtained, usually by trial and error or Fourier methods, the final values of the parameters (which may include K, f_j, the components of $\mathbf{B}_j$, and the components of $\mathbf{x}_j$) are usually obtained by carrying out a least-squares refinement on intensities I, the structure factors $F = (I/g(\theta))^{1/2}$, or F^2. As the errors in the intensities are rarely less than 5%, the ratio of the number of observations to the number of parameters is generally much greater than in some other applications of the least-squares technique. Typical problems in x-ray diffraction involve the determination of 100 parameters from 1000 pieces of data. Problems much larger or smaller than this are not uncommon, however.

It is easily seen that the problem is very non-linear. On the other hand, the errors in the parameters in a high quality investigation are generally small enough so that the problem is essentially linear in the parameter increments. The design matrix is thus composed of the first derivatives of the intensities with respect to the parameters. In current practice, these are usually evaluated explicitly from the analytical expressions, although some computer programs have been written which employ numerical evaluation of these derivatives. Serious problems in non-linearity can arise when the atom is located on or near a symmetry element in the crystal so that the first derivative is actually or approximately equal to zero. Such problems can usually be recognized and handled in a variety of ways, as suggested in Section 5–3.

Perhaps the greatest difficulty in this application of the least-squares method is that refinement is often begun before a really satisfactory trial structure is obtained. The intensities oscillate because of the trigonometric functions of the positional parameters which are involved, and if many of the parameters are on the wrong side of the resulting wave crests, the problem may well not converge to the correct answer. Occasionally structures which are very close to the correct one, but which will not converge to it, are found. (See, for example, Stout and Jensen (1962).)

Since the problems may often involve hundreds of parameters, large correlation coefficients between the parameters may cause some difficulty in the solution. Correlation coefficients near unity mean that the matrix of the normal equations is almost singular and that great care must be taken in its inversion. Frequently the failure of least-squares refinements to converge properly is the result of insufficient accuracy in the matrix-inversion step. With large ill-conditioned matrices, even the routine eight- to twelve-place accuracy of modern digital computers is not sufficient to produce a satisfactory solution. It should be emphasized that large correlation coefficients do not in theory prevent a refinement from converging satisfactorily, nor do they prevent the attainment of satisfactorily small errors in the parameter estimates. The principal troubles in this regard probably come from computational difficulties. Large correlations are likely to arise between temperature-factor parameters and scale factors. In complex situations, subtle relationships which cause large correlations between parameters may not be easily predicted or understood. Provided the correlations do not cause trouble in the matrix-inversion step, they should give no cause for worry, as their effects are adequately accounted for in the estimates of the marginal standard deviations and in the variance-covariance matrix.

REFERENCES

Busing, W. R., K. O. Martin, and H. A. Levy, 1962. ORFLS, a Fortran crystallographic least squares program. Oak Ridge National Laboratory Report ORNLTM-305.
Hedberg, K., and M. Iwasaki. 1964. Least squares refinement of molecular structures from gaseous electron-diffraction sector-microphotometer intensity data. I. Method. *Acta Cryst.* 17, 529–533.

HODGSON, L. I., and J. S. ROLLETT. 1963. An acceleration device and standard deviation estimates in least squares refinements of crystal structures. *Acta Cryst.* 16, 329–335.

HUGHES, E. W. 1941. The crystal structure of melamine. *J. Am. Chem. Soc.* 63, 1737–1752.

MERTS, A. L., and M. D. TORREY. 1963. Some analytic solutions of the Hartree-Fock equations by an iterative least squares method. *J. Chem. Phys.* 39, 694–700.

OVEREND, J., and J. R. SCHERER. 1960. Transferability of Urey-Bradley force constants. I. Calculation of force constants on a digital computer. II. Carbonyl hydrides and related molecules. *J. Chem. Phys.* 32, 1289–1303.

SCHACHTSCHNEIDER, J. H., and R. G. SNYDER. 1963. Vibrational analysis of the *n*-paraffins. II. Normal coordinate calculations. *Spectrochim. Acta* 19, 85–116.

STOUT, G. H., and L. H. JENSEN. 1962. Variable weighting and the solution of the false structure of rubrofusarin. *Acta Cryst.* 15, 1060–1061.

EXERCISE

6–1. Given a radioactive decay curve composed of two components with decay constants λ_1 and λ_2 and initial activities in the ratio $x_1/x_2 = R$. Derive an expression for preparing charts indicating combinations of initial total activity and counting times necessary to achieve a power of at least 95% in distinguishing between the two hypotheses,

$$H_0: \lambda_1 = \lambda_2$$
$$H_1: \lambda_1 = 1.1\lambda_2.$$

Appendix: Tables

TABLE I

Cumulative Normal Distribution

Values of $Y = \int_{-\infty}^{X} \phi(x)\, dx$ for $X = 0.00[0.01]2.99$

$X \rightarrow$ ↓	0.00	0.01	0.02	0.03	0.04	0.05	0.06	0.07	0.08	0.09
0.0	.5000	.5040	.5080	.5120	.5159	.5199	.5239	.5279	.5319	.5359
0.1	.5398	.5438	.5478	.5517	.5557	.5596	.5636	.5675	.5714	.5753
0.2	.5793	.5832	.5871	.5910	.5948	.5987	.6026	.6064	.6103	.6141
0.3	.6179	.6217	.6255	.6293	.6331	.6368	.6406	.6443	.6480	.6517
0.4	.6554	.6591	.6628	.6664	.6700	.6736	.6772	.6808	.6844	.6879
0.5	.6915	.6950	.6985	.7019	.7054	.7088	.7123	.7157	.7190	.7224
0.6	.7257	.7291	.7324	.7357	.7389	.7422	.7454	.7486	.7517	.7549
0.7	.7580	.7611	.7642	.7673	.7704	.7734	.7764	.7794	.7823	.7852
0.8	.7881	.7910	.7939	.7967	.7995	.8023	.8051	.8078	.8106	.8133
0.9	.8159	.8186	.8212	.8238	.8264	.8289	.8315	.8340	.8365	.8389
1.0	.8413	.8438	.8461	.8485	.8508	.8531	.8554	.8577	.8599	.8621
1.1	.8643	.8665	.8686	.8708	.8729	.8749	.8770	.8790	.8810	.8830
1.2	.8849	.8869	.8888	.8907	.8925	.8944	.8962	.8980	.8997	.9015
1.3	.9032	.9049	.9066	.9082	.9099	.9115	.9131	.9147	.9162	.9177
1.4	.9192	.9207	.9222	.9236	.9251	.9265	.9279	.9292	.9306	.9319
1.5	.9332	.9345	.9357	.9370	.9382	.9394	.9406	.9418	.9429	.9441
1.6	.9452	.9463	.9474	.9484	.9495	.9505	.9515	.9525	.9535	.9545
1.7	.9554	.9564	.9573	.9582	.9591	.9599	.9608	.9616	.9625	.9633
1.8	.9641	.9649	.9656	.9664	.9671	.9678	.9686	.9693	.9699	.9706
1.9	.9713	.9719	.9726	.9732	.9738	.9744	.9750	.9756	.9761	.9767
2.0	.9772	.9778	.9783	.9788	.9793	.9798	.9803	.9808	.9812	.9817
2.1	.9821	.9826	.9830	.9834	.9838	.9842	.9846	.9850	.9854	.9857
2.2	.9861	.9864	.9868	.9871	.9875	.9878	.9881	.9884	.9887	.9890
2.3	.9893	.9896	.9898	.9901	.9904	.9906	.9909	.9911	.9913	.9916
2.4	.9918	.9920	.9922	.9925	.9927	.9929	.9931	.9932	.9934	.9936
2.5	.9938	.9940	.9941	.9943	.9945	.9946	.9948	.9949	.9951	.9952
2.6	.9953	.9955	.9956	.9957	.9959	.9960	.9961	.9962	.9963	.9964
2.7	.9965	.9966	.9967	.9968	.9969	.9970	.9971	.9972	.9973	.9974
2.8	.9974	.9975	.9976	.9977	.9977	.9978	.9979	.9979	.9980	.9981
2.9	.9981	.9982	.9982	.9983	.9984	.9984	.9985	.9985	.9986	.9986

TABLE Ia

Percentage Points of the Normal Distribution

Values of X_P, where $\int_{-X_P}^{X_P} \phi(x)\, dx = 1 - P$ *

P	X_P	P	X_P
0	∞	0.025	2.241
10^{-9}	6.109	0.050	1.960
10^{-8}	5.731	0.100	1.645
10^{-7}	5.327	0.250	1.150
10^{-6}	4.892	0.500	0.674
10^{-5}	4.417	0.750	0.319
10^{-4}	3.891	0.900	0.126
10^{-3}	3.291	0.950	0.063
10^{-2}	2.576	0.990	0.0125

* P is thus the probability in the two tails of the normal distribution.

TABLE II

Percentage Points of Student's t Distribution*

Values of $t_{\nu,\alpha}$, where α is the probability that $|t| \geqslant t_{\nu,\alpha}$, ν is the number of degrees of freedom, and $\int_{-t_{\nu,\alpha}}^{+t_{\nu,\alpha}} \phi(t)\, dt = 1 - \alpha$ †

ν \ α	0.50	0.25	0.10	0.05	0.025	0.010	0.005
1	1.000	2.414	6.314	12.706	25.452	63.657	127.32
2	0.817	1.604	2.920	4.303	6.205	9.925	14.089
3	0.765	1.423	2.353	3.183	4.177	5.841	7.453
4	0.741	1.344	2.132	2.776	3.495	4.604	5.598
5	0.727	1.301	2.015	2.571	3.163	4.032	4.773
6	0.718	1.273	1.943	2.447	2.969	3.707	4.317
7	0.711	1.254	1.895	2.365	2.841	3.500	4.029
8	0.706	1.240	1.860	2.306	2.752	3.355	3.833
9	0.703	1.230	1.833	2.262	2.685	3.250	3.690
10	0.700	1.221	1.813	2.228	2.634	3.169	3.581
11	0.697	1.215	1.796	2.201	2.593	3.106	3.500
12	0.695	1.209	1.782	2.179	2.560	3.055	3.428
13	0.694	1.204	1.771	2.160	2.533	3.012	3.373
14	0.692	1.200	1.761	2.145	2.510	2.977	3.326
15	0.691	1.197	1.753	2.132	2.490	2.947	3.286
20	0.687	1.185	1.725	2.086	2.423	2.845	3.153
25	0.684	1.178	1.708	2.060	2.385	2.787	3.078
30	0.683	1.173	1.697	2.042	2.360	2.750	3.030
40	0.681	1.167	1.684	2.021	2.329	2.705	2.971
60	0.679	1.162	1.671	2.000	2.299	2.660	2.915
120	0.677	1.156	1.658	1.980	2.270	2.617	2.860
∞	0.674	1.150	1.645	1.960	2.241	2.576	2.807

* Adapted from the tables prepared by Maxine Merrington for *Biometrika*, vol. 32; reproduced with permission of the editors of *Biometrika*.
† α is thus a two-tailed probability.

TABLE III

Percentage Points of the χ^2 Distribution*†

Values of $\chi^2_{n,\alpha}$, where α is the probability that χ^2 exceeds $\chi^2_{n\cdot\alpha}$, and

$$\int_0^{\chi^2_{n,\alpha}} \phi(\chi^2)\, d\chi^2 = 1 - \alpha \ddagger$$

α / n	0.995	0.990	0.975	0.950	0.500	0.050	0.025	0.010	0.005
1	0.00+	0.00+	0.00+	0.00+	0.45	3.84	5.02	6.63	7.88
2	0.01	0.02	0.05	0.10	1.39	5.99	7.38	9.21	10.60
3	0.07	0.11	0.22	0.35	2.37	7.81	9.35	11.34	12.84
4	0.21	0.30	0.48	0.71	3.36	9.49	11.14	13.28	14.86
5	0.41	0.55	0.83	1.15	4.35	11.07	12.83	15.09	16.75
6	0.68	0.87	1.24	1.64	5.35	12.59	14.45	16.81	18.55
7	0.99	1.24	1.69	2.17	6.35	14.07	16.01	18.48	20.28
8	1.34	1.65	2.18	2.73	7.34	15.51	17.53	20.09	21.96
9	1.73	2.09	2.70	3.33	8.34	16.92	19.02	21.67	23.59
10	2.16	2.56	3.25	3.94	9.34	18.31	20.48	23.21	25.19
11	2.60	3.05	3.82	4.57	10.34	19.68	21.92	24.72	26.76
12	3.07	3.57	4.40	5.23	11.34	21.03	23.34	26.22	28.30
13	3.57	4.11	5.01	5.89	12.34	22.36	24.74	27.69	29.82
14	4.07	4.66	5.63	6.57	13.34	23.68	26.12	29.14	31.32
15	4.60	5.23	6.27	7.26	14.34	25.00	27.49	30.58	32.80
16	5.14	5.81	6.91	7.96	15.34	26.30	28.85	32.00	34.27
17	5.70	6.41	7.56	8.67	16.34	27.59	30.19	33.41	35.72
18	6.26	7.01	8.23	9.39	17.34	28.87	31.53	34.81	37.16
19	6.84	7.63	8.91	10.12	18.34	30.14	32.85	36.19	38.58
20	7.43	8.26	9.59	10.85	19.34	31.41	34.17	37.57	40.00
25	10.52	11.52	13.12	14.61	24.34	37.65	40.65	44.31	46.93
30	13.79	14.95	16.79	18.49	29.34	43.77	46.98	50.89	53.67
40	20.71	22.16	24.43	26.51	39.34	55.76	59.34	63.69	66.77
50	27.99	29.71	32.36	34.76	49.33	67.50	71.42	76.15	79.49
60	35.53	37.48	40.48	43.19	59.33	79.08	83.30	88.38	91.95
70	43.28	45.44	48.76	51.74	69.33	90.53	95.02	100.42	104.22
80	51.17	53.54	57.15	60.39	79.33	101.88	106.63	112.33	116.32
90	59.20	61.75	65.65	69.13	89.33	113.14	118.14	124.12	128.30
100	67.33	70.06	74.22	77.93	99.33	124.34	129.56	135.81	140.17

* Adapted from the tables prepared by Catherine M. Thompson for *Biometrika*, vol. 32; reproduced with permission of the editors of *Biometrika*.

† For more than 100 degrees of freedom, percentage points $\chi^2_{n,\alpha}$ of the χ^2 distribution may be obtained from the two-tailed percentage points X_P of the normal distribution by the approximate relation, $\chi^2_{n,\alpha} \approx n + (2n)^{1/2} X_P$, with $\alpha = P$.

‡ α is thus the probability in one tail of the distribution.

APPENDIX

TABLE

Percentage Points of

Values of $F_{\nu_1,\nu_2,\alpha}$, where ν_1 is the number of degrees of freedom for the numerator, ν_2 is

$\alpha =$

ν_1 ν_2	1	2	3	4	5	6	7	8	9
1	16211	20000	21615	22500	23056	23437	23715	23925	24091
2	198.50	199.00	199.17	199.25	199.30	199.33	199.36	199.37	199.39
3	55.552	49.799	47.467	46.195	45.392	44.838	44.434	44.126	43.882
4	31.333	26.284	24.259	23.155	22.456	21.975	21.622	21.352	21.139
5	22.785	18.314	16.530	15.556	14.940	14.513	14.200	13.961	13.772
6	18.635	14.544	12.917	12.028	11.464	11.073	10.786	10.566	10.391
7	16.236	12.404	10.882	10.050	9.5221	9.1554	8.8854	8.6781	8.5138
8	14.688	11.042	9.5965	8.8051	8.3018	7.9520	7.6942	7.4960	7.3386
9	13.614	10.107	8.7171	7.9559	7.4711	7.1338	6.8849	6.6933	6.5411
10	12.826	9.4270	8.0807	7.3428	6.8723	6.5446	6.3025	6.1159	5.9676
11	12.226	8.9122	7.6004	6.8809	6.4217	6.1015	5.8648	5.6821	5.5368
12	11.754	8.5096	7.2258	6.5211	6.0711	5.7570	5.5245	5.3451	5.2021
13	11.374	8.1865	6.9257	6.2335	5.7910	5.4819	5.2529	5.0761	4.9351
14	11.060	7.9217	6.6803	5.9984	5.5623	5.2574	5.0313	4.8566	4.7173
15	10.798	7.7008	6.4760	5.8029	5.3721	5.0708	4.8473	4.6743	4.5364
16	10.575	7.5138	6.3034	5.6378	5.2117	4.9134	4.6920	4.5207	4.3838
17	10.384	7.3536	6.1556	5.4967	5.0746	4.7789	4.5594	4.3893	4.2535
18	10.218	7.2148	6.0277	5.3746	4.9560	4.6627	4.4448	4.2759	4.1410
19	10.073	7.0935	5.9161	5.2681	4.8526	4.5614	4.3448	4.1770	4.0428
20	9.9439	6.9865	5.8177	5.1743	4.7616	4.4721	4.2569	4.0900	3.9564
21	9.8295	6.8914	5.7304	5.0911	4.6808	4.3931	4.1789	4.0128	3.8799
22	9.7271	6.8064	5.6524	5.0168	4.6088	4.3225	4.1094	3.9440	3.8116
23	9.6348	6.7300	5.5823	4.9500	4.5441	4.2591	4.0469	3.8822	3.7502
24	9.5513	6.6610	5.5190	4.8898	4.4857	4.2019	3.9905	3.8264	3.6949
25	9.4753	6.5982	5.4615	4.8351	4.4327	4.1500	3.9394	3.7758	3.6447
26	9.4059	6.5409	5.4091	4.7852	4.3844	4.1027	3.8928	3.7297	3.5989
27	9.3423	6.4885	5.3611	4.7396	4.3402	4.0594	3.8501	3.6875	3.5571
28	9.2838	6.4403	5.3170	4.6977	4.2996	4.0197	3.8110	3.6487	3.5186
29	9.2297	6.3958	5.2764	4.6591	4.2622	3.9830	3.7749	3.6130	3.4832
30	9.1797	6.3547	5.2388	4.6233	4.2276	3.9492	3.7416	3.5801	3.4505
40	8.8278	6.0664	4.9759	4.3738	3.9860	3.7129	3.5088	3.3498	3.2220
60	8.4946	5.7950	4.7290	4.1399	3.7600	3.4918	3.2911	3.1344	3.0083
120	8.1790	5.5393	4.4973	3.9207	3.5482	3.2849	3.0874	2.9330	2.8083
∞	7.8794	5.2983	4.2794	3.7151	3.3499	3.0913	2.8968	2.7444	2.6210

* Adapted from the tables prepared by Maxine Merrington and Catherine M. Thompson for *Biometrika*, vol. 33; reproduced with permission of the editors of *Biometrika*.

IV

the F Distribution*†

the number of degrees of freedom for the denominator, and $\int_0^{F_{\nu_1,\nu_2,\alpha}} \phi(F)\, dF = 1 - \alpha$

0.005

10	12	15	20	24	30	40	60	120	∞
24224	24426	24630	24836	24940	25044	25148	25253	25359	25465
199.40	199.42	199.43	199.45	199.46	199.47	199.47	199.48	199.49	199.51
43.686	43.387	43.085	42.778	42.622	42.466	42.308	42.149	41.989	41.829
20.967	20.705	20.438	20.167	20.030	19.892	19.752	19.611	19.468	19.325
13.618	13.384	13.146	12.903	12.780	12.656	12.530	12.402	12.274	12.144
10.250	10.034	9.8140	9.5888	9.4741	9.3583	9.2408	9.1219	9.0015	8.8793
8.3803	8.1764	7.9678	7.7540	7.6450	7.5345	7.4225	7.3088	7.1933	7.0760
7.2107	7.0149	6.8143	6.6082	6.5029	6.3961	6.2875	6.1772	6.0649	5.9505
6.4171	6.2274	6.0325	5.8318	5.7292	5.6248	5.5186	5.4104	5.3001	5.1875
5.8467	5.6613	5.4707	5.2740	5.1732	5.0705	4.9659	4.8592	4.7501	4.6385
5.4182	5.2363	5.0489	4.8552	4.7557	4.6543	4.5508	4.4450	4.3367	4.2256
5.0855	4.9063	4.7214	4.5299	4.4315	4.3309	4.2282	4.1229	4.0149	3.9039
4.8199	4.6429	4.4600	4.2703	4.1726	4.0727	3.9704	3.8655	3.7577	3.6465
4.6034	4.4281	4.2468	4.0585	3.9614	3.8619	3.7600	3.6553	3.5473	3.4359
4.4236	4.2498	4.0698	3.8826	3.7859	3.6867	3.5850	3.4803	3.3722	3.2602
4.2719	4.0994	3.9205	3.7342	3.6378	3.5388	3.4372	3.3324	3.2240	3.1115
4.1423	3.9709	3.7929	3.6073	3.5112	3.4124	3.3107	3.2058	3.0971	2.9839
4.0305	3.8599	3.6827	3.4977	3.4017	3.3030	3.2014	3.0962	2.9871	2.8732
3.9329	3.7631	3.5866	3.4020	3.3062	3.2075	3.1058	3.0004	2.8908	2.7762
3.8470	3.6779	3.5020	3.3178	3.2220	3.1234	3.0215	2.9159	2.8058	2.6904
3.7709	3.6024	3.4270	3.2431	3.1474	3.0488	2.9467	2.8408	2.7302	2.6140
3.7030	3.5350	3.3600	3.1764	3.0807	2.9821	2.8799	2.7736	2.6625	2.5455
3.6420	3.4745	3.2999	3.1165	3.0208	2.9221	2.8198	2.7132	2.6016	2.4837
3.5870	3.4199	3.2456	3.0624	2.9667	2.8679	2.7654	2.6585	2.5463	2.4276
3.5370	3.3704	3.1963	3.0133	2.9176	2.8187	2.7160	2.6088	2.4960	2.3765
3.4916	3.3252	3.1515	2.9685	2.8728	2.7738	2.6709	2.5633	2.4501	2.3297
3.4499	3.2839	3.1104	2.9275	2.8318	2.7327	2.6296	2.5217	2.4078	2.2867
3.4117	3.2460	3.0727	2.8899	2.7941	2.6949	2.5916	2.4834	2.3689	2.2469
3.3765	3.2111	3.0379	2.8551	2.7594	2.6601	2.5565	2.4479	2.3330	2.2102
3.3440	3.1787	3.0057	2.8230	2.7272	2.6278	2.5241	2.4151	2.2997	2.1760
3.1167	2.9531	2.7811	2.5984	2.5020	2.4015	2.2958	2.1838	2.0635	1.9318
2.9042	2.7419	2.5705	2.3872	2.2898	2.1874	2.0789	1.9622	1.8341	1.6885
2.7052	2.5439	2.3727	2.1881	2.0890	1.9839	1.8709	1.7469	1.6055	1.4311
2.5188	2.3583	2.1868	1.9993	1.8983	1.7891	1.6691	1.5325	1.3637	1.0000

† Values for $1 - \alpha$ can be obtained by using the relation $F_{\nu_1,\nu_2,\alpha} = (F_{\nu_2,\nu_1,1-\alpha})^{-1}$. Interpolation, when necessary, should be carried out on the reciprocal of the number of degrees of freedom.

APPENDIX

TABLE IV

$\alpha =$

ν_1 ν_2	1	2	3	4	5	6	7	8	9
1	4052.2	4999.5	5403.3	5624.6	5763.7	5859.0	5928.3	5981.6	6022.5
2	98.503	99.000	99.166	99.249	99.299	99.332	99.356	99.374	99.388
3	34.116	30.817	29.457	28.710	28.237	27.911	27.672	27.489	27.345
4	21.198	18.000	16.694	15.977	15.522	15.207	14.976	14.799	14.659
5	16.258	13.274	12.060	11.392	10.967	10.672	10.456	10.289	10.158
6	13.745	10.925	9.7795	9.1483	8.7459	8.4661	8.2600	8.1016	7.9761
7	12.246	9.5466	8.4513	7.8467	7.4604	7.1914	6.9928	6.8401	6.7188
8	11.259	8.6491	7.5910	7.0060	6.6318	6.3707	6.1776	6.0289	5.9106
9	10.561	8.0215	6.9919	6.4221	6.0569	5.8018	5.6129	5.4671	5.3511
10	10.044	7.5594	6.5523	5.9943	5.6363	5.3858	5.2001	5.0567	4.9424
11	9.6460	7.2057	6.2167	5.6683	5.3160	5.0692	4.8861	4.7445	4.6315
12	9.3302	6.9266	5.9526	5.4119	5.0643	4.8206	4.6395	4.4994	4.3875
13	9.0738	6.7010	5.7394	5.2053	4.8616	4.6204	4.4410	4.3021	4.1911
14	8.8616	6.5149	5.5639	5.0354	4.6950	4.4558	4.2779	4.1399	4.0297
15	8.6831	6.3589	5.4170	4.8932	4.5556	4.3183	4.1415	4.0045	3.8948
16	8.5310	6.2262	5.2922	4.7726	4.4374	4.2016	4.0259	3.8896	3.7804
17	8.3997	6.1121	5.1850	4.6690	4.3359	4.1015	3.9267	3.7910	3.6822
18	8.2854	6.0129	5.0919	4.5790	4.2479	4.0146	3.8406	3.7054	3.5971
19	8.1850	5.9259	5.0103	4.5003	4.1708	3.9386	3.7653	3.6305	3.5225
20	8.0960	5.8489	4.9382	4.4307	4.1027	3.8714	3.6987	3.5644	3.4567
21	8.0166	5.7804	4.8740	4.3688	4.0421	3.8117	3.6396	3.5056	3.3981
22	7.9454	5.7190	4.8166	4.3134	3.9880	3.7583	3.5867	3.4530	3.3458
23	7.8811	5.6637	4.7649	4.2635	3.9392	3.7102	3.5390	3.4057	3.2986
24	7.8229	5.6136	4.7181	4.2184	3.8951	3.6667	3.4959	3.3629	3.2560
25	7.7698	5.5680	4.6755	4.1774	3.8550	3.6272	3.4568	3.3239	3.2172
26	7.7213	5.5263	4.6366	4.1400	3.8183	3.5911	3.4210	3.2884	3.1818
27	7.6767	5.4881	4.6009	4.1056	3.7848	3.5580	3.3882	3.2558	3.1494
28	7.6356	5.4529	4.5681	4.0740	3.7539	3.5276	3.3581	3.2259	3.1195
29	7.5976	5.4205	4.5378	4.0449	3.7254	3.4995	3.3302	3.1982	3.0920
30	7.5625	5.3904	4.5097	4.0179	3.6990	3.4735	3.3045	3.1726	3.0665
40	7.3141	5.1785	4.3126	3.8283	3.5138	3.2910	3.1238	2.9930	2.8876
60	7.0771	4.9774	4.1259	3.6491	3.3389	3.1187	2.9530	2.8233	2.7185
120	6.8510	4.7865	3.9493	3.4796	3.1735	2.9559	2.7918	2.6629	2.5586
∞	6.6349	4.6052	3.7816	3.3192	3.0173	2.8020	2.6393	2.5113	2.4073

(Continued)

0.01

10	12	15	20	24	30	40	60	120	∞
6055.8	6106.3	6157.3	6208.7	6234.6	6260.7	6286.8	6313.0	6339.4	6366.0
99.399	99.416	99.432	99.449	99.458	99.466	99.474	99.483	99.491	99.501
27.229	27.052	26.872	26.690	26.598	26.505	26.411	26.316	26.221	26.125
14.546	14.374	14.198	14.020	13.929	13.838	13.745	13.652	13.558	13.463
10.051	9.8883	9.7222	9.5527	9.4665	9.3793	9.2912	9.2020	9.1118	9.0204
7.8741	7.7183	7.5590	7.3958	7.3127	7.2285	7.1432	7.0568	6.9690	6.8801
6.6201	6.4691	6.3143	6.1554	6.0743	5.9921	5.9084	5.8236	5.7372	5.6495
5.8143	5.6668	5.5151	5.3591	5.2793	5.1981	5.1156	5.0316	4.9460	4.8588
5.2565	5.1114	4.9621	4.8080	4.7290	4.6486	4.5667	4.4831	4.3978	4.3105
4.8492	4.7059	4.5582	4.4054	4.3269	4.2469	4.1653	4.0819	3.9965	3.9090
4.5393	4.3974	4.2509	4.0990	4.0209	3.9411	3.8596	3.7761	3.6904	3.6025
4.2961	4.1553	4.0096	3.8584	3.7805	3.7008	3.6192	3.5355	3.4494	3.3608
4.1003	3.9603	3.8154	3.6646	3.5868	3.5070	3.4253	3.3413	3.2548	3.1654
3.9394	3.8001	3.6557	3.5052	3.4274	3.3476	3.2656	3.1813	3.0942	3.0040
3.8049	3.6662	3.5222	3.3719	3.2940	3.2141	3.1319	3.0471	2.9595	2.8684
3.6909	3.5527	3.4089	3.2588	3.1808	3.1007	3.0182	2.9330	2.8447	2.7528
3.5931	3.4552	3.3117	3.1615	3.0835	3.0032	2.9205	2.8348	2.7459	2.6530
3.5082	3.3706	3.2273	3.0771	2.9990	2.9185	2.8354	2.7493	2.6597	2.5660
3.4338	3.2965	3.1533	3.0031	2.9249	2.8442	2.7608	2.6742	2.5839	2.4893
3.3682	3.2311	3.0880	2.9377	2.8594	2.7785	2.6947	2.6077	2.5168	2.4212
3.3098	3.1729	3.0299	2.8796	2.8011	2.7200	2.6359	2.5484	2.4568	2.3603
3.2576	3.1209	2.9780	2.8274	2.7488	2.6675	2.5831	2.4951	2.4029	2.3055
3.2106	3.0740	2.9311	2.7805	2.7017	2.6202	2.5355	2.4471	2.3542	2.2559
3.1681	3.0316	2.8887	2.7380	2.6591	2.5773	2.4923	2.4035	2.3099	2.2107
3.1294	2.9931	2.8502	2.6993	2.6203	2.5383	2.4530	2.3637	2.2695	2.1694
3.0941	2.9579	2.8150	2.6640	2.5848	2.5026	2.4170	2.3273	2.2325	2.1315
3.0618	2.9256	2.7827	2.6316	2.5522	2.4699	2.3840	2.2938	2.1984	2.0965
3.0320	2.8959	2.7530	2.6017	2.5223	2.4397	2.3535	2.2629	2.1670	2.0642
3.0045	2.8685	2.7256	2.5742	2.4946	2.4118	2.3253	2.2344	2.1378	2.0342
2.9791	2.8431	2.7002	2.5487	2.4689	2.3860	2.2992	2.2079	2.1107	2.0062
2.8005	2.6648	2.5216	2.3689	2.2880	2.2034	2.1142	2.0194	1.9172	1.8047
2.6318	2.4961	2.3523	2.1978	2.1154	2.0285	1.9360	1.8363	1.7263	1.6006
2.4721	2.3363	2.1915	2.0346	1.9500	1.8600	1.7628	1.6557	1.5330	1.3805
2.3209	2.1848	2.0385	1.8783	1.7908	1.6964	1.5923	1.4730	1.3246	1.0000

TABLE IV

$\alpha =$

ν_2 \ ν_1	1	2	3	4	5	6	7	8	9
1	161.45	199.50	215.71	224.58	230.16	233.99	236.77	238.88	240.54
2	18.513	19.000	19.164	19.247	19.296	19.330	19.353	19.371	19.385
3	10.128	9.5521	9.2766	9.1172	9.0135	8.9406	8.8868	8.8452	8.8123
4	7.7086	6.9443	6.5914	6.3883	6.2560	6.1631	6.0942	6.0410	5.9988
5	6.6079	5.7861	5.4095	5.1922	5.0503	4.9503	4.8759	4.8183	4.7725
6	5.9874	5.1433	4.7571	4.5337	4.3874	4.2839	4.2066	4.1468	4.0990
7	5.5914	4.7374	4.3468	4.1203	3.9715	3.8660	3.7870	3.7257	3.6767
8	5.3177	4.4590	4.0662	3.8378	3.6875	3.5806	3.5005	3.4381	3.3881
9	5.1174	4.2565	3.8626	3.6331	3.4817	3.3738	3.2927	3.2296	3.1789
10	4.9646	4.1028	3.7083	3.4780	3.3258	3.2172	3.1355	3.0717	3.0204
11	4.8443	3.9823	3.5874	3.3567	3.2039	3.0946	3.0123	2.9480	2.8962
12	4.7472	3.8853	3.4903	3.2592	3.1059	2.9961	2.9134	2.8486	2.7964
13	4.6672	3.8056	3.4105	3.1791	3.0254	2.9153	2.8321	2.7669	2.7144
14	4.6001	3.7389	3.3439	3.1122	2.9582	2.8477	2.7642	2.6987	2.6458
15	4.5431	3.6823	3.2874	3.0556	2.9013	2.7905	2.7066	2.6408	2.5876
16	4.4940	3.6337	3.2389	3.0069	2.8524	2.7413	2.6572	2.5911	2.5377
17	4.4513	3.5915	3.1968	2.9647	2.8100	2.6987	2.6143	2.5480	2.4943
18	4.4139	3.5546	3.1599	2.9277	2.7729	2.6613	2.5767	2.5102	2.4563
19	4.3808	3.5219	3.1274	2.8951	2.7401	2.6283	2.5435	2.4768	2.4227
20	4.3513	3.4928	3.0984	2.8661	2.7109	2.5990	2.5140	2.4471	2.3928
21	4.3248	3.4668	3.0725	2.8401	2.6848	2.5727	2.4876	2.4205	2.3661
22	4.3009	3.4434	3.0491	2.8167	2.6613	2.5491	2.4638	2.3965	2.3419
23	4.2793	3.4221	3.0280	2.7955	2.6400	2.5277	2.4422	2.3748	2.3201
24	4.2597	3.4028	3.0088	2.7763	2.6207	2.5082	2.4226	2.3551	2.3002
25	4.2417	3.3852	2.9912	2.7587	2.6030	2.4904	2.4047	2.3371	2.2821
26	4.2252	3.3690	2.9751	2.7426	2.5868	2.4741	2.3883	2.3205	2.2655
27	4.2100	3.3541	2.9604	2.7278	2.5719	2.4591	2.3732	2.3053	2.2501
28	4.1960	3.3404	2.9467	2.7141	2.5581	2.4453	2.3593	2.2913	2.2360
29	4.1830	3.3277	2.9340	2.7014	2.5454	2.4324	2.3463	2.2782	2.2229
30	4.1709	3.3158	2.9223	2.6896	2.5336	2.4205	2.3343	2.2662	2.2107
40	4.0848	3.2317	2.8387	2.6060	2.4495	2.3359	2.2490	2.1802	2.1240
60	4.0012	3.1504	2.7581	2.5252	2.3683	2.2540	2.1665	2.0970	2.0401
120	3.9201	3.0718	2.6802	2.4472	2.2900	2.1750	2.0867	2.0164	1.9588
∞	3.8415	2.9957	2.6049	2.3719	2.2141	2.0986	2.0096	1.9384	1.8799

(Continued)

0.05

10	12	15	20	24	30	40	60	120	∞
241.88	243.91	245.95	248.01	249.05	250.09	251.14	252.20	253.25	254.32
19.396	19.413	19.429	19.446	19.454	19.462	19.471	19.479	19.487	19.496
8.7855	8.7446	8.7029	8.6602	8.6385	8.6166	8.5944	8.5720	8.5494	8.5265
5.9644	5.9117	5.8578	5.8025	5.7744	5.7459	5.7170	5.6878	5.6581	5.6281
4.7351	4.6777	4.6188	4.5581	4.5272	4.4957	4.4638	4.4314	4.3984	4.3650
4.0600	3.9999	3.9381	3.8742	3.8415	3.8082	3.7743	3.7398	3.7047	3.6688
3.6365	3.5747	3.5108	3.4445	3.4105	3.3758	3.3404	3.3043	3.2674	3.2298
3.3472	3.2840	3.2184	3.1503	3.1152	3.0794	3.0428	3.0053	2.9669	2.9276
3.1373	3.0729	3.0061	2.9365	2.9005	2.8637	2.8259	2.7872	2.7475	2.7067
2.9782	2.9130	2.8450	2.7740	2.7372	2.6996	2.6609	2.6211	2.5801	2.5379
2.8536	2.7876	2.7186	2.6464	2.6090	2.5705	2.5309	2.4901	2.4480	2.4045
2.7534	2.6866	2.6169	2.5436	2.5055	2.4663	2.4259	2.3842	2.3410	2.2962
2.6710	2.6037	2.5331	2.4589	2.4202	2.3803	2.3392	2.2966	2.2524	2.2064
2.6021	2.5342	2.4630	2.3879	2.3487	2.3082	2.2664	2.2230	2.1778	2.1307
2.5437	2.4753	2.4035	2.3275	2.2878	2.2468	2.2043	2.1601	2.1141	2.0658
2.4935	2.4247	2.3522	2.2756	2.2354	2.1938	2.1507	2.1058	2.0589	2.0096
2.4499	2.3807	2.3077	2.2304	2.1898	2.1477	2.1040	2.0584	2.0107	1.9604
2.4117	2.3421	2.2686	2.1906	2.1497	2.1071	2.0629	2.0166	1.9681	1.9168
2.3779	2.3080	2.2341	2.1555	2.1141	2.0712	2.0264	1.9796	1.9302	1.8780
2.3479	2.2776	2.2033	2.1242	2.0825	2.0391	1.9938	1.9464	1.8963	1.8432
2.3210	2.2504	2.1757	2.0960	2.0540	2.0102	1.9645	1.9165	1.8657	1.8117
2.2967	2.2258	2.1508	2.0707	2.0283	1.9842	1.9380	1.8895	1.8380	1.7831
2.2747	2.2036	2.1282	2.0476	2.0050	1.9605	1.9139	1.8649	1.8128	1.7570
2.2547	2.1834	2.1077	2.0267	1.9838	1.9390	1.8920	1.8424	1.7897	1.7331
2.2365	2.1649	2.0889	2.0075	1.9643	1.9192	1.8718	1.8217	1.7684	1.7110
2.2197	2.1479	2.0716	1.9898	1.9464	1.9010	1.8533	1.8027	1.7488	1.6906
2.2043	2.1323	2.0558	1.9736	1.9299	1.8842	1.8361	1.7851	1.7307	1.6717
2.1900	2.1179	2.0411	1.9586	1.9147	1.8687	1.8203	1.7689	1.7138	1.6541
2.1768	2.1045	2.0275	1.9446	1.9005	1.8543	1.8055	1.7537	1.6981	1.6377
2.1646	2.0921	2.0148	1.9317	1.8874	1.8409	1.7918	1.7396	1.6835	1.6223
2.0772	2.0035	1.9245	1.8389	1.7929	1.7444	1.6928	1.6373	1.5766	1.5089
1.9926	1.9174	1.8364	1.7480	1.7001	1.6491	1.5943	1.5343	1.4673	1.3893
1.9105	1.8337	1.7505	1.6587	1.6084	1.5543	1.4952	1.4290	1.3519	1.2539
1.8307	1.7522	1.6664	1.5705	1.5173	1.4591	1.3940	1.3180	1.2214	1.0000

TABLE IV

$\alpha =$

ν_1 ν_2	1	2	3	4	5	6	7	8	9
1	1.0000	1.5000	1.7092	1.8227	1.8937	1.9422	1.9774	2.0041	2.0250
2	0.66667	1.0000	1.1349	1.2071	1.2519	1.2824	1.3045	1.3213	1.3344
3	.58506	0.88110	1.0000	1.0632	1.1024	1.1289	1.1482	1.1627	1.1741
4	.54863	.82843	0.94054	1.0000	1.0367	1.0617	1.0797	1.0933	1.1040
5	0.52807	0.79877	0.90715	0.96456	1.0000	1.0240	1.0414	1.0545	1.0648
6	.51489	.77976	.88578	.94191	0.97654	1.0000	1.0169	1.0298	1.0398
7	.50572	.76655	.87095	.92619	.96026	0.98334	1.0000	1.0126	1.0224
8	.49898	.75683	.86004	.91464	.94831	.97111	0.98757	1.0000	1.0097
9	.49382	.74938	.85168	.90580	.93916	.96175	.97805	0.99037	1.0000
10	0.48973	0.74349	0.84508	0.89882	0.93193	0.95436	0.97054	0.98276	0.99232
11	.48644	.73872	.83973	.89316	.92608	.94837	.96445	.97661	.98610
12	.48369	.73477	.83530	.88848	.92124	.94342	.95943	.97152	.98097
13	.48141	.73145	.83159	.88454	.91718	.93926	.95520	.96724	.97665
14	.47944	.72862	.82842	.88119	.91371	.93573	.95161	.96360	.97298
15	0.47775	0.72619	0.82569	0.87830	0.91073	0.93267	0.94850	0.96046	0.96981
16	.47628	.72406	.82330	.87578	.90812	.93001	.94580	.95773	.96705
17	.47499	.72219	.82121	.87357	.90584	.92767	.94342	.95532	.96462
18	.47385	.72053	.81936	.87161	.90381	.92560	.94132	.95319	.96247
19	.47284	.71906	.81771	.86987	.90200	.92375	.93944	.95129	.96056
20	0.47192	0.71773	0.81621	0.86830	0.90038	0.92210	0.93776	0.94959	0.95884
21	.47108	.71653	.81487	.86688	.89891	.92060	.93624	.94805	.95728
22	.47033	.71545	.81365	.86559	.89759	.91924	.93486	.94665	.95588
23	.46965	.71446	.81255	.86442	.89638	.91800	.93360	.94538	.95459
24	.46902	.71356	.81153	.86335	.89527	.91687	.93245	.94422	.95342
25	0.46844	0.71272	0.81061	0.86236	0.89425	0.91583	0.93140	0.94315	0.95234
26	.46793	.71195	.80975	.86145	.89331	.91487	.93042	.94217	.95135
27	.46744	.71124	.80894	.86061	.89244	.91399	.92952	.94126	.95044
28	.46697	.71059	.80820	.85983	.89164	.91317	.92869	.94041	.94958
29	.46654	.70999	.80753	.85911	.89089	.91241	.92791	.93963	.94879
30	0.46616	0.70941	0.80689	0.85844	0.89019	0.91169	0.92719	0.93889	0.94805
40	.46330	.70531	.80228	.85357	.88516	.90654	.92197	.93361	.94272
60	.46053	.70122	.79770	.84873	.88017	.90144	.91679	.92838	.93743
120	.45774	.69717	.79314	.84392	.87521	.89637	.91164	.92318	.93218
∞	.45494	.69315	.78866	.83918	.87029	.89135	.90654	.91802	.92698

(Continued)

0.50

10	12	15	20	24	30	40	60	120	∞
2.0419	2.0674	2.0931	2.1190	2.1321	2.1452	2.1584	2.1716	2.1848	2.1981
1.3450	1.3610	1.3771	1.3933	1.4014	1.4096	1.4178	1.4261	1.4344	1.4427
1.1833	1.1972	1.2111	1.2252	1.2322	1.2393	1.2464	1.2536	1.2608	1.2680
1.1126	1.1255	1.1386	1.1517	1.1583	1.1649	1.1716	1.1782	1.1849	1.1916
1.0730	1.0855	1.0980	1.1106	1.1170	1.1234	1.1297	1.1361	1.1426	1.1490
1.0478	1.0600	1.0722	1.0845	1.0907	1.0969	1.1031	1.1093	1.1156	1.1219
1.0304	1.0423	1.0543	1.0664	1.0724	1.0785	1.0846	1.0908	1.0969	1.1031
1.0175	1.0293	1.0412	1.0531	1.0591	1.0651	1.0711	1.0771	1.0832	1.0893
1.0077	1.0194	1.0311	1.0429	1.0489	1.0548	1.0608	1.0667	1.0727	1.0788
1.0000	1.0116	1.0232	1.0349	1.0408	1.0467	1.0526	1.0585	1.0645	1.0705
0.99373	1.0052	1.0168	1.0284	1.0343	1.0401	1.0460	1.0519	1.0578	1.0637
.98856	1.0000	1.0115	1.0231	1.0289	1.0347	1.0405	1.0464	1.0523	1.0582
.98421	0.99560	1.0071	1.0186	1.0243	1.0301	1.0360	1.0418	1.0476	1.0535
.98051	.99186	1.0033	1.0147	1.0205	1.0263	1.0321	1.0379	1.0437	1.0495
0.97732	0.98863	1.0000	1.0114	1.0172	1.0229	1.0287	1.0345	1.0403	1.0461
.97454	.98582	0.99716	1.0086	1.0143	1.0200	1.0258	1.0315	1.0373	1.0431
.97209	.98334	.99466	1.0060	1.0117	1.0174	1.0232	1.0289	1.0347	1.0405
.96993	.98116	.99245	1.0038	1.0095	1.0152	1.0209	1.0267	1.0324	1.0382
.96800	.97920	.99047	1.0018	1.0075	1.0132	1.0189	1.0246	1.0304	1.0361
0.96626	0.97746	0.98870	1.0000	1.0057	1.0114	1.0171	1.0228	1.0285	1.0343
.96470	.97587	.98710	0.99838	1.0040	1.0097	1.0154	1.0211	1.0268	1.0326
.96328	.97444	.98565	.99692	1.0026	1.0082	1.0139	1.0196	1.0253	1.0311
.96199	.97313	.98433	.99558	1.0012	1.0069	1.0126	1.0183	1.0240	1.0297
.96081	.97194	.98312	.99436	1.0000	1.0057	1.0113	1.0170	1.0227	1.0284
0.95972	0.97084	0.98201	0.99324	0.99887	1.0045	1.0102	1.0159	1.0215	1.0273
.95872	.96983	.98099	.99220	.99783	1.0035	1.0091	1.0148	1.0205	1.0262
.95779	.96889	.98004	.99125	.99687	1.0025	1.0082	1.0138	1.0195	1.0252
.95694	.96802	.97917	.99036	.99598	1.0016	1.0073	1.0129	1.0186	1.0243
.95614	.96722	.97835	.98954	.99515	1.0008	1.0064	1.0121	1.0177	1.0234
0.95540	0.96647	0.97759	0.98877	0.99438	1.0000	1.0056	1.0113	1.0170	1.0226
.95003	.96104	.97211	.98323	.98880	0.99440	1.0000	1.0056	1.0113	1.0169
.94471	.95566	.96667	.97773	.98328	.98884	0.99441	1.0000	1.0056	1.0112
.93943	.95032	.96128	.97228	.97780	.98333	.98887	0.99443	1.0000	1.0056
.93418	.94503	.95593	.96687	.97236	.97787	.98339	.98891	0.99445	1.0000

TABLE V

Percentage Points of the R Factor Ratio*

Values of $\mathfrak{R}_{b.N.\alpha}$, where α is the probability that $\mathfrak{R}$ exceeds $\mathfrak{R}_{b.N.\alpha}$

$$\alpha = 0.005$$

b \ N	5	10	15	20	30	40	60	120	240	480	∞
1	2.357	1.511	1.311	1.224	1.143	1.105	1.068	1.034	1.017	1.008	1.000
2	2.885	1.699	1.424	1.303	1.193	1.142	1.092	1.045	1.022	1.011	1.000
3	3.304	1.850	1.515	1.368	1.234	1.172	1.112	1.055	1.027	1.013	1.000
4	3.667	1.984	1.596	1.426	1.271	1.199	1.130	1.063	1.031	1.016	1.000
5	3.992	2.106	1.671	1.480	1.306	1.224	1.146	1.071	1.035	1.018	1.000
6	4.291	2.220	1.740	1.530	1.338	1.248	1.162	1.079	1.039	1.019	1.000
7	4.569	2.326	1.806	1.578	1.369	1.270	1.176	1.086	1.043	1.021	1.000
8	4.831	2.427	1.869	1.624	1.398	1.292	1.191	1.093	1.046	1.023	1.000
9	5.078	2.524	1.929	1.667	1.427	1.313	1.205	1.100	1.050	1.025	1.000
10	5.314	2.617	1.987	1.710	1.454	1.334	1.218	1.107	1.053	1.026	1.000
12	5.755	2.792	2.098	1.791	1.507	1.373	1.244	1.120	1.060	1.030	1.000
15	6.359	3.034	2.252	1.904	1.582	1.429	1.282	1.139	1.069	1.034	1.000
20	7.253	3.398	2.485	2.078	1.698	1.516	1.340	1.168	1.084	1.042	1.000
24	7.896	3.663	2.657	2.206	1.784	1.582	1.384	1.191	1.095	1.048	1.000
30	8.771	4.026	2.894	2.384	1.905	1.674	1.447	1.223	1.112	1.056	1.000
40	10.062	4.568	3.250	2.654	2.089	1.815	1.545	1.274	1.138	1.069	1.000
60	12.240	5.491	3.863	3.122	2.415	2.068	1.721	1.369	1.187	1.095	1.000
120	17.192	7.616	5.289	4.223	3.194	2.682	2.161	1.614	1.320	1.164	1.000
240	24.229	10.661	7.352	5.829	4.348	3.604	2.836	2.009	1.533	1.278	1.000
480	34.204	15.000	10.306	8.140	6.026	4.957	3.847	2.627	1.888	1.479	1.000

* Computed by the author from percentage points of F (Table IV) by the relation $\mathfrak{R}_{b.N.\alpha} = [(b/N)F_{b.N.\alpha} + 1]^{1/2}$.

TABLE V *(Continued)*

$\alpha = 0.01$

b \ N	5	10	15	20	30	40	60	120	240	480	∞
1	2.062	1.416	1.257	1.185	1.119	1.088	1.057	1.028	1.014	1.007	1.000
2	2.512	1.585	1.359	1.259	1.166	1.122	1.080	1.039	1.019	1.010	1.000
3	2.870	1.722	1.443	1.319	1.205	1.150	1.098	1.048	1.024	1.012	1.000
4	3.180	1.843	1.518	1.373	1.239	1.176	1.115	1.056	1.028	1.014	1.000
5	3.459	1.954	1.587	1.423	1.271	1.200	1.131	1.064	1.032	1.016	1.000
6	3.716	2.057	1.651	1.470	1.302	1.222	1.145	1.071	1.035	1.018	1.000
7	3.955	2.154	1.713	1.515	1.331	1.244	1.160	1.078	1.039	1.019	1.000
8	4.179	2.246	1.771	1.557	1.359	1.264	1.173	1.085	1.042	1.021	1.000
9	4.391	2.334	1.827	1.599	1.386	1.284	1.186	1.092	1.046	1.023	1.000
10	4.594	2.419	1.881	1.638	1.412	1.304	1.199	1.098	1.049	1.024	1.000
12	4.973	2.578	1.983	1.714	1.462	1.341	1.224	1.111	1.055	1.027	1.000
15	5.492	2.800	2.127	1.821	1.533	1.395	1.260	1.129	1.064	1.032	1.000
20	6.262	3.132	2.344	1.984	1.643	1.478	1.316	1.157	1.078	1.039	1.000
24	6.815	3.374	2.504	2.105	1.725	1.540	1.359	1.179	1.090	1.045	1.000
30	7.568	3.707	2.725	2.273	1.840	1.629	1.419	1.210	1.106	1.053	1.000
40	8.679	4.203	3.058	2.528	2.016	1.765	1.513	1.260	1.131	1.066	1.000
60	10.556	5.049	3.632	2.970	2.327	2.007	1.684	1.352	1.179	1.091	1.000
120	14.822	6.997	4.967	4.013	3.073	2.598	2.110	1.592	1.309	1.159	1.000
240	20.885	9.791	6.901	5.534	4.179	3.488	2.767	1.978	1.520	1.272	1.000
480	29.481	13.773	9.670	7.725	5.789	4.795	3.749	2.584	1.871	1.472	1.000

TABLE V (Continued)

$$\alpha = 0.025$$

b \ N	5	10	15	20	30	40	60	120	240	480	∞
1	1.732	1.301	1.189	1.137	1.089	1.066	1.043	1.021	1.011	1.005	1.000
2	2.091	1.446	1.279	1.203	1.131	1.097	1.063	1.031	1.015	1.008	1.000
3	2.379	1.565	1.353	1.257	1.166	1.122	1.080	1.040	1.020	1.010	1.000
4	2.629	1.670	1.419	1.305	1.197	1.146	1.096	1.047	1.023	1.012	1.000
5	2.854	1.766	1.481	1.350	1.227	1.167	1.110	1.054	1.027	1.013	1.000
6	3.062	1.856	1.538	1.392	1.254	1.188	1.124	1.061	1.030	1.015	1.000
7	3.255	1.940	1.593	1.433	1.281	1.208	1.137	1.068	1.034	1.017	1.000
8	3.437	2.021	1.645	1.471	1.307	1.227	1.150	1.074	1.037	1.018	1.000
9	3.609	2.098	1.695	1.509	1.331	1.246	1.162	1.080	1.040	1.020	1.000
10	3.773	2.172	1.744	1.545	1.355	1.264	1.174	1.086	1.043	1.021	1.000
12	4.082	2.312	1.836	1.614	1.402	1.299	1.197	1.098	1.049	1.024	1.000
15	4.504	2.507	1.965	1.712	1.468	1.348	1.231	1.115	1.057	1.029	1.000
20	5.130	2.799	2.162	1.861	1.570	1.426	1.284	1.142	1.071	1.036	1.000
24	5.580	3.013	2.307	1.972	1.646	1.485	1.324	1.163	1.082	1.041	1.000
30	6.194	3.307	2.507	2.127	1.753	1.568	1.381	1.193	1.097	1.049	1.000
40	7.099	3.745	2.810	2.361	1.918	1.696	1.471	1.240	1.122	1.061	1.000
60	8.630	4.493	3.331	2.770	2.209	1.925	1.633	1.329	1.168	1.085	1.000
120	12.110	6.219	4.548	3.733	2.910	2.484	2.040	1.560	1.294	1.152	1.000
240	17.060	8.697	6.313	5.143	3.951	3.329	2.670	1.935	1.501	1.264	1.000
480	24.078	12.229	8.842	7.174	5.469	4.572	3.613	2.523	1.846	1.461	1.000

TABLE V *(Continued)*

$$\alpha = 0.05$$

b \ N	5	10	15	20	30	40	60	120	240	480	∞
1	1.524	1.223	1.141	1.103	1.067	1.050	1.033	1.016	1.008	1.004	1.000
2	1.821	1.349	1.221	1.162	1.105	1.078	1.051	1.025	1.013	1.006	1.000
3	2.061	1.453	1.287	1.210	1.137	1.101	1.067	1.033	1.016	1.008	1.000
4	2.270	1.546	1.347	1.254	1.166	1.123	1.081	1.040	1.020	1.010	1.000
5	2.460	1.632	1.403	1.295	1.193	1.143	1.094	1.047	1.023	1.012	1.000
6	2.634	1.712	1.455	1.334	1.218	1.162	1.107	1.053	1.026	1.013	1.000
7	2.798	1.787	1.504	1.371	1.243	1.180	1.119	1.059	1.029	1.015	1.000
8	2.951	1.859	1.552	1.407	1.267	1.198	1.131	1.065	1.032	1.016	1.000
9	3.097	1.928	1.598	1.441	1.290	1.216	1.143	1.071	1.035	1.018	1.000
10	3.236	1.995	1.642	1.474	1.312	1.233	1.154	1.077	1.038	1.019	1.000
12	3.497	2.120	1.726	1.538	1.355	1.265	1.176	1.088	1.044	1.022	1.000
15	3.854	2.295	1.845	1.629	1.417	1.312	1.208	1.104	1.052	1.026	1.000
20	4.385	2.559	2.026	1.768	1.513	1.385	1.258	1.130	1.065	1.033	1.000
24	4.768	2.751	2.159	1.871	1.584	1.441	1.296	1.150	1.075	1.038	1.000
30	5.289	3.016	2.344	2.015	1.685	1.519	1.351	1.178	1.090	1.045	1.000
40	6.059	3.412	2.623	2.233	1.841	1.641	1.436	1.224	1.114	1.057	1.000
60	7.360	4.090	3.105	2.615	2.116	1.859	1.592	1.309	1.159	1.081	1.000
120	10.323	5.653	4.232	3.518	2.781	2.394	1.984	1.534	1.282	1.146	1.000
240	14.537	7.900	5.868	4.841	3.771	3.203	2.591	1.899	1.486	1.257	1.000
480	20.514	11.105	8.215	6.749	5.216	4.394	3.503	2.473	1.826	1.453	1.000

TABLE V (Continued)

$$\alpha = 0.25$$

b \ N	5	10	15	20	30	40	60	120	240	480	∞
1	1.157	1.072	1.047	1.034	1.023	1.017	1.011	1.006	1.003	1.001	1.000
2	1.320	1.149	1.097	1.072	1.047	1.035	1.023	1.012	1.006	1.003	1.000
3	1.460	1.217	1.142	1.105	1.070	1.052	1.035	1.017	1.009	1.004	1.000
4	1.586	1.280	1.184	1.137	1.091	1.068	1.045	1.023	1.011	1.006	1.000
5	1.701	1.339	1.224	1.167	1.111	1.083	1.055	1.028	1.014	1.007	1.000
6	1.809	1.395	1.262	1.196	1.131	1.098	1.065	1.033	1.016	1.008	1.000
7	1.911	1.449	1.299	1.224	1.150	1.112	1.075	1.038	1.019	1.009	1.000
8	2.007	1.500	1.334	1.251	1.168	1.127	1.085	1.042	1.021	1.011	1.000
9	2.099	1.549	1.369	1.278	1.186	1.140	1.094	1.047	1.024	1.012	1.000
10	2.186	1.597	1.402	1.304	1.204	1.154	1.103	1.052	1.026	1.013	1.000
12	2.352	1.689	1.467	1.354	1.239	1.180	1.121	1.061	1.031	1.015	1.000
15	2.580	1.817	1.558	1.425	1.289	1.219	1.148	1.075	1.038	1.019	1.000
20	2.920	2.012	1.698	1.536	1.367	1.280	1.190	1.097	1.049	1.025	1.000
24	3.166	2.155	1.802	1.618	1.426	1.326	1.222	1.114	1.058	1.029	1.000
30	3.503	2.353	1.948	1.735	1.511	1.393	1.269	1.139	1.071	1.036	1.000
40	4.001	2.650	2.169	1.913	1.641	1.497	1.344	1.180	1.092	1.047	1.000
60	4.847	3.161	2.553	2.227	1.875	1.684	1.480	1.256	1.133	1.068	1.000
120	6.777	4.348	3.458	2.974	2.443	2.150	1.828	1.460	1.247	1.129	1.000
240	9.528	6.059	4.778	4.076	3.297	2.862	2.374	1.797	1.442	1.237	1.000
480	13.436	8.505	6.677	5.669	4.547	3.914	3.198	2.330	1.769	1.429	1.000

Bibliography

In addition to the references listed at some of the chapter ends, the following books are cited as recommended reading. No attempt is made to provide a complete or representative bibliography for all fields of statistics, nor are all the classic works in the fields covered listed. These are simply books which have proved useful to the author, and the brief descriptions should be of some help in guiding the interested reader to those books which will be most useful to him. An excellent personal five-inch shelf might include the books by Brownlee and Graybill and the *Biometrika Tables*.

A. Tables

FISHER, R. A., and F. YATES, *Statistical Tables for Biological, Agricultural and Medical Research*, Oliver and Boyd, Edinburgh, 1953.

> Tables of N, t, χ^2, F, and miscellaneous other statistical tables and information, including the density of loose snow.

GREENWOOD, J. A., and H. O. HARTLEY, *Guide to Tables in Mathematical Statistics*, Princeton University Press, Princeton, N. J., 1962.

> One thousand pages of reviews and descriptions of virtually every table to be found in the literature. An extremely useful and *easily used* compilation.

HAIGHT, F. A., Index to the Distributions of Mathematical Statistics, *J. Res. Natl. Bur. Std.* 65B (1961): 23–60.

> This paper contains a compilation of references to tables and other references on many statistical distributions. Very useful.

PEARSON, E. S., and H. O. HARTLEY, *Biometrika Tables for Statisticians*, vol. 1, 2nd ed., Cambridge University Press, Cambridge, 1958.

> Compendium of all the tables needed by the amateur statistician and then some. At the price, no one should be without one. The publishers of *Biometrika* also supply, at nominal prices, reprints of many of the tables which have appeared in that journal.

RESNIKOFF, G. J., and G. J. LIEBERMAN, *Tables of the Non-central t Distribution*, Stanford University Press, Palo Alto, Calif., 1957.

Most good statistical texts include tables of the more common distributions and almost always at least one uncommon distribution of which the author is especially fond.

B. Books

ACTON, F. S., *Analysis of Straight-Line Data*, John Wiley & Sons, Inc., New York, 1959.

An excellent discussion of linear least squares and regression analysis for the bivariate case only. Much detail on confidence limits, hypothesis tests, and sampling procedure.

ADAMS, J. K., *Basic Statistical Concepts*, McGraw-Hill Book Co., Inc. New York, 1955.

Elementary treatment of the most commonly used single-variable statistical tests. Many detailed numerical examples are given, and the book can be recommended to the reader who lacks a strong mathematical background.

ANDERSON, T. W., *An Introduction to Multivariate Statistical Analysis*, John Wiley & Sons, Inc., New York, 1958.

An excellent book covering multivariate analysis, least squares, and linear hypothesis tests in great detail. Clearly written for the statistician but also to be recommended to the physical scientist who wishes to go into the subject more deeply than does the present text.

BAUER, E. L., *A Statistical Manual for Chemists*, Academic Press, New York, 1960.

Brief compilation of techniques, with special emphasis on those tests which involve the use of the range.

BENNETT, C. A., and N. C. FRANKLIN, *Statistical Analysis in Chemistry and the Chemical Industry*, John Wiley & Sons, Inc., New York, 1954.

A large text well illustrated with practical examples. With the exceptions of least squares and multivariate hypothesis tests, it covers in detail most statistical tests and procedures likely to be of use to the chemist.

BROWN, G. S., *Probability and Scientific Inference*, Longmans, Green & Co., London, 1957.

A delightful little essay on randomness, miracles, and science.

BROWNLEE, K. A., *Statistical Theory and Methodology in Science and Engineering*, John Wiley & Sons, Inc., New York, 1960.

A well-written book which is recommended for every scientist's bookshelf. Does not cover least-squares methods in great detail.

COX, R. T., *The Algebra of Probable Inference*, Johns Hopkins University Press, Baltimore, 1961.

A brief and scholarly presentation of abstract statistical inference.

FELLER, W., *Probability Theory and its Applications*, John Wiley & Sons, Inc., New York, 1950.

The best book on probability theory (not statistics) available for the non-specialist. Rigorous, complete, and extremely readable.

FISHER, R. A., *Contributions to Mathematical Statistics*, John Wiley & Sons, Inc., New York, 1950.

Collected papers. Highly recommended for their historical interest and the lucidity of presentation.

GRAYBILL, F. A., An Introduction to Linear Statistical Models, vol. I, McGraw-Hill Book Co., Inc., New York, 1961.

Modern and complete treatment of linear least squares, analysis of variance and regression. Exceptionally well written.

KENDALL, M. G., and A. STUART, *The Advanced Theory of Statistics*, Charles Griffin & Co., Ltd., London; vol. I, 1958; vol. II, 1961.

Extraordinarily complete and readable up-to-date advanced treatise on statistics and statistical methods. The exercises are particularly interesting and useful.

KOLMOGOROV, A. N., *Foundations of the Theory of Probability*, Chelsea Publishing Co., New York, 1956.

This translation of a classic work in abstract probability theory is brief, to the point, and highly recommended.

LANCZOS, C., *Applied Analysis*, Prentice-Hall, Inc., Englewood Cliffs, N. J., 1956.

A superb book on numerical analysis: large-scale linear systems, harmonic analysis, expansion in power series, and much more.

LEHMANN, E. L., *Testing Statistical Hypotheses*, John Wiley & Sons, Inc., New York, 1959.

A complete monograph on an advanced and rigorous level.

MOOD, A. M., and F. A. GRAYBILL, *Introduction to the Theory of Statistics*, 2nd Ed., McGraw-Hill Book Co., Inc. New York, 1963.

Readable text at the intermediate level. Complete and detailed with many interesting and instructive exercises. Revision of Mood's 1950 book of same title.

PLACKETT, R. L., *Principles of Regression Analysis*, Oxford University Press, Oxford, 1960.

One of the best monographs on linear least squares and the testing of linear hypotheses. Includes discussion of a number of special topics such as polynomial regression, experimental design, and effects of departures from assumed models. Many references to the recent literature. Not as detailed as the book by Anderson.

RAO, C. R., *Advanced Statistical Methods in Biometric Research*, John Wiley & Sons, Inc., New York, 1952

Very good sections on least squares and multivariate analysis. Some examples, largely anthropological.

SCHEFFÉ, H., *The Analysis of Variance*, John Wiley & Sons, Inc., New York, 1959.

A rigorous treatment in great detail of most of the variations of analysis-of-variance techniques of practical use. Advanced.

SNEDECOR, G. W., *Statistical Methods*, Iowa State College Press, Ames, 1956.

Complete treatment of the elementary methods, with a great deal of emphasis on the analysis of variance. Most examples are chosen from agricultural problems.

WILKS, S. S., *Mathematical Statistics*, John Wiley & Sons, Inc., New York, 1962.

A complete text, primarily for the mathematical statistician rather than the physical scientist.

Index